Richard Jefferies

Return to Jefferies' Land

Richard Jefferies

Michael Russell

First published in Great Britain 1985
by Michael Russell (Publishing) Ltd
The Chantry, Wilton, Salisbury, Wiltshire

Typeset and printed
by The Bournemouth Acorn Press Ltd
Bound by Biddles Ltd, King's Lynn

ISBN 0 85955 123 7

Contents

Publisher's Note

The prime mover in this publication has been Pamela Colman, Librarian of the Wiltshire Archaeological and Natural History Museum in Devizes since 1979. In the course of her Jefferies researches it occurred to her that the neglected 'History of Malmesbury', never published in book form, would be of considerable attraction to Wiltshire readers. It appeared in serial form in the *North Wilts Herald* in 1867 – a similar provenance to *Jefferies' Land,* subsequently published in 1896 and now a considerable rarity. As the present book is complemented with a collection of photographs of old Wiltshire, it was thought that the title *Return to Jefferies' Land* would not be inappropriate.

In her introduction to *Jefferies' Land* the Victorian editor stated, a little defensively, that 'these early efforts' were 'offered to the reading public as intellectual curios'. What she meant was that *Jefferies' Land* was bad Jefferies, but that there was some interest in comparing it with good Jefferies. The same applies, in general, to the present piece – indeed the young Jefferies groping in the mists of history is simply too punishing for the average reader, so we have preferred to join his chronicle at the time of Edward the Confessor, consigning Jefferies scholars to the library archives if they want to brush up on those early endeavours of Aldhelm and Offa. That said, first publication in book form of anything by Jefferies is a must for any serious collector and there is, undeniably, both a quaint charm about it and a good deal of local historical interest.

We should like to record our thanks to Dennis Bird for the use of the Swindon photographs. Other photographs appear by kind permission from The Wiltshire Archaeological and Natural History Society; Wiltshire Library and Museum Services; Mr M. Slater; and Mr F. Mead.

I
Edward the Confessor: State of the Abbey

The character of King Edward the Confessor, so far as it is possible to judge at this distance of time, appears to have been extraordinarily weak and vacillating. He seems to have been alternately dictated to by his nobles and priests, the last of whom gave him some return by making him a royal saint. Although his nobles, by dint of threats of physical force, at times had things their own way, it would appear that the private mind of the monarch was entirely in the hands of the priests. This is perhaps illustrated by his conduct towards the monastery of Malmesbury. Bishop Herman seems to have had no difficulty in obtaining the required permission to enable him to remove the episcopal see there from Wilton, and it was only through the influence of the Earl Godwin – influence probably purchased in some way or other by the monks – that the grant was rescinded. Edward was thus by one of his powerful nobles prevented from carrying out the favourite design of one of his priests. He seems, however, to have kept Malmesbury in his mind as a place to which he was pledged to present something in discharge of the promise to the bishop. About seven years after the election of Brithric as abbot, and when his life was rapidly drawing to a close, Edward seems to have bethought him of Malmesbury, and perhaps, in accordance with the religion in which he had so much faith, intended by benefacting the abbey to engage the prayers of the monks on behalf of his soul. In the year 1065 he granted important privileges to the abbey, contained in a charter from which the following is an extract:

All things that are written, observes the apostle, are written for our learning, that by patience, and consolation of the scriptures we may have hope. Therefore, eternable durable joys are to be purchased instead of earthly and fleeting ones, and good things are to be obtained by hope. For God himself will render retribution of all our actions in the day of examination, according to everyone's desert. Wherefore, I, Edward, through the divine favour governing the royal sceptre of the English, being asked by Brithric, abbot of the monastery of Malmesbury, with the consent of my bishops and nobles, for the honour of the holy mother of God, Mary, perpetual virgin, and for reverence of St Aldhelm, formerly abbot of the same monastery, afterwards Bishop of Sherborne, whose glorious body in the same church venerably reposeth, and shines with many miracles, do grant, and by my royal authority do enjoin, that the same church and all its lands and possessions which this day it holds, or hereafter by the bounty of my faithful people it may hold, in perpetual right and in perpetual peace they may hold.

And I do grant and enjoin that the same church be free from all wordly yoke, namely, of shires, and hundreds, and pleas, and quarrels, and all gelds and customs. I grant, moreover, to it full liberty, that is Saca and Toka, Tol and Theam, Infangtheoffe, Manbuche, &c. Whoever, therefore, assists this our donation of liberty, may it lead him to the enjoyment of Paradise. Whoever contemns it, may he with hands and feet bound, be plunged into the depth of hell.

The opening sentences of the charter contain evidence enough of the purpose for which it was granted. It was for the purchase of 'eternable durable joys'. The preamble is remarkable as showing how thoroughly Edward's mind had become imbued with the doctrines of religion, so that even in a legal deed he could not resist the opportunity of exhortation. 'All things that are written, observes the apostle, are written for our learning, that by patience and consolation of the scriptures we may have hope.' This might without suspicion of quotation from a deed of this character be made the opening sentence of a sermon. Certainly it may be quite correct that 'eternable durable joys are to be purchased instead of earthly and fleeting ones', but it seems difficult to discover the connection between the promise and the conclusion. Where is the why of the 'therefore'? That why instead of preceding follows. It is because 'God himself will render retribution of all our actions in the day of examination, according to everyone's desert'. Meantime it probably escaped Edward that whilst he thought himself of laying up treasures for future enjoyment above, his monks and priests who so highly extolled 'eternable durable joys' were remarkably fond of the 'earthly and fleeting ones' – such as gold and silver, woods, meadows, and lands. It was wonderful that no suspicion ever seems to have entered the heads of the gentlemen who lived in the good old times as to the sincerity of these professions. It never seems to have occurred to them that whilst they themselves parted with everything in order to obtain these 'eternable durable joys,', the monks who affected to put so low a value upon the 'earthly and fleeting ones' took good care to get as many as possible of them into their possession, and made noise enough if such 'impious wretches' as the Danes, for instance, dared to lay hands upon their sacred stores. Herein, too, again appears the name of the venerated St Aldhelm; he seems to have been then considered a saint worthy of being placed in close propinquity to 'Mary, perpetual virgin, who herself follows next to God'. It appears incidentally that the body of St Aldhelm was then still at Malmesbury 'and shines with many miracles'. This would seem to intimate that miracles were considered to be worked at the shrine of St Aldhelm in the same way as they were at that of Thomas à Becket, famous in after times. The grant of 'perpetual peace' would, no doubt, have been thought by the monks as an inestimable gift had not experience shown them that it was but a mere phrase. The following sentence was far more satisfactory. 'And I do grant and enjoin, that the same church be free from all worldly yoke.' Here was something substantial, and although a 'fleeting' earthly joy it does not appear that the monks were so wrapt up in the contemplation of 'eternable and durable' ones as to refuse its acceptance; nor, indeed, can it be supposed that they found fault with the next: 'I grant, moreover, to it full liberty, that is Saca, and Toka, Tol and Theam, Infangtheoffe, Manbuche. Very curious antique phrases these, and somewhat hard to decipher in their exact and indisputable meaning. They, however, may be taken as generally to imply those manorial rights which were so marked a feature of the feudal times, most of which all in the present day consider themselves in full possession of, without having ever received a charter from the reigning monarch − such as the liberty of sale or purchase, having markets, mills and fairs, and things of the like nature. There was another right now to be obtained, at least in that fullness and completeness which was characteristic of that period − the right of exercising jurisdiction over vassals. The Baron of Bradwardine, however, according to Sir Walter Scott, prided himself upon having in the middle of the eighteenth century documents which gave him full power to hang, draw and quarter his retainers, making him in fact a king upon a small scale on his estate; which rights the baron somehow thought it prudent not to exercise.

The most curious part of the charter is its conclusion – 'Whoever, therefore, assists this our donation of liberty, may it lead him to the enjoyment of Paradise. But whoever contemns it, may he, with hands and feet bound, be plunged into the depth of hell.' This blessing upon him who should follow out the purpose or intention of the donor, and curse upon him who should thwart it, seems to have been an ordinary wind-up to such deeds in those days. Some resemblance may perhaps be traced in it to the last verses of the Apocalypse, where the writer states that if any man should take away from what he had there put down, God would take away from him his 'part out of the book of life'. The charter makes no mention whatever of the town of Malmesbury, though conferring upon the monastery manorial rights which it may be supposed would be sure to affect the town more or less. It is conjectured at that date to have formed part of the royal demesnes. The authority of the abbots then probably extended only to the abbey lands and appendages, which, however, were very large. According to the charter of Edward the Confessor, the numerous manors which had been granted, or given to the monastery at various times, and by various persons, were no less than three hundred and forty hides of land. If the estimate which assigns one hundred acres to the hide be the correct one – some even assert that it was one hundred and twenty – there would then be the enormous number of thirty-four thousand acres of land in the possession of the abbey. All this was not of course under cultivation. Much of it was probably occupied or feudal tenure, and did not return a direct rent. But even then the income derived from it must have been immense. Allowing only one-third to be properly cultivated, or say ten thousand acres, then reckoned in modern money, and at the rents of the present day, this would give an income of at least fifteen thousand, if not twenty thousand pounds. The lands must have extended for miles and miles: it may be doubted whether the most extended view that it was possible to obtain from the abbey steeples would include the whole.

The abbey itself was a structure correspondingly grand. It was built in the form of a cross, and if tradition is to be trusted, covered a space of forty-five acres. This seems scarcely probable. Forty-five acres! There are many farms of less extent. But when examined, the tradition turns out to have a foundation in fact. In calculating the extent of the abbey there must not only be taken into consideration what is called the conventual, or abbey church. To this must be added the residence of the abbots, and the vast buildings set apart for the use of the monks. It must be remembered that in such edifices as that of Malmesbury, the peculiar offices which were the distinguishing feature of a monastery – such as the eleemosynaria or almshouse, the infirmary, and the sanctuary – were all separate structures from the main building. The monks had, too, their weavers, tanners, shoemakers, bakers, and the like, all of whom had, of course, their shops. In short, a monastery was a town in itself. There were the outdoor and uncovered appanages, such as ambulatories, or places for the monks to exercise themselves in, orchards, rabbit warrens, fishponds, gardens. There were also dove-yards, and even vineyards. The Malmesbury dove-yard long after it had disappeared gave its name to the spot upon which it had once stood, if it does not do so now. The historian of Malmesbury states that a Grecian monk, one Constantine, travelled there from his own land, and bringing with him a knowledge of the treatment of the vine, he planted a vineyard. This, it appears from the same writer, was situated towards the south and west of the Worthys. These monks of Malmesbury seem to have been well provided for. When all these circumstances are taken into consideration, there seems little room to doubt the afore-mentioned tradition. Reckoning abbey church, monastery proper, abbot's mansion, the various offices, and the surrounding gardens, orchards, and vineyards – all probably under the immediate superintendence of the monks – it certainly may have covered forty-five acres, which the tradition assigns it.

It may here be remarked that there was a farm no great distance from the town, and upon the road to Chippenham, which was a grange belonging to the monastery; that is, it was under the superintendence of one of those individuals known as *grangiarii* and its produce perhaps especially applied to the sustenance of the monks.

These numerous houses and farms, scattered all over the country and known as the granges, seem all to have been at one time or another connected with some monastery. The monks at Malmesbury seem to have had no necessity – at least in so far as material comforts were concerned – to repine at their lot. They had a magnificent house to live in, an enormous income both in corn and kind. If they delighted in gardening, as men of their class generally did, there were acres upon acres of land attached to the abbey upon which to exercise their skill. If they had a literary taste they had every means to gratify it at their disposal. They had, indeed, their religious routine to be attended to, but it does not seem to have been of a very onerous character. It must certainly have taken up some time, and been found at first rather awkward; but no doubt time accustomed them to perform it without difficulty.

The day was divided into eight services. The first of them began at twelve, or one o'clock in the morning, and was called matins. The next was lauds, at three, after which the majority retired to the dormitory, but some spent the interval to prines at six in private prayer. Then at eight or nine – authorities differ, and so may the customs at different times and in different places – came thirds; after which the monks repaired to the chapter house. Here the prior proclaimed a sort of petty sessions by pronouncing the words 'Lo-quamur, de ordine nostro', that is, 'Let us speak of our order' (or of the affairs of our order). When there were any complaints to be made, or submissions to be heard, there were they listened to, and proceeded with. To this succeeded the service of the sixth hour, after which study and literary work was the order. Now came the nones, when a service was sung. It was now time to dine, and dinner was accordingly served up in the refectory; whither went the monks; even this could not be done without psalm-singing or praying. It is not improbable that the modern custom of saying grace before and after meat originated in the monasteries. After dinner succeeded the vespers, and that service concluded, the monks were free to dispose of their time until five, which was the ancient supper time. Then came a conference of sacred subjects, to which succeeded the office called compline, at six. That over, and the day's work was done. They might retire to bed, wherein they are said to have taken their slumber without undressing – at least such was the custom in some abbeys.

Like modern clergymen, on Sunday the monks delivered exhortations. It is obvious that the monks could never have engaged in all these services. They were probably divided by a kind of tacit agreement amongst them. Here and there might perhaps be one who either from the absolute want of something else to occupy his mind, from real piety, that is in sincerity, or else from a desire to gain a name for it, was careful in his attendance upon them all; but in all probability when once the novelty of the thing had worn off, the majority shirked the routine as much as possible. It was not such a pleasant thing to get up at one o'clock of a cold rainy winter's morning, to go through a service as cold and inanimate as routine could make it. Nor could it have been altogether agreeable to be obliged to retire to rest so very early in the evening in order to be able to arise at the required moment. It must have been far pleasanter to sit over the burning logs of wood, and dip deep into the circling horn of mead; whilst some old greybeard told the tale of the days of long ago – to the smoke that curled up the chimney probably, since such gentlemen are apt to be remarkably diffuse and digressive.

The principal officers over the monasteries which were independent of the bishops – of which was Malmesbury – were the prior and sub-prior. The prior was next to the abbot, and governed the abbey when he was absent. The sub-prior had also a share in the controlling of the monks. Below him was the cellarer – that is, the house-steward, a place of no mean importance in certain places, since it is related that the city of Ely was under the government of the cellarer of that ancient abbey. Next came the almoner, or distributor, or at least superintendent of alms which each day were distributed to the poor; the pittancer, who took care of the extra provisions shared out on certain occasions; the chamberlain, who looked after the sleeping department or dormitory, and supplied the monks with some part of their clothing; lastly came the lay-brethren, who elected them to the service of the proper monks – performing menial offices, or tilling the land. Here was an establishment of a wonderful extent, and, as might have been expected, the monastical monarchs – the abbots – who were the heads of the concern, lived in no small state. Not only had they their proper mansion adjoining the monastery, but actually had country seats and parks upon the estates belonging to the abbey. Cole Park, in the neighbourhood of Malmesbury (anciently known as Cowfolde Park), was one of the parks of the Malmesbury abbots. Only one – mark that! Such was their sumptuousness. These abbots were almost entirely, if not quite, independent of the bishops, and were known as mitred abbots. Their jurisdiction was supreme in their district, and they even had seats in the House of Lords. It could scarcely be expected that with all these dignities the abbots should be remarkable for their humility. Accordingly it is related that when upon their travels they were attended by a vast train of retainers; he of Glastonbury, when he went out, had upwards of one hundred – so that it was said their trains resembled the triumphal processions of a Caesar, that is of an emperor! No wonder with the chance of arriving at this elevation that men of an ambitious turn became monks, and submitted to deprive themselves of pleasures by vows which, moreover, in later times at least, they were absolved from keeping in anything but name. The ceremony of initiation was very simple, at least in the order of St Benedict, which was that professed at Malmesbury. The aspirant was taken into the church, Miserere sung, appropriate prayers offered up, the benediction given, the secular habit put off, and the monastic assumed, which was followed by prayer, then came the kiss of peace, and after three days of silence the novice had become a monk.

Such was the vast establishment which arose from the hermit's cell of Meyldulph. No wonder Herman wished to remove his episcopal see to Malmesbury; nor that the monks, who perhaps saw that if such a project was carried into execution their chance of becoming abbot was gone, vehemently opposed him.

2
The Monk Oliver: William the Conqueror

Whilst the public affairs of the abbey were receiving so much attention – and, it may be added, the possessions of the monastery were
being so much extended – the internal affairs of the establishment
once more became conspicuous. The monks for whom all these
benefits were designed and received, and who through them became
celebrated, again spring into notice for their own peculiar accomplishments, or rather those of one of them. For perhaps three-
quarters of a century Malmesbury had not produced a man who had
made himself famous, and through his exertions added new laurels
to those already in the possession of the abbey. Since the death of the
celebrated Ælfric, or rather his translation from Malmesbury to the
bishopric of Crediton, there had been no man of Malmesbury who
had lifted himself into notice. Malmesbury monastery had itself
become famous through the connection with such men as King
Edgar and Edward the Confessor and no doubt the memory of St
Dunstan, who enshrined the bones of St Aldhelm, was held in much
reverence here; but the monks themselves, like the ten abbots whose
names alone survive, do not seem during this three-quarters or more
of a century to have rendered themselves more distinguished than
usual. There was now, however, a plant growing up within the
shelter of the Malmesbury monastery who was destined again to
attract, through his own personal exertions, the attention of the
world. Those ancient walls that had witnessed the performances of
such men as Aldhelm and Athelard were again to behold an extraordinary man.

Somewhere about this time the monk Oliver rises into notice. Of
his birth, parentage, and early days, like those of so many of his
celebrated contemporaries, little or nothing seems known with cer-
tainty. His very name has not been uniformly spelt. Besides Oliver,
he has also been called Egelmer, or Elmer. There is an apparent

difference between these two last names enough to arouse a suspicion of the existence of another who had been confounded with the Malmesbury man. But the fact seems to be that in the ancient writings not only was 'g' very near in its form to 'y', but that the early printers often confounded the two. Eyelmer would naturally be contracted to Elmer. Neither of these names is suited to the modern tongue, hence that of Oliver has been here preferred.

Until Oliver became a monk of Malmesbury monastery, little or nothing seems known concerning him, though it has been asserted that he was born there. But he was not a man of the ordinary stamp, who upon mingling with so many monks would lose his identity amongst them. His genius could no more be mixed and lost in their uniformity than oil with water; though he joined them, and lived with them, he was still separate and individual. Study amongst them, like almost everything else, religion not excepted, had been reduced to a routine. Regularly after the service called sixths, which was that immediately preceding nones, or the midday service, they were marched off into the cloisters, there to spend their time until dinner in what was called study. This chiefly consisted in such manual labour as transcribing or illuminating. It cannot certainly be denied that they transcribed with the greatest care; nevertheless mistakes were made. But allowing their transcriptions to have been perfectly correct, this cannot entitle them to more praise than that of possessing patience. There could be nothing original in the mere act of copying. Illuminating on the other hand was a process which certainly required some considerable skill, taste, and even genius. It consisted in ornamenting those works which had been transcribed with figures, borders, or gigantic initial letters in colour. The works over which they appear to have spent most time in this way were the Mass-books, or missals, many of which are still preserved and even under glass cases, as at Oxford and in the British Museum, strike the eye with the brilliance of their hues. The reason probably that the missal received so much attention was the reverence in which it was held, almost approaching that paid to the Bible itself, persons being sworn upon the missal as they are now upon the Testament in the present law courts – to which practice indeed it may be conjectured that the monks with respect to their missal gave rise. The figures

with which the missals were ornamented, though sometimes only
remarkable for their oddity, often did the designer and executor
much credit, while the illuminated initial letters are of so dazzling
and brilliant a description that it is difficult to conceive how the
novices contrived to fix their attention upon the text. A practice
somewhat similar to this prevails even at the present day, though it is
now done by the aid of engraving.

From these illuminated works much curious information has been
gathered concerning the residences of our ancestors, and from the
portraits to be found upon them a regular series has been formed
illustrating the features possessed by our earlier kings or rulers.
Although it is of course impossible to place much reliance upon this,
yet the thing is very curious, since in the nineteenth century may be
seen through the labours of the monks approximate portraits of the
monarchs of the ninth. Such were the usual studies of the monks.
But Oliver could not be thus confined. Although he appears to have
been a man of much learning, and had no doubt perused the works of
the ancients, it was not so much as a man of deep erudition that he
was to become famous as for one who originated something. His
favourite study seems to have been mathematics, since he is recorded
to have written a work upon geometry, nor did he scorn the darker
mysteries of divination, since he, like his celebrated predecessor, St
Aldhelm, is also related to have issued a book upon astrology, then
by no means a science in so much disrepute as at present. Neither of
these has survived the ravages of time.

It was not as an author that Oliver was to be famous. His favourite
study, mathematics, probably led him by insensible degrees to turn
his attention to mechanics. But in this science he was not to be
bounded by the narrow circle of productions which had preceded
him. He did not make himself renowned by constructing a mill to
grind the abbey corn, nor did he search for the fulcrum – which
Archimedes so much desired – whereupon to rest a lever that should
enable him to overturn the world, and thus shoot far beyond Alexander, who merely conquered its surface. Oliver, confined in his cell,
seems to have envied the free denizens of the air, since, like the
Psalmist, he appears to have wished for the wings of the dove, that
he might fly away; though as for rest it would perhaps in those days

have been difficult to discover a place more favourable to that than the Malmesbury monastery, guaranteed as it was by Edward the Confessor's charter, in the possession of perpetual peace. Oliver, in short, had a great longing to emulate the doves who cooed and circled around the haughty steeples of the abbey. He found that his monastic habit was no magic mantle by which, like that used by Mephistopheles, he could raise himself up and float through the atmosphere like a swift winged swallow. He required the aid of artificial means. He set himself to work, and no doubt after many trials, deep thought and much monastical meditation, came to the conclusion that he had at length discovered the means which was to open up a new element – the air – to man's dominion.

It has been said that he was a bold man who first ate an oyster. He must have been not less bold who could do what Oliver did. Ascending one of the abbey towers he placed his machinery in order and, fearlessly trusting himself upon it, launched himself forth into the atmosphere. Nor did he sink immediately to the ground, as no doubt the monks had confidently predicted. What must have been their astonishment to behold him floating high in the air over those gardens and orchards amongst which they had no doubt seen him roam like other men upon his feet? What must have been Oliver's own sensations as he felt himself borne along by the wind in a region no great distance beneath the clouds? What did the doves and swallows think upon beholding this unfeathered, huge, unwieldy bird skimming along beneath the sky? So gigantic a hawk it would be difficult to elude had he a power of turning, twisting, and rapid flight corresponding to his size. But their apprehensions upon that head were quickly laid. Oliver, after floating no less than a furlong, or over two hundred yards, was seen to descend rapidly, apparently compelled by a power over which he had no control. He had fallen. When assisted to rise it was discovered that the shock of his descent had fractured both his legs; thus dearly had he paid for a few moments of success. This adventure must have caused an enormous amount of talk amongst the Malmesbury men at that date. Legends they might indeed have heard of witches cutting through the air on a moonlit night by merely bestriding a besom, and greasing it to go faster. The monks themselves had no doubt heard from their learned companions of Daedalus and Icarus's unfortunate attempt. But all these were nothing more than traditions. Here was the real thing. They had seen it. It was perhaps fortunate for Oliver that he did injure himself, since otherwise it would have been ten to one if he were not set down as a magician, like the celebrated Roger Bacon, who flourished no great while afterwards. As it was, he could not be accused of sorcery, since he would certainly in that case have provided for his own safety, if not success. Of what construction his machinery was seems open to dispute. It certainly was not a balloon. He is described as placing wings upon his hands and feet; but such an account is too wide and loose to be accepted in its literal sense. These wings were probably something which spread out and supported him – like a huge umbrella or parachute. No matter whatever it was. He flew, though his flight was a short one. He must have been a man of no little courage, since there does not seem to be any record of any one having previously made such an attempt either in Britain or abroad. Malmesbury, then, was the scene of the first English aeronautic attempt.

Oliver's accomplishments, moreover, did not end here. Not only did he study astrology, but is related to have been something of a prophet. In those days, as is well known, and indeed for long after, the appearance of a comet was beheld with awe as the forerunner of dearth, death or disaster. Such superstitions were not confined to comets. A curious instance is given in Ethelwerd's *Chronicle:* 'A.D. 734 . . . The moon appeared as if stained with spots of blood, and by the same omen Tatwine and Bede departed this life'; and previously in 729 'a comet appeared, and the Holy Bishop Egbert died'. It happened that shortly after the death of a French monarch in 1060 or thereabouts, one of those mysterious skyey strangers, a comet, made its appearance in the heavens. Oliver upon seeing it gave utterance to the following prophecy: 'Art thou arrived, O messenger of evil, omen of that destruction which shall cause many mothers to pour forth lamentations!'

Nor was he wrong. A day was fast approaching which certainly should cause 'many mothers to pour forth lamentations' and even perhaps force tears from eyes that had never wept before. A foreign yoke was preparing for England. Events were thickening fast.

William, called the Conqueror, landed upon the British coast near Hastings on September 28, 1066 and after defeating King Harold, whose forces had been exhausted by contests in another part of the kingdom, seized the crown. However great a misfortune this even may have been for the English of that date, it in the end had at least the effect, strange as it may seem, not of destroying all vestiges of the ancient state of Britain, but of preserving them. Just as an heir upon taking possession of an estate hitherto unsurveyed would probably cause it to be mapped out at earliest convenience; so King William on a gigantic scale had his newly gained kingdom surveyed, and the accounts written down in a work since known as the Domesday Book. That work fortunately is still in existence, and, even were it ever destroyed, has been so carefully copied that little real loss would be sustained. It enables the antiquary to become acquainted with the state of the land in the days of the Conqueror. When the surveyors reach Wiltshire it appears that Malmesbury was the first place investigated. The following is an extract from a translation of that part of Domesday Book, relating to the Malmesbury manors:

The king has 26 messuages in the borough of Malmesbury, and 25 other messuages that pay no taxes. These houses pay ten pence each as rent, in all forty-two shillings and sixpence. Half a ruined messuage, part of the fee of the Bishop of Bayeux, does no service. The Abbot of Malmesbury has four messuages and a half, and the out-burgesses have nine cottages [coscez] who are assessed with the burgesses. The Abbot of Glastonbury has two messuages. Edward the Sheriff three messuages. Radulf de Mortemer has one and a half. Durand de Gloucestre one and a half. William de Ou one. Humphrey de L'isle one. Osbern Giffard one. Alured de Merlebergh has half a ruined messuage. Geoffery Mariscul the like. Tovi has one messuage, and the fourth part of another. Drogo, son of Ponz, half a one. The wife of Edric has one. Roger de Berchelai holds one under the king, and Ernulf de Hesding the like; which he unguardedly took possession of. These two do no services. The king has a waste tract of land which belonged to Azòr.

The king received from the third penny of Malmesberie six pounds. Walter Hosed pays the king eight pounds from two parts of the borough of Malmesbury, and the borough itself paid as much T. R. E. [*Tempori Regis Edwardi;* that is, within the reign of Edward the Confessor], and the pleas of the hundreds of Cicemtone and Sutelesbery were holden in this manor, which belonged to the king. The borough pays one hundred shillings in money. The Earl Harold had an acre of land in this borough in which are four messuages, and six other minors, and a mill pays ten shillings. All this paid T. R. E. one hundred shillings; and when he undertook any expedition by sea or land he accepted either twenty shillings, towards the maintenance of the sailors; or took with him one man for the honour of five hides [say five hundred acres of land]. The Bishop [of Coutances] held Malmesberie. Gislebert held it T. R. E., when it was assessed at one hide. Here is half a yardland. Three yardlands are in demesne, where is half a plough land, with three borderers [bordarii]. Here are four acres of meadow, and the pasture in length two furlongs, and in breadth one. It is worth thirteen shillings.

Chetel holds one hide at Malmesberie. Goodwin held it T. R. E. Here is one ploughland, which is in demesne. With the borderers [bordarii] there are six acres of meadow; and the pasture is three furlongs in length, and half a ploughland. It is worth twenty shillings.

The commission set afloat by William may have performed their labours in a manner suited to his expectations, but their survey would scarcely have satisfied a modern monarch. It would appear that in those days Malmesbury belonged to the crown. The King is described as having no less than fifty-one messuages there in the first sentence quoted above. The rent certainly was not in modern estimation much to find fault with – only tenpence each – but the value of money in those days was far higher than at present. The Bishop of Bayeux, if we remember aright, also held extensive property in the neighbourhood of Swindon. The term coscez is supposed to have arisen from a French word meaning to lie down, and those who held possessions under that tenure were obliged to furnish their lord with lodging should he pass that way. There were nine cottages in coscez in the possession of the out-burgesses of Malmesbury. The name of Alured de Merlebergh seems to intimate that he also had some connection with Marlborough – anciently spelt Marlebrough, a very near approach to Merlebergh.

Ernulf de Hesding is mentioned as holding one messuage 'which he unguardedly took possession of'. Did he then seize it when unguarded? Such a thing would have been by no means out of character with the times. The Bishop of Coutances is described as holding Malmesbury, probably as other manors were held. A ploughland has been estimated at about one hundred and twenty acres; and a fourth of a ploughland, or say thirty acres, was called a yardland. Three of these yardlands are represented as in demesne, that is, they were in possession of the lord of the manor, and cultivated for his especial benefit by his *servi,* a word whose meaning very nearly approached that of slaves. The service which the *bordarii* performed was that of providing such articles as poultry and eggs for their lord; such being those which they are supposed to have possessed in the greatest quantity. The other terms used in the above quotation respecting land are meadow and pasture – pasture being that which is now generally called leaze, that land fed by cattle, and meadow meaning such land as was mowed for hay. The pasture here spoken of was 'in length two furlongs [over four hundred yards] and in breadth one furlong. It is worth thirteen shillings.' Was this the annual rent or the actual value? If the actual value it appears almost ridiculously small, and even if only the rent was to be understood would be in modern times utterly out of proportion. The Abbot of Malmesbury held four and a half messuages. The word messuages appears to be derived from a French term meaning house-room. It is now written by them *maison.* Here it probably means a house and adjoining land. All these terms are now sufficiently wide and loose to cause a deal of discussion, but were then probably understood well enough.

They do not seem to have cared much for details, these noble ancestors of ours. If they cooked meat it was often whole animals, and it is an indisputable fact that they measured their meat just as we do land, by the yard and foot. Imagine a yard of beef! About three square inches would perhaps puzzle a modern, but the capacious maws of the Conqueror's companions – capacious enough to swallow up all England – were not probably satisfied with less than half a foot on their platters, if it were only for dignity's sake. They used the same daggers with which they stuck their enemies instead of knives. They cared little about detail. The same disregard was carried into everything, and land did not escape. A plough-land must have frequently varied in extent, if it was as much as one plough could properly till, and consequently its divisions. What matter – they who measured their meat by yards were scarcely likely to care about a rood more or less.

3
Estates of the Abbey: William the Conqueror

Nothing that the most cruel and tyrannous ingenuity could have devised could in all probability have brought home to the minds of the Saxon thanes or nobles – and, indeed, their followers – the condition of subjection to which they had been brought than the system of surveying set on foot by the Conqueror. There must have been many a distant outlying place – far away from the fatal field where the battleaxe of the Saxons went down before the lance of the Normans; far, too, from the capital, as was Malmesbury – which had never yet beheld the steel headpieces or prancing chargers of the dreaded and hated invaders. But there was not a nook in England into which the commission sent out by the Conqueror was not to penetrate, not a homestead that was not to be registered, not a cottager but he must tell whether he was one of the coscez, and obliged to give lodgings upon occasion to his lord, or a *bordarius,* and compelled to provide him with poultry and similar provisions. This must have been extremely irritating to the Saxon population. Few things at this day are more unpleasant than the rendering up an account to the tax-gatherer of the extent of property in possession; how must it have been then? When no man knew not but that the ancient home of his fathers might attract the attention of some Norman knight, and then what could save it for his family? For the Conqueror was most liberal – as well he might be – to his companions. Not only did he dispose of property which never had been and was never likely to come into his personal possession, but by spreading out his band over the country each Saxon earl, or churl, each Saxon thane or noble was taught to feel the power of the Norman, and no combination could be made to dispossess him of his conquest since he had willing spies in every direction. His companions thus received their reward, and most liberal these rewards were. Witness the couplet in one of the cantos of *Don Juan,* when, speaking of his own ancestors, Lord Byron writes:

> Ernulf and Radulfus – eight and forty manors
> Were their reward for following Billy's banners.

These names, Ernulf and Radulfus – or Radulf with the Latin termination 'us' – both occur in the preceding quotation from that part of Domesday Book relating to Malmesbury given in the last chapter. Yet says the poet very truly

> I can't help thinking it was scarcely fair
> To strip the Saxons of their *hides* like tanners.

The pun is a good one – hides not only meaning skins but, as has already been shown, a Saxon measure of land. How the term originated it would be difficult to decide, unless there was once in old time an English Queen Dido. Dido, be it known, landing with a few subjects in a foreign land, asked of its prince as much land to build a city upon as she could cover with an ox's hide. He laughed, and granted her modest request. Thereupon that deceiver Dido cut the hide up into long thin strips, and so encompassed a goodly measure of land, sufficient for her purpose.

Still, however disagreeable the working of the Conqueror's commission may have been to the then inhabitants of the land, it was most advantageous to the antiquary, since through their record – the Domesday Book – he has, as it were, a map of England in the latter part of the eleventh century. In the last chapter this was sufficiently well shown by quotations from it which referred chiefly to the manor of Malmesbury. But the advantages of it do not stop there. Even the sacred seat of St Aldhelm was not to be left unpolluted by the Norman steel-clad tread. The halls of this ancient abbey at Malmesbury had to re-echo the scarce subdued laugh of the invader, and the guardians of the wide lands which, since the Saxons had founded it, had grown wider and wider, were to render up an account of their possessions. What must have been the sensations of the Malmesbury monks when they beheld the Conqueror's commission at the gates of their monastery? If they suffered, the present generation have got the benefit. Things are balanced after seven hundred years have elapsed. This is a warning not to judge hastily. Through the record contained in Domesday Book, not only can we ascertain the extent of the property then belonging to the abbey between the years 1081 and 1086, during which the record was preparing; but its actual value at that date and approximately at the present; while curious facts concerning the ancient names of places in the neighbourhood of Malmesbury may also be gathered.

It must be understood that the Norman pound – unlike, very unlike, the sovereign of today whose weight is estimated by grains – the Norman pound actually *weighed* a pound. It was a pound's weight of silver. Like the present sovereign it was divided into twenty shillings, but there again the likeness ends. The Norman shilling must have been equal in weight to three of the shillings in use at the present day, consequently its value even nominally must have been three times that of the modern coin. But to get at its true value another thing must be taken into consideration, namely the relative proportion which a certain coin bore in those days to the amount of kind to be obtained by it. In other words, what could you in 1081 have bought with a Norman shilling? How many men could you have employed with it for a week? Or how long would a single man have laboured to gain possession of it? Then by comparing the modern value of labour or provisions with that of the ancient, the value of that certain coin is arrived at – that is, approximately.

Now authorities differ concerning the price of labour in those days, some placing it as *high* as eleven pence a week, others reducing it to nine pence; and both supporting their opinions by diverse good and satisfactory reasons, which, however, only prove what must at once be evident to all, that just as the value of labour varies at the present day in various places and at various times – even in the different months of the year – so it did then, seven hundred years and more ago. A modern would estimate the price which he had to pay for labour by striking an average; the same process applied to these different accounts makes the usual pay for labour in the days of William the Conqueror as ten pence a week. Ten pence a week! With what joy would farmers hail a return of such 'good old times'! They might, however, find themselves mistaken. Labourers had to support themselves then as now, although, no doubt, they received a good deal in kind from their employers, but this added to their ten pence would be against the employer. It cannot then be otherwise than supposed that the ten pence a week of the ancient labourer was equal to the ten shillings of the modern one. From this calculation – and exactness is out of the question – it follows as a matter of necessity that in those days provisions and the other requirements of life were worth about twelve times as much as at present; that is, it was then possible to buy for a penny what would now be bought for a shilling, and what would then have cost a shilling would now be worth twelve. To estimate properly then the actual value of the rents, which will presently be given in modern money, it is not only necessary to multiply them by three in order to get the nominal value of the money, but also by twelve, that the actual value of the coin in these days may be arrived at. In other words to obtain a correct idea of the annual income of the abbots of Malmesbury in 1081, or in the day of the Conquest, as recorded in Domesday Book, it is necessary to multiply the sums therein given by thirty-six times.

The first manor which seems to be mentioned as in the possession of St Mary's Church at Malmesbury in the days of William the Conqueror is that of Hiwei, in Wiltshire, and it was valued – the extent being eleven hides – at eight pounds per annum. At that time it may be observed the ancient church of St Aldhelm was dedicated to him in conjunction with the Virgin Mary. Hence it was called the church of St Mary. The modern name of this manor is Hywaye. If the hide be estimated at one hundred acres, it must in those days have extended over no less than eleven hundred acres of land; and would form in itself in these days a very pretty present from a prince to a favourite. The rent of this estate was then eight pounds. Eight pounds for eleven hundred acres! At the present day that man would think himself extremely fortunate who could get it into his possession at £800. But it must not be forgotten that this eight pounds to be understood in modern money requires to be multiplied by thirty-six times. This makes only £288, still a very low sum. The annual rent, allowing the previous estimates to be correct, of a single acre would on this estate in the reign of William I have been only about five shillings.

There were, however, still several drawbacks. In the first place it cannot have been supposed to be so well cultivated as at present. No land was, nor was it possible for it to be so. Hence, the return it would make would be far less than at present. At this day in the backwoods of America land can be obtained for that sum. There must be also taken into consideration the fact that all land was in those days held in some form of feudal tenure. Now it was a distinguishing characteristic of this description of tenure that payments were often made in kind, and that the tenant was considered in a great extent personally under the control and at the disposition of his lord. Did the king undertake an expedition by sea or land he either expected (and in fact exacted) a certain amount of pecuniary assistance, or took with him 'one man for the honour of five hides'. Hence this estate, over and above paying certain annual rent, might also in case of emergency be called upon to furnish two men – no slight drawback. An instance of this had occurred in the reign of King Ethelred the Unready. Between the years 1006 and 1008 great preparations were made to resist the ever-increasing numbers of the Danes, under the celebrated Sweyn, and it is recorded that every owner of nine hides of land – say nine hundred or in round numbers a thousand acres – had to provide a man armed with headpiece and breastplate; while those who possessed three hundred and ten hides – say thirty thousand acres, much such an estate as that which the present Duke of Rutland is so famous for farming – had to furnish forth a ship for the contest. Again the tenant was expected, had his lord any private feuds against his neighbours, to assist him not only by proxy but in person. To these drawbacks, too, must be added the incessant danger from marauders or the incensed retainers of another lord, so that no man knew that his house might not be burned over his head during the night; himself murdered with a crossbow bolt as he endeavoured to escape; and his daughter, if she happened to be beautiful, carried off to satiate the sensuality of some brutal Saxon thane or a dissolute Norman noble. Moreover, in all probability, his estate was partially settled upon by cottagers from whom he could get but little, perhaps its borders were ill marked and consequently liable to encroachment, or a great part of it moorland or furzeland, unfit for much except breeding rabbits. Altogether these eleven hundred acres at a fraction over five shillings an acre would have been scarcely so desirable a possession as a modern homestead at a modern high rent. The modern English farmer has at least peace – so essential to success. To us it has always been a matter of wonder and admiration of their perseverence how in those days farmers did contrive to get a living at all. What with Danes and Normans, private feuds, and public quarrels, marauders, and feudal obligations, the life of a yeoman must have been in those days one of unceasing toil and incessant care. It had, however, perhaps one good effect, that of exercising almost all in the use of arms, and to this may probably be traced the rapid progress which England made in gaining the respect of the world when once she became united in herself. Still to look around at the smiling English landscape of the present day, to gaze along the banks of such a river as the Avon at Malmesbury, one can but earnestly hope that the last drop of blood has been shed upon British sod, and that never more may British water be mingled with British gore. The men of Malmesbury, with their traditions of the glorious days of Athelstan, would doubtless echo the sentiments of the two townsmen in *Faust:*

2nd Townsman
Nothing I know to me has greater charms
Upon a Sunday or a holiday (say the second Tuesday after Trinity),
Than a snug chat of war and war's alarms
While people fight in Turkey far away.
One stands besides the window – takes his glass,
Sees down the stream the painted vessels pass,
Then gladly home returns as evening chimes,
With blessings upon peace and peaceful times.

3rd Townsman
Yes, neighbour, yes! I little care,
How matters may be managed there,
All things they there may overthrow,
And break each other's heads at will,
Only at home pray let us go
According to old custom still.

The next place that is mentioned in the Domesday Book record is what then called Dantesie, which extended over ten hides and paid six Norman pounds, or £204 modern money. This is now known as Dantsey – a very slight change in the spelling for so many centuries. Upon this estate there stood a mill which paid a rent of twenty shillings. Mills in those days, as at present, seem to have been very profitable concerns. The reason then was their scarcity. It was one of the manorial rights of the lord to be allowable to erect a mill or to allow another to do so, and none who lived within the boundaries of his manor dared to carry his corn elsewhere to be ground. This no doubt was a right that was often abused and must have led to great oppression of the poor, as all such monopolies invariably do. Twenty shillings was a large sum of money in those days. Multiplied by thirty-six to get its real value and it amounts to £36. At Dantesie, there was also a wood no less than three-quarters of a mile square. The next place is spelt Brecheorde, which brought in a rent of four Norman or 142 modern pounds. The extent was five hides. This estate contained another wood whose breadth was one furlong, and length two. Brecheorde is supposed to survive in the modern name Brinkworth.

Nortone, now Norton, where were five hides of land, paid four Norman pounds. Here also was a mill which paid fifteen shillings. Chemele, now Kemble, and Newentone, now Newton, each were recorded as consisting of thirty hides; the former paid £13, the latter £12. In Chemele there was a wood no less than a mile and a half long and three fulongs broad; as also two mills, which latter paid fifteen shillings. Two more mills in Newentone, or Newton, paid thirty shillings. Cerletone manor extended over twenty hides of land, say at least 2,000 acres; and paid eight pounds. It contained a wood two furlongs in length and one in breadth. A mill upon it paid fifteen shillings; which sum appears to have been the ordinary rent of a mill. This manor is now well known in the neighbourhood of Malmesbury as Charlton. The 'h' has often been added to Saxon words originally spelt without; as 'ceorl', now pronounced and written 'churl', originally meaning a husbandman, now a rude rustic fellow. Charles is said to be another variation of this word. So Charles's Wain, the constellation, would mean the waggon of the husbandman.

Gardone, three hides, paid five Norman or £180 modern money. It is now known as Garsdon, and then contained a wood two furlongs broad and three-quarters of a mile long; together with two mills paying twenty-five shillings. Credvelle, now Crudwell, forty hides, say four thousand acres, paid four pounds Norman, or £144

modern money. This vast estate was rented at about eighteen pence
an acre in the money of the present day! The reason soon becomes
evident – it had a wood within it three miles square. Wood in those
days was not so valuable as now. Breme, now Bramhill, thirty-eight
hides, or about three thousand eight hundred acres, was rented at £16
Norman money, or £576 modern money. This estate was probably
in a higher state of cultivation than the preceding, and it, moreover,
contained two mills paying thirty shillings. There was also a wood
three miles long, and a quarter broad. Piritone, better known as
Purton, of thirty-five hides paid also sixteen Norman pounds, or
£576 in modern money. In this there was a wood three miles square,
and a mill upon it paid five shillings – a lower sum than usual.
Liteltone, or Littleton, in Gloucestershire, also belonged to the
abbey, and was rented at five pounds, it containing five hides.
Another estate in Warwickshire, then known as Nieuebold now
Newbold, of three hides, paid £210 Norman money. But the largest
estate of all was one in the immediate neighbourhood of Malmesbury; now well known at least as a place – Brokenborough, then
spelt Brochenberge. Here were fifty hides, or five thousand acres,
rented at thirty Norman pounds or £1,080 in modern money. In this
too then was a large wood – extending indeed over an area four miles
and a half in length, and in breadth three miles! There were upon it,
too, eight mills paying £6.12s.6d Norman money. Altogether there
were fifteen manors containing 290 hides, say thirty thousand acres,
and yielding an annual income of £138.10s in Norman, or – allowing
the previously made estimation of the relative value of coin to be
correct – about £5,000 in modern money, in the possession of the
abbey of Malmesbury when Domesday Book was compiled in the
year 1081 A.D. Upon this vast estate – which afterwards received
additions – there were twenty-one mills, and woods of enormous
extent, at a rough calculation, say over twenty miles square.

No wonder that the abbot rode in state, no wonder that it was a
generally received idea that the monks lived comfortably! With a
money income of £5,000, and no doubt a vast quantity of provisions
was paid in kind, they could indeed afford to make Malmesbury
monastery one of the most magnificent in the kingdom; so that it
afterwards was commonly said the highest steeple at Malmesbury in

the days of the abbey's grandeur towered seven yards, or 21 feet, above that of the cathedral at Salisbury. And all this had resulted, all this had grown up from the simple hermit's cell erected by the wandering Scot – Meyldulph! An overwhelming illustration of the extraordinary power possessed by the Roman Catholic religion over the minds of its votaries. For all this was made up of gifts. Nothing had been taken by force. In those days truly the monks must have seemed the monarchs of Malmesbury.

When William the Conqueror landed in 1066, Brithric, who had been 'appointed' by Edward the Confessor, was abbot of the Malmesbury monastery. But when thanes and nobles were ejected from their estates all over the kingdom, it could not be expected that so valuable a living – if that term may be admitted – as Malmesbury would be left undisturbed. The Normans were even harder masters to the monks than the Danes; and Brithric was compelled to give up his place. The monk Turald was made abbot in his stead by the Conqueror – who made even the monks of Malmesbury feel that he was conqueror in reality as well as in name. Turald came from a place called Fescamp, in Normandy. He remained abbot until 1070, and was then being translated to Peterborough, succeeded by Warrin de Lara, who died in the same year that the surveying commission was set on foot – 1081. The Conqueror then appointed one Godfrey Gerneticensis abbot, whom he translated here from being the procurator of the famous abbey of Ely. Somewhere about this date the Conqueror himself became a benefactor of the abbey, and his charter, like that of Edward the Confessor, denounces maledictions upon those who should interfere with it, and blessings upon those who should add to the possessions of the abbey. His queen Matilda, too, whose character seems to have been very estimable, gave some land at Garston to the abbey. It may be doubted, however, whether her husband's gifts were dictated by pure piety. Here is his character given by the *Saxon Chronicle,* written by a contemporary:

He was a very wise man, and very rich and more splendid, and stronger than any of his predecessors were. He was mild to the good men who loved God [the clergy], and beyond all measure severe to the men that gainsayed his will. So stern was he, and wrathful, that one durst not do anything against his will. In his time had men much distress, and very many sorrows.

Castles he let men build, and miserably swink the poor. The king was very stern, and took from his subjects many a mark of gold, and many hundred pounds of silver, that he took with right and with great might from his people for little need. He was fallen into covetousness and greediness in land withal. He made great deer-parks, and therewith made laws that whoso killed a hart or a hind, that man should be blinded. He forbade [to touch] the harts, as also the hares; he loved the tall deer as if he were their father. He also set by the hares and they must go free. His rich men murmured, and the poor men shuddered at it; but he was so stern that he recked not all their hatred, for they must follow all the king's will if they would have life or have land, or even his peace.

He, however, refused to do homage to Pope Gregory VII and asserted his supremacy over the English clergy. He founded churches and monasteries; yet scarcely found burial in one of them. His death took place in 1087. He was about to be interred in the church of St Stephen's at Caen, when a voice was heard crying, 'Clerks and bishops, this ground is mine; it is the site of my father's house; the man you are praying for *took it from me to build this church*: on the part of God I forbid the body of the despoiler to be covered with my mould.' His demand was found just, and sixty shillings were paid him for the ground, which was too small and in putting down the body it burst, driving all from the church by the stench. Such was the end of the man who conquered England and deposed Brithric, the abbot of Malmesbury monastery.

4
Unsettled Times

The abbot of Malmesbury monastery, Godfrey Gerneticensis, whilome procurator of Ely, who had been translated from thence by William the Conqueror, enjoyed that office for some twenty-four years. He died in 1105. The Monk Edulf of Winchester then supplied his place, and reigned until the year 1118. He was then deposed by the celebrated Roger le Poer, Bishop of Sarum, or Salisbury. Roger le Poer was one of the most remarkable men of his age, and gave in his own person a striking instance of the unsettled state of the times which allowed men to rise from obscurity by the most singular paths. He appears to have been a Norman by birth and extraction. He early entered the Church, and became a curate at Caen, a place in Normandy, Here he might have remained, perhaps undistinguished, until his death, had it not been for his gaining the notice of Prince Henry, who afterwards became King of England, and was then surnamed Beauclerck, or fine scholar. The way, however, in which Roger was fortunate enough to attract the young prince's attention scarcely agrees with the character which that prince afterwards gained when a monarch. It is said that Roger mumbled over a Mass before the prince, whom he probably saw to be in a hurry, at such a rate that the royal worshipper swore aloud that he had at length discovered a priest fit to be the chaplain of a soldier. From that date Roger's fortune rapidly increased. He was attached to Henry's person forthwith, and no doubt made use of the many opportunities that position must have given him to ingratiate himself with the future monarch. Roger became Bishop of Sarum, the ancient name of Salisbury, in the year 1107. Henry, his patron, ascended the throne in 1110, and henceforth Roger became one of the chief men of the kingdom. He was advanced to the post of Lord Chief Justice, a place which was then it seems by no means deemed unfit for an ecclesiastic to hold. In that age the spiritualities and temporalities appear to have been intimately intermingled. The next step up the ladder of fortune

made him Lord Treasurer, and he finally became Lord Chancellor.
Even yet the scale of dignities which were to be showered upon him
had not been exhausted. He was so much in the confidence of Henry
that whilst the monarch was abroad or absent, Roger actually, if not
nominally, held the office of Regent of the kingdom. What must
have been the sensations of the man? Once a poor curate, now a king
in all but name. His was a life of strange vicissitudes. He had now
been advanced to the highest place which it was in the power of the
monarch to bestow: he had gained the summit of the mountain. It
was now his turn to descend. Henry died in 1135. Had justice been
regarded in those days his daughter, Matilda, would have succeeded
to the crown; but right was not yet strong enough to combat
ambition combined with ingratitude. Forgetting the benefits he had
received at the hands of Henry, Roger le Poer assisted Stephen
against the daughter of his dearest patron. Matilda's partisans were
too few and too little accustomed to act in concert, and Stephen
gained the throne.

Meantime Roger had not been idle at Malmesbury. He knew full
well that the times were of a character in which might was superior
to right. His own life had been an instance of that. The very king
upon the throne reigned in despite of right. It was not to be expected,
if royalty itself thus acted, that the subject's property would be safe.
Roger accordingly set about fortifying Malmesbury. He built a castle
which seems to have been adjacent to the abbey. It was an edifice that
did great credit to the architect and mason, the stones, according to a
historian, being so closely set together that their joints were not
perceivable, while the structure itself was magnificent. Roger also
built walls. In those days, as has been already remarked, the contractor, and the rapid rate of modern building operations, were unknown, and these fortifications seem to have been long in course of
erection. Roger, however, did not confine his attentions to Malmesbury; but seized also upon Abingdon Abbey. From such attentions in
all probability the abbot of Abingdon would have willingly been
excused.

Roger's reign was now rapidly drawing to a termination. His
black ingratitude to Henry would seem to have recoiled upon himself; and to those who are so inclined his downfall may furnish an

instance of reparation upon earth. King Stephen, it seemed, had acted as arbitrator between him and the Earl of Richmond, perhaps then better known as Allan of Bretain, with whom he had quarrelled. Roger le Poer, no doubt proud beyond measure, does not seem to have considered himself fairly treated, and in the plentitude of his power set at naught the majesty of the crown by attacking the earl. Herein he committed a fatal error. His ingratitude to Henry – his treachery to Matilda – had no doubt been observed and noted down by Stephen, who would probably draw from it the conclustion that, did opportunity serve, the offended bishop would not hesitate to turn traitor the second time. Moreover, the King had become alarmed at the enormous increase of ecclesiastical influence. Here was a fair pretext for striking a blow at its progress. Accordingly Stephen hesitated not to arrest both Roger and the Bishop of Lincoln, his nephew. Another of Roger's nephews even shut himself up in his uncle's castle at Devizes, and obstinately refused to surrender it. Stephen was successful, and the castle fell into his hands, as did also Roger's castles at Salisbury and Sherborne. Malmesbury Castle was also seized by the King. These events do indeed reveal the immense strides which the ecclesiastics had made to usurping both temporal and spiritual power in the kingdom. Here is one of the head members of the body, Roger le Poer, in possession of at least three castles, namely, Malmesbury, Sherborne, and Salisbury. Roger had held possession of Malmesbury not less than twenty years, when he was at length compelled to deliver it into the hands of the King. He was not, moreover, a solitary instance. Numerous other prelates held similar possessions – although so seemingly out of character with their sacred professions – and these of course beheld with alarm the fall of the most prominent of their order. So powerful was the influence they brought to bear upon Stephen that it has even been conjectured the crown would have been compelled to give way to the cowl – the monarch to the monk – as in many other instances, had not the hopes of the party been suddenly disappointed by the death of Roger. It has been surmised that grief for loss of his property which had fallen into the hand of the King so preyed upon his mind that it resulted in depriving him of life. Besides his castles, his fortifications, his jewels and plate, Stephen had also seized upon no less than fifty thousand marks in money, an enormous sum in those days. Roger in fact was a millionaire of the twelfth century. His avarice, it is said, increased with his gains; hence the blow fell upon him with irresistible force, and he succumbed beneath it. Whatever may have been his faults, and they were not a few, his genius was undoubted. After his death Stephen does not seem to have feared the ecclesiastical party, for he knew that their leader, their rallying point, the man who could unite all their varying interests in one, was gone to return no more. Roger's rise was rapid, and remarkable; his fall no less so. His character may be summed up in two words – ambition, avarice.

In the year that followed the usurper's death – 1140 – the monks of Malmesbury seem to have recovered themselves, and returned to their usual routine so rudely disturbed by Roger. The monk John, who was an inmate of the monastery, was by then elected to fill the office of abbot; but the legate of the Pope when applied to refused to give his sanction to the proceeding. Simony seems in those days to have been rampant. The refusal was probably only a contrivance to extort money. It was like the judges in Rabelais who paid but little attention to the case before them, merely saying 'Gold! Gold!' Gold satisfied them, gold satisfied the legate, and John was allowed to become abbot. His reign which had commenced so unpropitiously was fated to be unfortunate. The castle at Devizes, probably partially dismantled and deserted since the siege of it by Stephen, was taken possession of by one Robert, a sort of British buccaneer or filibuster. His other name does not seem to have survived, if indeed he had another. Men in those days often contented themselves with a single name – such as John or Robert, to which was added that of the place where they drew their extraction, had performed some remarkable action, or usually resided. So this soldier may be called Robert of Devizes. He was robber, marauder, and sacrilegist all in one: a very incarnation of all that was wicked in those days. All Wiltshire felt his terrible scourge, and mourned the feeble hand of government which permitted such outrages to be committed with comparative impunity. Cruelties were perpetrated in all directions: churches were no longer sanctuaries of safety; in fact it was against them and monasteries that Roger, who was doubtless duly cursed with bell, book, and candle, directed his attacks. Malmesbury monastery was too near to escape his notice. The monks must have trembled at his approach. Many, probably most, fled; for he threatened to put them to death. So dire was the vengeance that Robert vowed against the ecclesiastical order that one seems driven to conclude that he had suffered some terrible injury at their hands. Not content with threatening the monks, and desecrating the monastery, Robert actually attempted to destroy the abbey. But the solid structure that had been reared above the bones of St Aldhelm resisted his attacks, and no doubt the saint got credited with another miracle. The monks knew how to turn all things to their advantage. Amongst them probably this Robert of Devizes was known as Robert the Robber. They had reason to hate the letter R. Firstly had come Roger, now it was Robert. Whether or no these terrible events had anything to do with the death of the abbot seems to be unrecorded, but it is most probable that they had, since he died during the month of September, in the same year of his election, having upheld the reins of government a few months, and those most troubled ones. The abbot John is related to have been an estimable man, possessing two qualities ill fitting him to live in those days, benificence and liberality. The latter may have been one cause why his election was objected to.

Stephen is by one writer related to have besieged Malmesbury in 1140, when it was held by the partisans of Maud, and it has been surmised that a place called Castle Ground, or Burnt Ground, at Malmesbury was the spot where a battle was fought between the rival parties. Nothing seems known as to the issue of the fight.

The successor of the abbot John was one Peter, who is related to have taken part in a procession when Matilda entered the city of Winchester, probably after she had defeated Stephen early in 1141. Stephen, however, regained his crown, as Matilda, having disappointed the hopes of the people, found it necessary to withdraw to Normandy. She did not yet despair of the throne. Her son Henry was now approaching man's estate, and promised to make a formidable enemy to the usurper; who had, however, alienated many of his old supporters by insisting upon the delivering up of their castles into his hands, and who had, by resisting the encroachment of the Pope, got his party laid under an interdict – then a serious matter. At length a declaration appears to have been made in young Henry's favour and he crossed over from France to assist his partisans, whom Stephen had shut up in the town of Wallingford and was closely besieging. In order to distract Stephen's attention, and to relieve the garrison of Wallingford, Henry shortly after his arrival in England marched upon Malmesbury, which was held by the supporters of Stephen. His attack was most successful, the town and the castle – probably that which Roger le Poer had erected – fell into his hands; and only one incident occurred to check his career. A desperate defence was made by one of the castle towers – since known as Jordan's, such was the name of the defender – and despite his most energetic attempts Henry was unable to gain possession of it. He then determined to starve out the garrison and accordingly block-aded all approach, and sat down to form a camp between the walls of the town and the banks of the Avon. King Stephen fell into the snare. Leaving Wallingford, Stephen with a large army marched upon Malmesbury. Upon arriving, he found that he had not much bet-tered his position, as Henry, well aware of the smallness of his forces, would not leave the defence which his camp afforded him. Stephen, in consequence, was compelled to attack under the most disadvantageous circumstances. Not only did his army suffer severe-ly from the cold, but he was allowed scarcely any time to make proper dispositions, being under the impression – probably a correct one – that if he delayed to destroy the little army of Henry, that prince's partisans would have time to collect their forces, and either come to his assistance or attack him in the rear. The local conforma-tion, too, was greatly against him. Henry occupied the opposite side of the river, which it was necessary to pass in order effectually to attack him; yet despite these drawbacks it is related that Stephen determined upon an assault, probably influenced in a great measure by the desire to relieve the brave defenders of Jordan's tower, which still held out. He ordered an advance to be made, but the weather itself was against him. Hail and sleet coming on obscured all sight of the enemy, who, with it in their backs, were but little discomforted; while their weapon's force was augmented by being driven forward by the wind. Stephen's men at length, despite all these obstacles, seem to have advanced to the very edge of the river, but to their dismay found it impassable, being swollen by rain. Their courage, half dead as they were with the rain and the cold, failed them, and Stephen was compelled to retire. It was not until then – when they found all hope of relief gone – that the tower which had so long held out was given up to Henry. A compromise was shortly afterwards effected between the two claimants of the crown, by which Stephen was to retain it during life, and Henry returned to Normandy. Stephen died in the following year. His reign had been a turbulent one, and full of evils for the men of Malmesbury; who would probably have fully subscribed, especially the monks, to the picture given by the Saxon Chronicler, of those dreadful days:

In this king's time was all dissension and evil, and rapine; for against him soon arose the rich [great] men that were traitors; when they found that he was a mild man, and did no justice [execution] . . . They sorely oppressed the wretched men of the land with castle-works, and when the castles were made they filled them with devils and evil men . . . Many thousand did they kill with hunger . . . Wretched men died of hunger, some took to alms who were once rich men . . . Never yet was more wretchedness in the land, and never did heathen men worse than they did; for after a time they spared neither church nor churchyard but took all the goods that were therein, and then burned church and all together [this would seem a correct description of the deeds of Robert of Devizes at Malmesbury], neither did they spare bishop's land nor abbots, nor priests, but robbed monks and clerks, and every man who was able robbed another; if two or three men came riding to a town all the township fled before them, believing that they were robbers. The bishops and learned men cursed them evermore, but nought thereof came on them, for they were all accursed, and foresworn and abandoned. Such, and more than we can say, we tholed [knew, suffered] nineteen winters for our sins.

Yet it was in the early part of the twelfth century that Malmesbury monastery became famous as the residence of a writer whom Archbishop Usher is said to have called 'the first of our historians'. His family name was Somerset, but he is better known as William of Malmesbury. He appears to have become early connected with the town, if he was not born there; and to have joined the community of monks in his youth. In time he became librarian and it was then that he conceived the idea of writing that work which has rendered his name celebrated as the preserver of many facts which probably would otherwise have fallen into oblivion. This he is said to have compiled from ancient manuscripts which he discovered in the library. The first part of this history extends from the arrival of the Saxons to the decease of Henry I. The original title is *De Gestis Regum Anglorum, Libri V,* that is 'Of the acts or exploits of the kings of England'. *Historiae Novellae, Libri II* is the name of the continuation of this work, which extends down to 1143. These two works are dedicated to Robert, Earl of Gloucester. Much that is known of Malmesbury in early times is gathered from this history. William seems to have been perfectly contented with his situation of precentor and librarian of Malmesbury, since he appears to have continued in it until his death in 1143 or 1148, a few years after the date at which his history ceases. William seems to have had a very modest opinion of his own works, if it be possible to judge from the following quotation:

I am not anxious concerning the precise censure of my contemporaries. But I hope that when partiality and malevolence are no more, that I shall receive from after times the character of an industrious though not an eloquent historian.

His desire has been more than gratified. No history of the early days of the English monarchy could be written without examining his writings. He certainly was a most industrious author, as, besides his history, he also wrote the following works: *De Gestis Pontificum Anglorum, Libri IV,* that is 'Of the acts of the English bishops (or pontiffs)', and accordingly it consists of an account of the various bishoprics of Britain – a sort of ecclesiastical history, or chronicle; and *De Vita Aldhelmi,* or the life of Aldhelm. All these works have been printed and republished at divers periods, both in the original and translated. Malmesbury may justly be proud of this man. Without ostentation or ambition he has yet contrived by means of his history to make the name of Malmesbury familiar as a household word to all who have searched the history of the past; and whilst the works of Aldhelm, so celebrated in his day, now lie only upon the shelves of the antiquary, his history has became a classic. All honour

to William of Malmesbury. A contemporary of his, and it is supposed from a passage in his writings a companion, was one Peter
Baldwin, also a monk of Malmesbury; who made himself famous in
his own day for poetry. Nor was William the only historian of
Malmesbury. In the same century – the twelfth – lived Godfrey of
Malmesbury, a monk of the same order; who, something after the
manner of William, wrote the 'annals' extending from the coming of
the Saxons into Britain up to the time of Henry I. The fame of
William has, however, and it would seem justly, swallowed up that
of these lesser writers.

5
Malmesbury from 1154 to 1533

After the tremendous disturbances to which Malmesbury had been subjected in Stephen's reign, the affairs of that place seem to sink into comparative insignificance for several centuries. The notices of it which occur in history are scattered, and incapable of forming a flowing narrative. The abbots were no longer celebrated for their great ability – of many of them nothing is known beyond the date at which they flourished. Hence it has been thought convenient, both for reference and reading, to arrange the notices that do occur in their chronological order, as nearly as can be ascertained.

Henry II, who reigned from 1154 to 1189, presented six pounds ten shillings of Norman silver to the monastery; it is supposed in some slight acknowledgment of the attachment the monks had shown to this mother. During this reign Robert Fitzhardinge is related to have had the castle and town of Malmesbury, which was granted to him by the monarch, together with the appendages – lands and hundreds. The rent was thirteen pounds ten shillings. This favour he purchased for one hundred marks in money. A mark was generally taken as 13s. 4d.; one hundred marks, then, would be nominally less than £60. Robert Fitzhardinge was the first who held the title of Lord Berkeley, of Berkeley.

1159 Gregory is mentioned as abbot.
1174 Robert was abbot.
1180 Albert Foliott, whilome prior of Glastonbury, became abbot, and on his death in 1181 or 82 was succeeded by the monk Nicholas of St Albans.

This Nicholas, ere translated to Malmesbury monastery, had been prior of Wallingford, and whilst occupying that place was despatched about the year 1175 into Ireland by Henry II, carrying with him a bull of Pope Alexander III which confirmed that of Adrian IV, also that bull of Adrian which made over the lordship of Ireland to that monarch. Such was the way in which those proud Popes *granted* lordships to English monarchs in those days! Nicholas was accompanied by William Fitzadelm. Fitzadelm interpreted means son of Adelm, or Aldhelm. This, however, could scarcely have been a son of the saint.

1187 Nicholas was deposed, and the subprior of Winchester, Robert de Mehun, elevated to his place.
1205 Death of Robert de Mehun, and succession of Walter Loring.

John was now king, and by his permission the castle, which had been built adjoining the abbey and obstructed its enlargement, was razed to the ground in order that the monastery might receive the additions which were necessary for the convenience of the monks. John granted to the abbots of Malmesbury the mead; and in the same reign the town fell into their possession. The monks were now, indeed, the monarchs of Malmesbury. John's widow, Queen Isabel, gave a charter to the abbots, confirming them in possession of the town in fee-farm. The rent was fixed at twenty pounds. Conceive holding a town such as Malmesbury for £20! In modern ears it sounds ridiculous.

1122 Death of the abbot Walter Loring, and accession of John Wallensis, whose name has become historical, he having attested Magna Charta, in the ninth year of Henry III, or in 1225.
1246 Election of Jeffry as abbot.
1260 William de Colerne became abbot.

Somewhere about this date the celebrated order of St John of Jerusalem raised a hospital at Malmesbury. It was governed by a prior who had under him the usual inferiors, brethren and sisters of the order. They had a chapel, and all things accustomary. A decree relating to them issued by Constantine, an officer of Walter, then Bishop of Sarum or Salisbury, is said to be still extant. It was concerning some tithe matters which required to be adjusted between them and the vicar of the parish of St Paul at Malmesbury; and bore both the seal of the office, and that of the abbot of the monastery, who was then the patron of the church. It is considered that this hospital stood adjacent to the South Bridge.

Edward surnamed Longshanks ascended the throne in 1272. It has been generally supposed that it was in his twenty-third year, or 1295, that the borough of Malmesbury was first required to return members to Parliament. Other authorities, however, consider it to have been in 1298, of which year there is said to remain a return of knights, citizens, and burgesses. Two burgesses were returned for Malmesbury with their mancipators. Chippenham, Downton, and Devizes likewise returned two; while New Sarum – Salisbury – sent up two citizens; and two knights were returned for the county. The constable of Merleberge, and the bailiff of Wortle and Calne, likewise received writs; but made no response ('qui nullum inde dederunt responsum').

1296 Death of William de Colerne, who had been abbot for 36 years, and successor of William de Badminton whose decease took place in 1323, when Adam de la Hooke, or Att Hok, became abbot.
1340 Adam de la Hooke died at Malmesbury and was succeeded by John de Tintern.
1348 Death of de Tintern and accession of Simon de Aumeney.

Much dispute has taken place concerning these last two abbots, as to which of them it was who concealed from justice Robert de Gurnay, an accomplice in the cruel assassination of Edward II at Berkeley Castle, and which of them received the pardon which Edward III was pleased to grant. There seems no possibility of settling it indisputably. The murder took place in 1327. Adam de la Hooke was then abbot, but it does not of necessity follow that it was he who concealed Gurnay.

1360 Death of de Aumeney, and accession of Walter Camme.
1396 Succession of Thomas de Chelesworth.

Edward III had chosen the abbot of Malmesbury to be one of the twenty-five fixed upon by him to sit in the House of Peers. Two priors were also so qualified, to these again two more abbots were afterwards added. The following were the local parliamentary companions of the abbot of Malmesbury: the abbots of Cirencester, Gloucester, Abingdon, Evesham and Tavistock. In this reign the abbey is understood to have received considerable additions and decorations. Two members were returned for Malmesbury with their mancipators in the thirty-sixth year of Edward III, 1339. Malmesbury also returned two members in the forty-third year of that monarch; yet in his twelfth year, as the sheriff neglected to make his precept, it must be supposed that the corporation of Malmesbury had omitted to exercise their power of electing representatives.

King Richard III granted in 1389 to the Malmesbury men a confirmation of their existing privileges. The deed is said to still exist in the British Museum and to be thus headed: 'A charter of divers liberties, with a heath [Bruera, Burnt Heath], containing five hides of land granted [*concess*] by King Athelstan to the burgesses of the town of Malmesbury, for a victory gained against the Danes.' Richard also granted a mitre to the Abbot of Malmesbury, who had not hitherto been able to wear that headdress, although he had been independent of the diocesan. The life of this monarch was written by a monk of the Malmesbury monastery, and has been printed and republished.

Henry IV, who ascended the throne in 1399, also granted a confirmatory charter to the burgesses of Malmesbury, renewing their privileges and franchises. It has been found from examination of the patent rolls that in their reign the vicar of St Paul had an income from the property of the monastery, situated in Brokenburgh, Milbourn, Burton, and Malmesbury. The amount mentioned is seven shillings.

Henry V also granted a deed to the corporation, restoring them a field which had been hitherto set apart for the support of a chapel under the jurisdiction or protection of a foreign abbey. As this was the monarch who conquered so large a portion of France it may readily be conjectured that he thus made use of his conquest to free many places in England which had hitherto been under French administration and restore them to English hands. So that the men of Malmesbury felt personally benefited by their monarch's expensive expeditions.

1423 One William became abbot.
1424 Election of Robert Persue as abbot.
1434 Death of Persue and accession of Thomas Bristave.
1456 Death of Bristave and succession of John Andover.
1462 Andover died and was succeeded by John Aylee, who is supposed to have departed this life in 1479.

Henry VI applied the fee-farm of the abbey of Malmesbury to the royal purveyance in the early part of his reign; but in his thirty-first year granted it to William Elton, Esq. Whilst this monarch sat upon the throne, William of Worcester, a well-known writer, was journeying through the land, writing down such particulars as he thought worthy of preservation. Coming to Malmesbury he measured the abbey church by striding it, and recorded its dimensions. They were as follows. Length of the whole church, including the choir, one hundred and seventy-two steps; breadth, forty-two. Length of the chapel dedicated to Mary at the east end, thirty-six steps; breadth, fourteen. Length of cloisters (severally) about sixty-four steps. Breadth of the principal nave beyond the wings, twenty-two. Allowing three feet to each of these steps, and the breadth of the church of St Aldhelm would be 516 feet, and the breadth 126.

In the thirty-third year of Henry VI (1445), the parliamentary affairs of Malmesbury took a new phase, a separate indenture being returned. This was the first time. The election was made by the burgesses and aldermen; but the seal has been destroyed. The document is said to still be in existence but in a very unsatisfactory state, much of it being mutilated.

Malmesbury also made a return – recorded in the reign of Edward IV, 1477. He also gave two charters to the town, which, like so many others, confirmed existing privileges, and therefore contain no feature of much interest. They give another name to Malmesbury; Medulfunesi's Villa. This prince passed through Malmesbury in 1477, after his victory over Warwick the Kingmaker, upon the memorable field of Barnet. He was marching to meet Queen Margaret, who, although terribly dispirited by the defeat, managed to rally herself; and then followed the bloody Battle of Tewkesbury, in which she was made prisoner. This monarch's queen had twenty pounds a year paid her from Malmesbury as pin-money – toilette money, or private income.

1509 Thomas Olvesten, who had become abbot, died and was succeeded by Richard Frampton.

Evil days were now rapidly approaching the monks of England. The great – in more senses than one – Henry VIII sat upon the English throne. The power of the monks had reached its height. Their influence had rolled over England like a mighty torrent, which had increased from a small spring – pure at the source – until, combining with smaller muddy rivers, it inundated the surrounding country. The monstrous legends of the monks were never so absurd as now, their trickeries had never been so brazen, their impieties so outrageous. Some of these legends are so curious, and display so great an amount of superstition, that it may not be amiss to relate a few, since they show clearer than any amount of reasoning the mental degradation of the day. Lucifer left a minstrel in care of hell, and went out to walk about upon the earth. St Peter thereupon lured the minstrel to play at dice, staking the souls that were in torture under his care. St Peter won, and Lucifer, upon returning, found his fire out and the place empty. Whereupon he kicked the minstrel out of hell, swearing none of that profession should henceforth darken his doors.

The whole great drama of the Christian dispensation was displayed on the stage – God himself being introduced as an old man – and the spectators are stated to have been at one time convulsed with laughter at the antics of mimic demons, at another shuddering with fear at the representation of the lake of sulphur. From the books which still survive, containing entries of the various sums paid for articles used by the actors, the following strange items have been extracted. 'A new hook to hang Judas, 6d. Fuel for keeping the fire at hell-mouth, 4d. Girdle of God, 9d. God's coat of white leather, 3s.' The infamous John Tetzel had aroused the wrath of Luther. Tetzel is said to have declared that he had saved more souls from hell by the indulgences he had sold than St Peter had by preaching! Had any one ravished the mother of God he could *sell* a pardon for it! Such was the mental condition of the day. The morality of the monks was at a still lower scale. Despite their vows of chastity their dissoluteness had almost passed into a proverb. The picture drawn by Rabelais is probably an exaggerated one; but one tenth of the dissipation he describes as passing within the walls of monasteries and convents would have been sufficient to justify his bitter satire and their suppression. Sir Daniel Lindsay's works are full of references to the dissoluteness of the Roman clergy; of which he was an eye-witness. One piece of his, called 'Kittie's Confession', displays the immorality which resulted from private confession. It is too long and too coarse to be quoted at length; but the opening lines give a good idea of its contents:

> The curate Kittie culd confesse,
> And scho [she] told on baith mair and lesse;
> Quhen scho was tellaud as she wist [knew]
> The curate Kittie would have kist . . .

The ballads of the day are full of singular allusions, as that one beginning:

> A lovely lass to a friar came
> To confess in the morning early.

Byron aptly expressed this tendency of monastical seclusion:

> And apropos of monks their piety
>   With solitude has found it hard to dwell.
> These vegetables of the Catholic creed
>   Are apt exceedingly to run to seed

These were the men who had vowed chastity. Such were the vows of the Malmesbury monks, as appears from the following bull of Pope Innocent:

Innocent Bishop, lowest of the servants of God, to his beloved sons the abbot of the monastery of Malmesbury and his brethren both present and to come; dedicated to a regular mode of living. It is meet that those who choose a religious life should be under apostolical protection, lest any rash intrusion should shake them from their purpose – which God forbid – and lessen the strength of religion. Therefore, beloved ones in the Lord, we have graciously assented to your reasonable petitions, and taken the monastery of Malmesbury, in the diocese of Sarum, in which by divine service

Above: Cross Hayes, Malmesbury.

Below: Corsham High Street.

bove: Market Cross, Malmesbury, decorated for 1887 Jubilee.

pposite: Engraving of Malmesbury Abbey, west end ruins.

Above: Marlborough, 1887 Jubilee.

Opposite: (above) H. Banks, coachbuilder, Station Road, Corsham; (below) a smart turn-out.

Above: Ladies with 'twopenny farthings' outside The Spotted Cow, Coate Road, 1880.

Below: Verger's cottage, Church of St John, Devizes.

Opposite: Malmesbury Abbey from the north.

Above: GWR Works entrance, Swindon.

Below: Bridge Street, Swindon, c. 1890.

Above: Church Street, Lacock.

Below: Outside Niblett's, mineral water manufacturers, Milford Street, Swindon.

Bradford-on-Avon.

Above: In Cromwell Street, Swindon.

Below: Outside Devizes Post Office.

Above: Regent Street, Swindon.

Below: Imber.

Opposite: Portrait study by local photographer, Honey of Devizes and Trowbridge.

Above: Roller skating at The Rink, Swindon.

Below: Original engine at Marlborough Water Works, with Engineer Lewis.

Opposite: Edward Simpson, flint jack.

Above: Biddestone.

Below: Malmesbury Old Corporation, assembled on Coronation Day, 1911.

you are engaged, under our crown and St Peter's protection, ordaining that the monastic order, which is instituted in the said monastery (according to God and the rule of St Benedict), be there and at all times inviolably observed.

Yet notwithstanding the apostolical protection, the monks had much fallen away from their vows. A day of reckoning was at hand. At length the fiat went forth for the suppression of monasteries, and they were ordered to be delivered into the King's hands. Richard Frampton, the last abbot of Malmesbury, quietly gave up his charge on the December 15 1539; and accepted a pension. Other of his inferiors were also to receive salaries in order to maintain them decently until their death, to be paid them twice a year by the commission appointed for such purposes, namely, upon the Feast of the Annunciation and of St Michael the Archangel. The first payment was to begin in the following year, 1540, on the Feast of the Annunciation. The amounts of these pensions were as follows: Robert Frampton, otherwise known as Selwin, whilome abbot, 200 marks, say £120. Walter Stacye, sen., the land steward and chamberer, £13.6s.8d. John Codrington, B.D., prior, and Walter Suttan, B.D., sub-prior, each £10. John Gloucester, sen., and tierce (or third prior) Richard Pilton, abbot's steward, Phillip Bristowe, and Thomas Tewkesbury, sens., each £6.13s.4d. John Cantine, chapel warden, £8. Rauf Sherwood, sen., Richard Asheton farmerer, Antonie Malmesbury, sub-sexton, William Alderley, Thomas Dorselye, Thomas Gloucester, John Horselye, chaunter, Thomas Stanley, pittancier, William Brystone, Thomas Froster, student, Robert Elmore, priest, William Wynchecombe, and William Byfley, each £6. The abbot Frampton was also to have a tenement, situate in the High Street of Bristol (Bristowe), which had until lately been occupied by Thomas Harte, and also a garden in the suburbs of the town near the Red Cross, late in the tenure of the same person. Robert Southwell, Edward Carne, John London, William Beners sign their names to this. The whole amount of the incomes allowed to these twenty-two monks scarcely amounted to £270 – a strange contrast to the princely revenue they had hitherto enjoyed. Of these twenty-two only seven – Walter Stacye, Richard Asheton, Thomas Froster, Thomas Stanley (married), and Walter Suttan, Anthony Malmesbury, John Horseley

– received pensions in 1553; or fourteen years after the suppression of the monastery. The rest had either died, been dispersed, or neglected to claim their pension. And such was the end of the magnificent abbey of Malmesbury – insofar as the monks were concerned. Dating from the death of the founder Meyldulf in 676 to the suppression in 1539, no less than eight hundred and sixty-three years had elapsed since the foundation of the Malmesbury monastery.

6
Henry VIII: Hobbes: Charles I

Henry VIII became more intimately connected with Malmesbury than was brought about by the issuing of his decree for the dissolution of monasteries, which took effect there. In 1531 he granted a charter to the corporation, which like some many other documents confirmed them in the possession of their rights. It has been supposed that this was purchased from the monarch. The burly king was, however, now destined to become personally acquainted with Malmesbury. After the dissolution he is known to have kept a stud of horses in Cole Park, anciently called Cowfolde Park, which had been one of those in the possession of the abbot of the monastery, in order to enable him to enjoy the pleasures of hunting. One day, after having pursued the chase until he was satiated in Bradon Forest (about four miles from Malmesbury), the monarch, followed by his train, alighted at the door of a rich inhabitant, one Mr Stumpe, who had gained a large fortune in the clothier's trade. Although entirely unprepared for the royal visit, Stumpe was not the man to lose his wit at the moment it was most wanted, and accordingly ordered the meal which had been prepared for his workmen to be served up, doubtless with due explanations, before the hungry monarch. Through the influence of this William Stumpe, the abbey church was converted into that for the parish, and was thus preserved from destruction to delight the antiquarian and to be the pride of Malmesbury. The library which the monks had formed was however almost, if not entirely, destroyed, like that of so many others at that period. So great was the number of manuscripts taken from some of these monastical libraries, and so little were they valued, that they were actually used to wrap up wares in shops, to scour candlesticks, or clean boots! A wanton destruction, the results of which have been keenly felt in later times. Stumpe, however, does not seem to have got the abbey presented to him as a sort of acknowledgment for satisfying the hungry monarch. Harry the Eighth knew too well the value of money, and is recorded to have sold the abbey and demesne to his whilome entertainer for £1,500. The date of Stumpe's death is unknown. His son James became a knight, and married the daughter of Sir Edward Baynton. Sir James Stumpe was High Sheriff of Wilts in Edward VI and Queen Elizabeth's time.

It was during the reign of Henry VIII that the great archaeologist Leland visited Malmesbury. He describes the abbey as 'most magnificent'. There were then two steeples. One was standing at the west end of the church; the other had partially fallen in memory of man, and had been rebuilt. The immense extent of offices which had belonged to the abbey were filled with looms for the weaving of cloth. So great was the demand, and in so flourishing a state was the trade, that it had been determined to build two streets for the clothiers in the rear of the abbey; which, once all monks and meditation, had become all cloth and clothiers. One can imagine a passing monk exclaiming – doubtless in Latin, that none might understand nor take offence – 'Ye have made my house a den of money changers!' Three thousand cloths, according to Leland, were then the annual produce of the place. Leland saw also weavers in a little church adjacent to the south side of the transeptum of the abbey; and tradition then said that it was here Johannes Sectus was murdered by his scholars in the reign of Alfred the Great. He speaks too of no less than three nunneries which had once been in existence in the town. One of these is supposed to have stood outside the town, on the road to Chippenham, close to the south bridge. The site of the other two is not certain, though one has been conjectured to have stood in Burnivale – on the very spot were Meyldulph erected his hermitage. In the time of Leland some part of the gates and walls were standing, but even then were much decayed. He speaks of a work since known as the *Eulogium Historiarum,* as the *Malmesbury Chronicle.* It was the work of a Malmesbury monk. Here is an extract from it:

The town of Malmesbury standeth on the very top of the great slaty rock, and is wonderfully defended by nature; for Newton water cometh two miles from north to the town, and Avon water cometh by west, and they meet about a bridge at the southeast part of the town, and run so near together in the bottom of the west suburb that there within a burbolt shot the town is peninsulated. It has four gates all ruinous. The walls in many places stand full up, but now very feeble; nature hath diked the town strongly. It was sometime a castle of great fame, wherein the town hath since been builded; for in the beginning of the Saxon's reign, as far as I can learn, Malmesbury was no town. The castle was named of the Britons Caer Bladun; the Saxons first called it Ingelburn, and after of one Maidulphus, a Scot, that taught good letters there, and after procured an abbey there to be made; it was named Maidulphorhyri: i.e. *Maidulphi curia*. The King of the West Saxons and a Bishop of Winchester were founders of this abbey. Aldhelm was then, after Maidulph, abbot there, and after Bishop of Sherburn. This St Aldhelm is patron of the place. The town hath a great privilege of a fair about the feast of St Aldhelm at the which time the town keepeth a band of harnesid men [armed men] to see peace kept, and this is one of the brags of the town, and they be furnished with harness . . . There were in the abbey churchyard three churches. The abbey church, a right magnificent thing, where there were two steeples, one that had a mighty high pyramis and fell dangerously *in hominum memoria* [in the memory of man]; it stood in the middle of the transeptum of the church, and was a mark to all the country about, the other yet standeth a great square tower at the west end of the church. The townsmen of late bought this church of the king, and made it their parish church.

In the first year of the reign of Queen Mary the election of members for the town was made by the burgesses. The indenture is said still to remain, and to have the common seal of the burgesses attached to it. The indenture of the next year's election does not mention the alderman.

In the time of Queen Elizabeth a part of the lands once belonging to the Knights Hospitallers at Malmesbury, an order that was suppressed in 1540, are recorded to have been in the possession of John and William Marsh, who handed them over to John Stumpe – probably a descendant of William Stumpe – of Malmesbury. Stumpe also bought other of the lands from two London gentlemen – Andrew Palmer and John Herbert. In 1580 Stumpe generously transferred this property to the corporation for the nominal sum of £26.13s.4d. It was to be held in common socage under the sovereign manor of East Greenwich. During the reign of Elizabeth one Henry Knynett claimed the demesne of Malmesbury, and is understood to have managed to make it good, since in 1566 he allowed the abbey church to continue in use as a parish church. The estate appears to have afterwards come into the family of the Suffolks through marriage. In 1578 some portion of Stumpe's property was in the hands of a clothier of Malmesbury, one Adam Archarde. The reign of Elizabeth seems to have seen the break-up of the Stumpe family, which had been so influential at Malmesbury in that of Henry VIII. There seem, however, to have been persons of that name connected with the town until the days of James I.

Malmesbury was a noted place for the clothing trade in the time of Elizabeth. The town seal was cut in the year 1615. The principal figure upon it is a castle, which has three towers, one on each end – these two are embattled – and one domed in the centre. A pennon waves over the last. On both sides of the castle are three ears of wheat upon a stalk. On the dexter side, in chief, a six-pointed mullett; on the sinister side a unicrescent, also three balls – two at the edge of the sinister tower, and the other near the domed one. Water forms the base of the escutcheon. It was in the latter part of the sixteenth century in all probability that those brass or copper coins, which may still be seen – those tokens which were issued by the clothiers and tradesmen of the town – were struck. The almshouse has been supposed to have been founded in the reign of Elizabeth; though not established until 1629. A little later than this – in 1631 – William Cale, of Bristol, was the lessee of the manor of Malmesbury; which seems to have been in the hands of one Anne Warneford. On her death the husband of her third daughter – William Plomer – became heir.

Meantime there had been growing up at Malmesbury a plant which was designed to render it famous. In the year 1588 a Mr Hobbes was the minister of the parish of Westport, Malmesbury; and his wife (it is said in terror of the Spanish Armada, then on its progress towards England) was prematurely delivered of a son. He was named Thomas. The house in which he was born has been down some seventy years. When eight years old the young Hobbes became a scholar of Robert Gatimer, master of the Malmesbury Grammar School; where by his evident capacity for study he seems to have been a favourite. From here, in 1603, he was taken to Magdalen Hall, Oxford. He had, ere this, translated Euripides, the Greek author's

Medea, into Latin verse. He was now fifteen. His charges at college were chiefly disbursed by a relation, Francis Hobbes, alderman of Malmesbury, who seems to have been very fond of his nephew, since at his decease it was found that he had left an annuity to him. With this Hobbes was enabled to pursue his studies, and took in 1607 the degree of B.A. Next year, 1608, he became tutor to the son of Lord Hardwicke, who was afterwards Earl of Devonshire. He obtained this place by the assistance of the Principal of Magdalen. In company with his pupil he left England and made a tour through Italy and France in 1610. On his return Hobbes sent forth into the world his first literary attempt – which was a translation of Thucydides' *History.* That author, together with Euripides, Virgil and Homer, was his favourite study. Hobbes again went abroad in 1631 as the companion of Sir Gervase Clifton, and afterwards became tutor to the young Earl of Devonshire; going abroad with him nor returning until 1637. Four years later he went to Paris, and here was allowed the honour of teaching mathematics to King Charles II, who had fled his country. When Charles grasped the sceptre, Hobbes shared in that good fortune, being allowed a pension of £100 per annum. He seems to have passed the remainder of his day with the Earl of Devonshire.

Hobbes was now famous as an author. His works were: *Elements of Law, Moral and Politic; The Leviathan, or, The Matter, Form and Power of a Commonwealth, Ecclesiastical and Civil; Behemoth, or, The History of the Causes of the Civil Wars in England; Human Nature, or, The Fundamental Elements of Policy; An English Version of the Iliad and Odyssey of Homer; Ten Dialogues on Natural Philosophy;* together with several small pieces, and treatises on mathematics. *The Leviathan,* which was written whilst he was at Paris, caused an immense amount of sensation, as also a book of his called *De Cive.* The ecclesiastics were up in arms against him. *The Leviathan* was even suppressed, or rather condemned, by Parliament, being classed in a bill against atheism and profanity, which passed in October 1666. *De Cive* was also condemned by the convocation of 1683; and it had *The Leviathan* burnt. He has been much vilified as an atheist, yet it would appear that he was himself a Christian, since he took the sacrament. His learning was undoubted – it is borne testimony to by Lord

Clarendon, who was his friend and passes a high encomium upon him. Perhaps one of the reasons of the extreme dislike with which he seems to have been held by a certain class of clergy, and of the charges which have been brought against him, was his political opinions – well calculated to be heard with favour by King Charles, but not so by the opposition of that day. Those charges are not only unsupported but are in themselves unworthy of hearing. Yet such is the force of prejudice that Hobbes has never been looked upon with favour – never found readers except amongst those who were determined to investigate things for themselves. One cause perhaps of his being charged with atheism was the dread with which he is said to have contemplated death; but this is no proof – the most orthodox have felt a similar fear of the unknown. He is, too, understood to have dreaded a visit from the spirit-land; to have doubted the existence of his own soul, yet feared the visit of other people's. Byron alludes to this failing in one of his poems, where his hero is awaiting an apparition he imagined he had seen the previous evening:

> In short he felt some qualms very
> Like those of the philosopher of Malmesbury.

Hobbes certainly was the philosopher of Malmesbury.

Malmesbury has indeed been famous for literary characters – Aldhelm in the seventh century, William of Malmesbury in the twelfth, and Hobbes in the seventeenth. Hobbes's genius was recognised in his own day, and procured him the notice of illustrious inhabitants of foreign countries. Amongst those who visited him was the celebrated Cosmo Medicis, once Prince, later Duke of Tuscany. At length, after some ninety-one years chiefly spent in study, Death whom Hobbes so much dreaded cut off the philosopher of Malmesbury. This was on December 4, 1679. Hobbes was another instance of the extraordinary longevity of Malmesbury men. He was interred at Hault-Hickwall in the church; and a monument raised to commemorate him.

This short account of Hobbes has led us to forestall somewhat other portions of our history. It is now necessary to retrograde to the year 1645, in which it is said King Charles passed through Malmesbury and was entertained by the corporation at the banqueting house, on the east side of the tower. The spot is supposed to have been that which had been formerly an *hospitium* to the abbey. Previous to this Henry VIII had been entertained by William Stumpe upon the same place. The building was afterwards converted into a workhouse. Charles, however, was too closely beset by the Parliamentary forces to be allowed even a quiet night's rest in the town of Malmesbury. Prince Rupert, who was in possession of Cirencester, learning that the King was in danger from a Parliamentary party, rode over to Malmesbury to rescue him. He was in time, and Charles escaped to Cirencester behind the Prince. Shortly afterwards, in the same year, Waller, a Parliamentary officer, made a forced march through Wiltshire and captured the garrison of Malmesbury, which was entirely unprepared. Waller had with him a force of some 2,000 horse. However, Waller and Essex being defeated at Roundway Down, near Devizes, by the King, whose soldiers henceforth called it Run-away Down, it would appear that Wiltshire was cleared of the rebels, and consequently that Malmesbury fell once more into the King's hands. An entry in the parish register supports this conjecture. It is the baptism of the daughter of Thomas Dahridgecourte, lieutenant-colonel in the King's army, and deputy-governor under Colonel Horne, or Howard, of Malmesbury. The date is November 6, 1643.

Another change of the fortune of the field threw Malmesbury again into the possession of the Parliamentary party; and tradition says of Cromwell himself, pointing out a hole in the wall of the abbey church, reported to have been caused by a cannon ball, as a witness of the fact; like the bricks in the chimney of Shakespeare. Tradition also maintains that the Wortheys was the site of a camp; from which site it is supposed the Parliamentary forces made their attack upon the town, as certain houses once standing in the Abbey Row are known to have been destroyed by fire in the civil wars. Marmaduke Pudsie, says the register, lieutenant-colonel of the garrison, was married to Margaret Serge, of the abbey, on September 30, 1644. Thomas Serge, Esq., held the manor of Malmesbury in 1656. The question is – on whose side was the garrison? Malmesbury is known to have been garrisoned up to June 1646, but very little more beyond that fact seems to have transpired.

Charles I in 1636 grated a new charter to the corporation, which created an alderman, twenty capital burgesses, and twenty-four assistants. The alderman then became a justice of the peace. This charter seems to have been merely the royal recognition of laws previously existing.

In 1654, as is learnt from a deed, the clothing trade was still carried on at Malmesbury; and even so late as 1729 the manufacture of medley-clothing, drugget-making, and Spanish clothing is recorded to have been persevered in. These occupations dropped before the expiration of the eighteenth century. During this period the election of Members of Parliament seems to have been almost entirely made by the capital burgesses and alderman, the common seal being used; but the free burgesses remaining inactive, as if having full confidence in their superiors. When, however, the Prince of Orange ascended the English throne the return was made in the ancient manner by the alderman, ten capital burgesses, fifteen assistants, nineteen land holders, and twenty-seven commoners, altogether seventy-two persons. This was in 1689, and was a sort of reassertion of right. Charles II having required the surrender of all charters, Colonel Wharton was the person elected, but he, being chosen for another place, a second election occurred; sixty electors signed their names. The first contest appears to have taken place in 1697, when, although the members elected by the capital burgesses were returned, a petition was presented against it on December 14, 1698. Another election took place in 1699, and another petition went up against it. The upper portion of the corporation now seem to have determined to keep the right of election amongst themselves. David Parker, Esq., however, stood up for the popular interest in 1701, but failed, having preferred a petition against the members returned of the capital burgesses, and being unable to prove a charge of bribery which he had made against them, he was ordered to be prosecuted by the Attorney General, and even taken into custody. In 1702 the whole of the corporation appear to have exercised their rights: but later the capital burgesses again usurped the power. In 1722 a contest occurred – there being a split amongst the capital burgesses; and a petition was presented against the return of Sir John Rushout and Lord Hillsborough. It seems to have failed of effect. In 1796 a contest also took place, this time between men who represented the two branches of the corporation. Thelluson and Smith were the candidates supported by the capital burgesses; Vassar and Luxford appealed to the others. The two first were returned, and a petition followed from Vassar and the free burgesses. Mr Vassar's was examined by a committee but rejected, as was also one which he presented in the following year. That of the free burgesses passed unnoticed.

The year 1664 must have been very pleasant in one respect to the inhabitants of Malmesbury. The number of paupers relieved was *eight,* and the amount of the poor rates was £18.7s.2d. Distilling was carried on here in 1674. Silk weaving appears also to have been the occupation of some Malmesbury men in 1687. Woollen cloth manu-facturing was given up about 1750, but afterwards revived in the latter part of the eighteenth century by Mr Francis Hill.

7
A Marquess and a Poetess

A relation of the Stumpes – a name celebrated at Malmesbury – held the manor in 1671. His name was Godwyn Wharton, Esq. He appears to have represented the town in Parliament in 1695; and from him it has been supposed the property descended to Thomas Lord Wharton who became Marquess of Wharton and Malmesbury. Philip Duke of Wharton is also conjectured to have held it for a time. It then came into the hands of the Northwick family. The Marquess of Wharton was a very remarkable man. He was a great politician, and was fortunate enough to attract the attention of no less than three sovereigns – William, Anne, and George I, under which last monarch he was Privy Seal. In 1706 Anne made him Viscount Winchenden in Bucks and Earl of Wharton. He then in 1708 became the Lord Lieutenant of Ireland. Six years afterwards the title of Marquess of Wharton and Malmesbury was added to his other honours. Wharton had not been entirely idle in the Revolution of 1688. His character seemed to have been an estimable one. He bestowed his patronisation upon worthy men, one of whom, Sir Richard Steele, a well-known writer of the day, acknowledged the debt in the *Spectator* in the most warm and ample terms. The Marquess died in 1715. On the death of Philip Duke of Wharton in 1731 the title became extinct.

It was during this period that the poetess of Malmesbury flourished. Mary Chandler drew her first breath at Malmesbury in 1687. Her father was a dissenting clergyman, not entirely unknown to literature, having published a tract in 1705. His daughter was brought up as a milliner, and when arrived at a proper age was entrusted with the care of a shop at Bath. One of her poems on Bath gained much applause, and attracted the attention of Pope. Pope even paid her a visit. She had displayed a taste for poetry from childhood, often amusing her companions with riddles in verse; and when older devoting herself to the study of classical authors. Horace pleased her better than Homer or Virgil – he descended to private life; they soared where none could follow. Her person was unfortunately somewhat deformed, but her mind and morality amply made up for her physical disfigurement; so that she attracted the notice of a gentleman who came from a great distance to offer her his hand, which, however, the poetess declined. She appears to have lived single her whole life. Her death took place after much illness on September 11, 1745, at the age of fifty-seven. She was not the only one of the family who displayed some literary ability. Her father had appeared in print, and his son Dr S. Chandler produced *A Critical History of the Life of David,* together with other works. His death took place in 1766 at the age of seventy-three years.

Numerous titles have been derived from Malmesbury. Amongst these were Marquess of Malmesbury, Duke of Malmesbury to the Whartons; Earl and Baron to the Right Hon. James Harris, Earl of Malmesbury, Viscount Fitzharris, of Heron Court, Hampshire, Baron Malmesbury and Knight of the Bath.

That part of our history which relates to ancient Malmesbury is now rapidly drawing to a close; and, as it were to put the finishing stroke, we have not thought it out of place to give the names of the parliamentary members for Malmesbury since 1741:

1741   Giles Erle, Esq.; W. Rawlinson, Esq.

1747   John Lee; James Douglass, Esq.;

1751   Hon. Ed. Digby.

1754   Rt. Hon. Lord G. Bentinck; Brice Fisher, Esq.;

1760   Wm. Conolly.

1761   Rt. Hon. Richard (Tylney), Earl Tylney in Ireland;
        Thomas Conolly.

1763   Rt. Hon. John (Child), Earl Tylney in Ireland.

1768   Rt. Hon. Arthur (Chichester), Earl Donegal in Ireland;
        Hon. Thomas Howard.

1774   Hon. C. J. Fox; Wm. Strahan, Esq.

1780   Hon. G. (Legge) Viscount Lewisham; Hon. Art. (Hill),
        Viscount Fairford.

1784   Rt. Hon. Peniston (Lamb), Viscount Melbourne in Ireland;
        Hon. J. Maitland, Viscount Maitland.

1790   B. B. Hopkins, Esq.; Paul Benfield, Esq.
1791   Sir J. Saunderson.
1795   Francis Glanville, Esq.
1796   Peter Isaac Thelluson, Esq.; – Smith, Esq.;
1797   Phillip Metcalf, Esq.
1802   Claude Scott, Esq.; Sam. Scott, Esq.

8

Modern Malmesbury (I)

A more didactic subject could scarcely be chosen than a simple description of a modern town – with the names of streets, the number of chimney tops, gutters and lamp posts. Such a description cannot fail being dry and uninteresting. Hence we have considered it best in the present work to approach the town of Malmesbury as it were from a distance, to describe its appearance from afar; then to enter and pass through it taking all that is worth seeing on our way.

Most strangers would probably attempt to reach Malmesbury by rail, but in such an attempt they would be miserably disappointed: since although the first sod of railway was turned near the town a few years ago with great ceremony and exultation the enterprise was abandoned, in spite of the most energetic efforts on the part of several landowners interested in the welfare of the town, and the grass has grown green above the spot. The nearest railway station is Minety – a small place upon the South Wales branch of the Great Western line; this is seven miles from the ancient seat of Aldhelm. The road, however, is good, and as it perhaps affords the best view that can be obtained of the town, will amply repay the journey.

The first mansion which is seen stands about a gunshot distance from the station, half-hidden amongst trees. It belongs to Mr Fitz-gerald. Further on a magnificent wood runs for a great way beside the road; it is known as Stone-Hill and is the property of the Earl of Suffolk, who indeed owns an immense estate in the neighbourhood. Upon the left will be noticed some fir plantations of considerable extent overshadowing with their dark and sombre foliage a broad sheet of water well known as Braydon Pond. This is an American nomenclature – it would certainly be pronounced a lake by a visitor; and a most beautiful one too. Even the glimpse that can be obtained of it from the road is sufficient to show its great extent: it is said to be 'three miles round', that is, it is a three miles' walk around it. A piece of water of this size can scarcely be called a pond in this post-diluvian age. When mammoths, leviathans and behemoths crashed through primeval forests, wallowed in original mud or drank streams dry at a draught, it might have – had it then existed – been termed a pond. But now when things do not go upon such a gigantic scale Braydon Lake or Braydon Mere would be a far more elegant and fit appellative.

The traveller if on foot would soon become conscious of the antiquity of everything near Malmesbury. The very milestones are defaced and utterly illegible through age. The farm-houses which frequently occur on either side of the road are roofed with the ancient 'stone-slates', brown and mossy with age. The scenery is pleasant but not grand – it is that peculiar, rich English landscape, characteristic of the Western counties: green meadows, wide woods, brawling streams, farm-houses, labourers' cottages, orchards – an air of peace, contentment, and rural wealth and happiness: these are its charms. There are no dangerous precipices, no frowning rocks, or wild, bare heaths; all is smiling and softly beautiful. The road now rises and falls, but there is nothing abrupt even in this; everything steals upon the sight. The first and only village is Charlton. Here the road to Malmesbury branches to the left; that which apparently continues straight on goes but a short distance through the village, and terminates at the entrance to Charlton Park. On each side of it stand ancient houses, suggestive of the seventeenth and eighteenth centuries, with that peculiar colour and look – the result of age and exposure to the weather – which cannot be successfully imitated. At the very edge of the park stands Charlton Church, its tower grimly frowning over the smiling pleasure grounds. A first glance is sufficient to show the great antiquity of this place of worship. The graveyard is full – the stones lie thick as leaves in autumn – so that it has become necessary to enclose a semi-circular piece of ground, encroaching upon the park, in addition to the old 'God's Acre'. Over the porch is the face of a sundial – but the gnomon is gone, and it is consequently useless. There is an inscription upon it – 'Jno. Stump, Ch. Warden, 1792'. Within the porch, upon the left hand, is an inscription in memory of John Waters, gent., who departed this life in 1676. Above the door which gives entrance to the church is a niche, which probably once contained an image, which has disappeared. Within is a magnificent, though modern, monument. The church tower is firmly bound up with a luxuriant growth of ivy, whose stem has attained a diameter equal to that of a small tree. This probably is a great assistance to the erection, enabling it to weather the storm of winter with safety. Close by is a large yew tree – sombre and melancholy enough, especially in contrast with the adjoining gardens.

Leaving Charlton Church, and returning to the Malmesbury road, another church tower will be descried upon the left. This is Garsden. Near it, but much hidden by the trees, is the hamlet of Milborne. Here the road becomes skirted upon the right by a high bank, covered with trees and shrubs, giving it what is called a picturesque appearance. It crosses a stream, which runs to join the Avon, coming through Charlton Park, the wall of which forms a barrier upon the right side of the road. This wall is said to extend for a distance of five miles completely encircling the park – and to have been eight or nine years in course of erection. A little further a glimpse may be obtained of Charlton House, the seat of the Earl of Suffolk. The entrance from Malmesbury is beneath lime trees, which form a pleasant canopy of shade to the weary traveller; who can here, through the lodge gates – if he be tall enough – see a little of the park. The mansion is situated a great distance from the road, almost hidden by numerous trees; many clumps of which, scattered about the park, give it a very beautiful look, and as on account of its great extent it is impossible to see more than one boundary at a time, it has a perfectly natural appearance, and requires none of artificial aid to render it private and secluded. The mansion itself is a study, and – unless by an architect in technical terms – baffles description. The most striking peculiarity are four turrets, with eastern domes; which, taken together with several other circumstances, has made us often institute a comparison between this mansion and the chateau at Valençay, long the favourite residence of Prince Talleyrand. The stables and offices are completely hidden by trees, and separated from the main building.

To return to the Malmesbury road. A glimpse may now and then be here obtained of the steeple of St Paul's, Malmesbury and upon approaching Whychurch turnpike gate, a partial view, through the interstices of the trees, may be got of the abbey itself. Passing

through the turnpike, upon the right hand stands Whychurch farm –
a very ancient building, which it has been conjectured once had some
connection with the Roman Catholic clergy. It appears to have been
formerly spelt Whit-Church – perhaps *White*-Church, from the
White Friars, or the colour of the building. The field upon the right is
known as the Worthy's. The road here dips down, and the abbey is
lost sight of – hidden not only by the conformation of the ground,
but by some magnificent chestnut trees which overhang the way. A
few steps further and the traveller hears the rushing sound of water –
he stands upon a bridge over the Newnton river, Malmesbury is
before him upon the hill, and the abbey, dark with the storms of
ages, looks loweringly down upon the winding vale and willow-
guarded stream. The colour of the abbey walls has been compared to
that of the Duke of Beaufort's mansion at Badminton. It appears to
us like the darkness of a monk's hood, whence the spirit of the past
looks down, frowningly and sorrowfully, upon the present. After
crossing the bridge the road again rapidly rises and Malmesbury is
entered. This part of the town is known as Holloway. On either side,
but particularly upon the left, arise high and massive walls forming
on the left hand a kind of bastion, considered to be a remnant of the
old town wall. The road here divides into two branches, one running
through to Cross-Hayes Square, the other and main branch coming
into Oxford Street, and placing the traveller·opposite the Market
Cross. This is an octagonal erection. Eight pillars surround a centre
column. From these eight spring arches to each other, and to the
central column. Above this towers a sculptured turret, much mutilated; but upon which two figures may still be made out. They both
face the abbey. One is St Peter with his key, the other is probably St
Lawrence with his gridiron. There are also traces of a crucifix. The
turret is said to have been formerly surmounted by a cross, which is
now broken off. Beneath it forms a shelter from the storms of
heaven. Over the right arches are balls or other ornaments, some
mutilated, others perfect. That to the south, facing High Street, had
formerly a sundial; part of which still remains. The cross is now
looked upon with very little veneration. Vehicles are run into it for a
temporary shelter, and the pillars are covered with printed bills of
different colours; men out of work and other idlers here have their

great rendezvous. Children play in and out. The stonework has consequently become much defaced, though in some places there still remain a few inches showing its original smoothness and polish. There are two entrances.

This cross was standing when Leland visited the town in the reign of Henry VIII; and he describes it as having been erected in the memory of man to shelter poor market people from the rain, which certainly the vault is well calculated to do. These crosses, however, served other purposes, to deliver sermons from, or to lead men to prayers. A more conspicuous spot could scarcely have been chosen at Malmesbury. High Street, the most populous and best built in the town, runs down the hill exactly opposite its south side. St Paul's steeple towers up upon the right – it is all that remains of St Paul's Church, and here a chime of five bells used to call to divine service as required – and to the north rises the abbey. The view of the abbey is, however, much interrupted by some low ancient houses, one of which has a curious projecting balcony, if that term might be used – it is rather the roof or part of it, flat and used as a sort of flower garden. Here too is a Friendly Sabbath School and the Malmesbury Reading Room. On the right will be readily found the White Lion, an inn of very antiquated appearance. The walls are said to be of immense thickness. It is considered to have been an appendage to the abbey, used as an *hospitium,* or place to entertain travellers, which office it still fulfils. Proceeding down High Street evidences will be seen on every side of the present and former prosperity of Malmesbury. There are, however, no attempts to attract attention by the enormous extent of plate glass displayed in more modern towns which have grown up under the influence of a floating population brought in by rail. A modest display of goods, a name, and that is all the indication which can be seen. A great amount of business is nevertheless said to be transacted. A peculiarity – the result of the great antiquity of the place and of the custom of intermarrying in order to preserve corporation rights – is the number of similar names, such as Hanks, Heys and others. It is even said that the true Malmesbury population are all more or less intimately related – one great family. This is one advantage of a corporation – it makes men perhaps greater friends, more attached to their native place, and imbues them with what is called the *esprit de corps*. At the same time it debars progress. Some even stigmatise the corporation as the ruin and bane of Malmesbury, asserting that there is not a single large tradesman in the place who is really a Malmesbury man in proof of the statement. Such may now be the case, but it is evident that of yore the corporation has been of the greatest service to this town. It consists of commoners, who are said to be nearly three hundred in number, 'twenty-fourths', from whom the burgesses are chosen, who are twelve. These twelve elect an alderman, who cannot take office unless he is able to entertain the others with a dinner. The alderman is chief magistrate. The present alderman is Mr William Grant, a rope maker. There is also a High Steward. At present this office is filled by Colonel Miles, who appoints a Deputy Steward, Mr Chubb.

High Street is the principal street of the place. Here are two large inns. The first is the George Commercial Hotel, where good accommodation can be obtained for man and horse at moderate charges, and where the antiquary may congratulate himself upon residing in a house that has been established nearly two centuries. Further down on the other side of the street is the Red Lion. At the bottom of the hill upon the left may be seen an ancient arch of very peculiar workmanship. It forms the end of the almshouse. This is the spot where stood the convent of British nuns in the sixth century, under Dinooth, abbot of Bangor; which establishment was suppressed by Augustine, then Archbishop of Canterbury. Here, too, was the hospital of the Knights of Jerusalem – Knights Hospitallers as they were called – and it has been conjectured that this ancient arch is a remnant of their hospital. It is defended from defacement by iron railings. Near by is the entrance to the almshouse – an ancient porch, over which there is a curious figure carved in the stonework. Immediately over the arch there is a tablet with the following inscription of eighteen lines:

[1] Memorand. that whereas King Athelstan [2] did give unto the free school within this [3] borough of Malmesbury ten pounds, and to [4] the poor people my [this word is scarcely legible] Almshouse of St John. [5] Ten pounds to be paid yearly by ye alderman [6] and burgesses of ye same burrough for Ever. [7] That now Michael Weekes, esq., late of [8] This s'd

Burr'h and now Citizen of London [9] hath augmented and added to ye afores'd gift [10] Vizt to ye S'd Free School ten pound to ye [11] S'd Almshouse ten pounds more to be Paid [12] yearly at St. John's aforesa'd within this [13] Burr and by his trustees for Ever and hath [14] also given to ye Minister of this town [15] For ye Time being x 20 s by ye year for Ever [16] to preach a Sermon yearly on ye x 19 day [17] of July and to his said Trustees x 20 s by the year beginning and to his said Trustees x 20 s by the year begining on the 25th day of March. Anno Domn, 1694.

This inscription is merely a memorandum of gifts, and explains itself. A short distance further the traveller stands upon a bridge over another river – the Avon, which flows upon the south-west side of the hill upon which Malmesbury is built; just as the Newnton does upon the north-east. Malmesbury is in fact almost surrounded by water – there being no less than six bridges, five of which are thoroughfares; while it is only possible to enter the place without crossing a stream upon one side, namely the Sherston road. This bridge near the ancient arch is called South Bridge, and is the entrance to the town from Chippenham. Standing upon it two conspicuous erections are at once apparent. Upon the left at the back of the Almshouses is the Gas House and Gasometer; over the river is the extensive silk-ribbon manufactory of Messrs Thomas Bridges and Co. The silk arrives here in a raw state and is unpacked in the upper storeys of the building. Much of it is Chinese, and the packages often contain small slips of paper stamped with Chinese characters. The operation of cleaning employs a large number of children who tend the machinery used for that purpose. Most of these are very young and sing at their work. Overseers superintend them, and talking is not allowed, for the simple reason that attention is required to be exercised to manipulate the silk properly. Beneath is the winding department; lower still the looms where the ribbons are made. The machinery is of an order impossible to describe. There is a sameness in it. Apparently the greatest attention is paid to the comfort of those employed. The rooms are very large, well lighted, and though necessarily warm, not overheated. Nevertheless, from being so early put to work the children have an old look; but nothing of that careworn expression sometimes seen in factories. The machinery is driven by water power.

Leaving the factory the road rapidly rises and turns to the left, splitting into two. That to the left runs to Cowbridge, where there is a strange but extensive mansion and some beautiful gardens, the seat of S. B. Brooke, Esq. A little beyond it is Cowbridge – a very long bridge over the Avon. This road is the one to Brinkworth and Wootton Bassett. Brinkworth was formerly a manor belonging to the abbey of Malmesbury. It is a beautiful village. The church is an ancient structure. A clock in the tower must from its appearance be very old. The face is square – much like a sundial. The rectory is also a very ancient erection. Away to the right the downs are covered with wood for many a wide acre. This is known as the Great Wood, Grittenham. On the left, but some distance on, are Braydon Woods. At Brinkworth there was formerly a mill which was rated at so much in Domesday Book. There is a mill here still of very old appearance, and of somewhat unusual construction; there being six sails instead of four. Here remain some portions of the village stocks.

The other branch of the road after crossing South Bridge is known as the Chippenham. On the right hand, not far from Cowbridge Gate, stands the mansion of Colonel Miles, High Steward of the borough. Here are some beautiful gardens, which at certain seasons are, by the kindness of the owner, thrown open to the public. A row of fine lime trees runs parallel to the road. Near by stands an old farmhouse upon the left hand. This is thought to have been the spot where stood one of the nunneries anciently existing at Malmesbury. It has lately been undergoing repairs, during which an iron plate was found with an inscription of the date of 1606. Adjacent is a field known as the Chapel Close, which perhaps once belonged to the nunnery. By means of a footpath upon the left side of the road it is, from here, possible closely to approach Cole Park, anciently known as Cowfolde Park, which was once a country seat of the abbots of Malmesbury, but is now the residence of A. Lovel, Esq. Here too Henry VIII once kept a stud of horses. The mansion appears to be in great part modern, but is surrounded by a broad moat filled with water, which gives it an air of antiquity. The principal approach is by a splendid avenue of elms, wherein the rooks have made a settlement. Turning to the left the path goes over the hill to Cowbridge. This hill is known as Cam's or Camp's hill, there being some indications of a camp or castle upon its summit. The entrenchments or mounds remaining are of great extent, and well marked. On the south-west side of the hill they run down some considerable distance. To the south-east there is a well-marked mound or bank thrown up, which appears to be particularly known as the castle. This spot is also known as the Burnt Grounds – tradition relating that a battle was once fought here by King Stephen against some of his numerous enemies. It may have been then that the castle was burnt down. Cennis Hill is the highest ground near Malmesbury, and consequently just such a spot as the ancient armies would choose for an encampment. The view from it is very fine. Malmesbury Abbey can be seen to the north, the Avon flows by to the south-east, and a large stream joins it at the foot of the hill, where stands Cowbridge. Downs and green dales, woods, parks, and meadows extend for miles. Standing here, and noting the fertility of the surrounding country, it is impossible not to observe the wisdom which led the monks to settle at Malmesbury; nor of Dunwallo Molmutius, who chose a spot equally well wooded and watered to build a city, which, situated upon a hill between two rivers, might in those days have been easily defended. The River Avon is not famous as a fishing stream, but trout are occasionally caught in it. It is certainly surprising that no small skiffs are kept – it would afford a fine row; but the people of Malmesbury, like those of Lechlade – who have the Thames, and only use it to float coal-barges – do not seem to be of that opinion, since the only boat we ever saw was a flat-bottom, sunk to the bottom, near South Bridge.

9
Modern Malmesbury (II)

Returning to South Bridge, and turning to the right, after passing the Almshouse, brings the traveller to another bridge on the Newnton river, which joins the Avon but a little farther – just past a mill. The view here is very beautiful, the river winding along at the foot of a steep bank, or escarpment, upon which the town of Malmesbury is built. This hill has much the appearance of having once been fortified – probably the town wall ran along its summit, while the river at the foot would answer the purpose of a moat. The other side of the river is level, and forms a beautiful meadow, which has lately fallen – by will – into the possession of some Roman Catholics, who have accordingly come to take up their residence in the town, once so celebrated for its connection with them. Retracing these steps to the Almshouse, a small steep street will be noticed upon the right hand – this is Silver Street. It leads into Cross Hayes Square. Here is Ebenezer Chapel, enlarged in 1848. Mounting a short distance up High Street, it will be observed that there is an offshoot from it upon the left hand. This is King's Wall. It is a narrow, dark passage between two walls, one of which is built upon the every edge of the hill, and over it a tall man may obtain glimpses of the Avon winding along far beneath. The old town wall, or fortification erected in Stephen's time, probably ran along here. The present wall would be useless for defence, since it is too high to fire over, and too thin to withstand a cannon-ball. At the extremity of King's Wall lies the suburb of Burnivale, deep down in the hollow, between the hill upon which the abbey stands, and the River Avon. Mr Luce's brewery stands here. Further, once stood an ancient building known as the Chapel House. It seems to have now entirely disappeared, its place being occupied by a sort of almshouses, inhabited by poor persons. Near this spot it is supposed that Meyldulph erected his hermitage over a thousand years ago. Here, too, stood the third nunnery, and it has been supposed that the Chapel House was a remnant of that establishment. Whoever inquires on the spot for the Chapel House, in the expectation of seeing an ancient erection, will be much amused upon having a modern wooden building pointed out to him, used as a chapel and ragged school by the Methodists of this part of the town.

Burnivale leads into that quarter of the town known as Westport. Close here stands a Primitive Methodist chapel, erected in 1856. A little further the road divides into two. That to the right leads to Sherston, and is the only way by which the town can be entered without crossing the water. On this road stands the Malmesbury Union Workhouse, a large and extensive building. The present number of inmates is considered to be about 150. Malmesbury Union, if we remember aright, contains twenty-five parishes. The other road crosses a bridge over the Avon known as Turketul Bridge. Here is a beautiful view of the western end of the abbey, which towers up above the surrounding house. Burnivale appears from here to be built something in the form of a parti-amphitheatre; it is certainly seen to best advantage at a distance. Near this bridge is a tannery. Very shortly after crossing the bridge the road turns to the right, and has something of a romantic appearance on account of the overhanging trees and steep banks. At a short distance upon the left hand stands the house known as the Arches. The next place of any note is upon the same side and is known as Thornhill. From here there is a fine view of the vale through which the Avon flows. Across it – far away on the right – stands Higham farm house, apparently an ancient building. After passing Thornhill the road commences to rise. The summit of this hill – known as Shade Hill – affords a good look out over the much celebrated common of Malmesbury, and the land granted by King Athelstan to the corporation, in recompense for the services of the town people which enabled him to gain a victory over the Danes at Sodbury. Shade Hill is the highest part of this land. The common is now almost all arable land, well cultivated. It extends, it is said, for two miles, and covers a space of some five hundred acres. It is held by the burgesses and corporation generally in allotments varying with circumstances. Some have eight, some twelve, others fifteen, and it is said a few have as much as thirty acres; which they can till themselves or let out. The alderman by support him. The effect of this arrangement – this allotmenting – is said to be deprecatory of progress; since men who have a few acres, enough to supply them with the necessities of life, do not trouble themselves in the endeavour to rise from the position to which they have been born, or come by right of inheritance, or marriage. The common appears from Shade Hill almost perfectly level. Upon the left run downs, known as Ail's Heath, White Heath, and Burnt Heath. The village of Corston lies in its extremity, while upon the right it is bounded by Higham Wood. It certainly was a most magnificent gift – this land presented by King Athelstan, and it is no wonder that his memory is still fresh in the minds of the inhabitants of Malmesbury, even after an interval of so many slow-circling centuries.

All these places – Burnt Heath, Higham – are connected with the history of ancient Malmesbury. Bruera or Burnt Heath was anciently in the occupation of the corporation, held of the abbey. Higham is mentioned in the already given extracts from Domesday Book. Everything in the neighbourhood of Malmesbury carries back the mind into the past, and it is difficult to believe when not actually in the town and in sight and hearing of the various branches of industry there going forward that one is living in the nineteenth century. Looking over this corporation ground, one would not be in the slightest surprised, and for a moment while in that mood not consider it extraordinary, if the 'stout King Athelstan' should himself appear riding at the head of his victorious army returning from the conquest of the Danes. The very air that blows around Shade Hill, fresh from the woods and winding river, whispers strange things of olden times as it sighs through the green-leaved trees. It is not until some labourer passes, employed by a burgess upon his land, that the spell is broken; for he carries a hoe or a spade, not a spear, and whistles a merry modern tune, instead of making the welkin ring with the blast of the horn.

Returning to Turketul Bridge, it will be noticed that there is an offshoot from the main road upon the left. This leads up into Westport-high-town, if it might be so termed. On the left hand of this branch road or street stands the National School, a substantial-looking structure, in strange contrast with the anything but firm-looking houses near. It might easily be taken for a place of worship at first sight. Upon the top of the hill, on the same side, is the piece of ground enclosed for burial purposes by the Baptists; on the right Malmesbury Cemetery, which does not contain a chapel. Further is the police station which, although it stands so near Westport, is in Brokenborough parish. Brokenborough, as has been before mentioned, is a village some distance from Malmesbury, said to have been once a Roman settlement, certainly a British and Saxon one. Its ancient name was Caerderburge. It is mentioned in Domesday Book, and then belonged to the abbey. The police station is tenanted by the superintendent, Mr Woodman, an able and most intelligent officer, and by a staff of men. It is a small but neat and comfortable dwelling, of the usual type. The situation is dry and healthy. From here the road leads into a three-cornered open space – it could be called square – known as the Horse Fair. Two streets branch out of it upon the right. The first goes down to Turketul Bridge, passing the front of the Independent, or New Congregational Chapel, now in course of erection, or rather of reconstruction. The other passes by the entrance to the same chapel yard. Here, on the right hand, close to the gateway, is a strange and very ancient building, occupied by poor persons. The porch, or entrance, is arched and evidently very old, while a window, built up, also gives indications of extreme antiquity. This is the house in which the former philosopher of Malmesbury – Thomas Hobbes – lived. Hobbes was born in Westport in 1588. His father was then minister of Westport Church. Wishing to learn what reputation the celebrated Hobbes had left behind him in his native place, we one day accosted a woman, apparently an inhabitant of the house, asking her, while pointing to the arched window, if it had ever been a chapel. No it hadn't – it *were* a mansion in times past. 'Who lived in it?' 'Oh it were an infidel.' And who was he? She could not remember his name. Was it Hobbes? 'Oh, yes, that were it.'

A short distance further stands Westport Church or Westport St Mary, which is a chapel of ease to the vicarage of Charlton. The living is worth £520 per annum with residence, and is in the gift of the Lord Chancellor. The present incumbent is the Rev. George Hutchinson, M.A. We were informed by an inhabitant of Westport that before the restoration of this church, which had taken place in his memory – some thirty years ago, it was a very small, and dilapidated building, resembling a 'barn' but very ancient. The oldest inscription was dated 1672.

The road here turns to the right – this leads to Tetbury, over a bridge. Tetbury is distant from Malmesbury five miles, and the inhabitants of both places have considerable dealings with each other. Turning to the right from Westport Church leads into a street which is known as the Abbey Row. This next to High Street is the best-built street in the town, and certainly the most pleasant situation. The houses are all situated upon the left side of the road; upon the other is a stone wall or parapet, part of it defended with sharp spikes apparently placed there to prevent children climbing over, or to sharpen up the unwary who should sit down upon them. Beneath this wall, which is built upon the edge of the hill, lie terrace gardens; lower still Burnivale, the hill terminating in meadows which run to the side of the Avon river. Over it the ground again rises. Upon the left hand – facing the river – is the abbey and the steeple of St Paul's Church, upon the right Westport, beneath the suburbs of Burnivale, Turketul Bridge, and the river. From this spot there is a very pleasant view. The Abbey Row, in fact, makes the most pleasant promenade in Malmesbury. Here the road is wide, and there being no houses upon one side, nothing obstructs the sight. Immediately below stood the hermitage of Meyldulph, near that the ancient nunnery, of which the chapel house was considered a remnant. The antiquity of the greater part of Malmesbury is immediately evident from here. Looking down upon the tops of the houses they are seen to be roofed with the ancient stone-slates; bricks are not used here, stone is too plentiful, which circumstance contributes to give the place generally an ancient appearance. Numbers of the houses have a dingy, yellowy-white look, having been washed over with something. This is far more pleasant to the eye than glaring red bricks.

In the Abbey Row stands the Baptist Chapel, almost hidden by lime trees, which overshadow the graves in the yard before it, placed in unpleasant proximity to the houses. At the extremity of the Abbey Row stands the steeple of St Paul's Church. It is said that the vicar of Malmesbury is still inducted in this steeple. The church has long been down. When Leland visited the place in the reign of Henry VIII, the body of it had disappeared, the remainder at the east end was used as a Town Hall. Its use as such was discontinued in 1623. The steeple appears to be still perfectly firm, though it has a very ancient appearance. From here two ways lead to the Market-Cross – one for horses and carriages by the White Lion, the other for foot-passengers behind the block of houses standing below the steeple. This latter way will be preferred as affording a beautiful view of the south side of the ancient abbey. From the Market-Cross a street leads to that part of the town known as Holloway. Here stands a tower or observatory said to have been built by Dr Player, and now, with the house beneath it, in the occupation of Messrs Jeston and Kinneir. Upon this spot it has been supposed, from some relics of antiquity which were found here, stood an *hospitium* belonging to the abbey, or place to entertain strangers wth monkish hospitality. Here, too, it was that the celebrated clothier of Malmesbury, Mr Stumpe, was suddenly called upon by the burly King, Henry VIII; who with his retinue had ridden in hungry enough, probably from hunting in Braydon Forest. Mr Stumpe was equal to the occasion as has been already related. On the same spot stood the Banqueting House in which King Charles I was entertained by the corporation of Malmesbury about 1643. His flight from here to Cirencester behind Prince Rupert has been alluded to previously. Nearly a century ago there stood here a summer-house in which tradition related the king slept a short time before he started. This place was afterwards called the workhouse.

Turning to the right from here the street leads into Cross Hayes Square. On the right hand, opposite the tower, stands the Moravian Chapel. Cross Hayes Square is of considerable extent, and of rather an oblong form. It is surrounded with buildings, but being nearly all old, and without the least attempt at regularity, they do not call for any especial comment. Here is the Town Hall – a modern erection, used for the purpose of law courts. On the left hand is an infant school, erected and supported by Mrs Kemble and S. B. Brooke, Esq. It is easily found by a conspicuous gilt ball upon the roof. The date is 1857. Further down, upon the same side, stands a house in which the Roman Catholics, who have recently entered the town, hold service upon Sundays. They are said to contemplate building a chapel. Their sensations upon looking at the abbey must be very strange. They were at first subject to much annoyance by the lower class of children disturbing their services which has been very properly put a stop to. On the right-hand side of the square is the back entrance to the George Hotel. Lower down, upon the same side, a narrow street communicates with High Street. Here dip-candle making is carried on. The Malmesbury volunteer corps are assembled and drilled in this Square. The corps is in a very flourishing condition, at least as regards numbers, there being over ninety members. The range for rifle practice is at the south end of the town, near Carris Hill.

Malmesbury gives its name to the hundred, and stands in the diocese of Gloucester and Bristol. The deanery is called Malmesbury North. The living of St Paul's, with Corston and Rodbourne annexed, is worth £430 per annum. It is in the patronage of the Lord Chancellor. At Corston, which is two miles distant from Malmesbury, though in the same hundred, there is a free school supported by R. H. Pollen, Esq., and others. Rodbourne is also at some distance. R. H. Pollen, Esq., has a residence there. The incumbent of St Paul's, Malmesbury is the Rev. Charles Pitt, M.A. It so chancing that when the dissolution of monasteries took place in the reign of Henry VIII that this church was dilapidated, the abbey church was purchased by Mr Stumpe, the clothier, and used in its place by means of a licence from the celebrated Archbishop Cranmer. Mr Stumpe thus conferred a double benefit upon posterity – providing them with a place of worship, and preserving the ancient abbey from destruction.

The municipal population of Malmesbury is over three thousand. It now only sends one member to Parliament. The present representative is Viscount Andover, eldest son of Lord Suffolk, of Charlton Park. The number of registered electors was 315 in 1859. By the addition of eleven parishes with a population of nearly seven thousand the constituency has been much enlarged. Numerous trades are and have been lately carried on at Malmesbury. Amongst these are silk ribbon manufactory, pillow lace, cloth, breweries, tanneries, dip-candle manufactory, &c. Although the place has no railroad, and is situated ten miles from Chippenham, the nearest station of any importance, a large amount of business is carried on. The two rivers greatly contribute to keep up something of its ancient importance. They supply a motive power much less costly than steam – especially where coal has to be brought ten miles in waggons – which is availed of in driving the machinery of silk ribbon manufactory, and several mills. The water of the town is forced up by a pumping engine from the river into a large tank placed near the abbey, and from thence distributed to the houses. Almost all the sects of religion have places of worship in or near the town. The average population of Malmesbury and Westport is 7,920.

Several noblemen and gentlemen of high standing in society own estates or residences in or near Malmesbury. The first of these is the Earl of Suffolk, who is spoken of with much respect by the inhabitants. His estates are of vast extent, comprehending several villages. George (Lord) Northwick is lord of Malmesbury manor; but does not reside here. Sir Hungerford Pollen and Sir John Neeld own estates in the neighbourhood. The Duke of Beaufort's mansion at Badminton is ten miles distant. Hunting is much indulged in by the gentlemen of the neighbourhood.

Modern Malmesbury (III)

The most striking entrance to the abbey is through a battlemented archway, close to the Market Cross, facing High Street. This is the south side. Immediately after passing beneath the wall the abbey, the upper portion of which can be alone seen from the street, bursts upon the sight, and seems to grow larger and more grand as it is approached, until standing opposite the porch it is almost impossible not to allow an exclamation of wonder to escape one. The abbey here presents its whole south side to the observer. It is immediately seen to be as it were of two storeys, as from over the lower arched windows – pointed arches like mute stone hands in the attitude of prayer – the roof falls back; then rises the second storey, supported by flying buttresses, ornamented with pointed pyramidical pillars. Here are six windows of equal extent. The upper roof appears to be of modern slate, the lower the old stone slate; giving the upper part a light, and the lower a more heavy appearance. A general air of extreme antiquity pervades the whole erection – gloomy and dark, like the dim vistas of the past. The entrance to the interior is here beneath a magnificent stone porch of enormous size. The arch towers high above the head wide enough to admit numbers at the same time. It is strangely sculptured. From the battlements of the porch look down mutilated faces carved out of the stonework, the sphinxes of England cut by her ancient priesthood, to be the surprise and puzzle of posterity. Many a century must have passed away since first those curious countenances stared down stolidly upon the stone flags beneath, on the passing processions of the monks, the gay dresses of the Cavaliers, the prim Parliamentarians, the strange dresses of the seventeenth century – on the black palled coffin, and the babe about to be christened. They must have witnessed curious scenes of sorrow and of joy; and have yet remained unmoved, unchanged through all, as if mocking at the human beings who made

them. Three arches there are to this porch at the entrance, one within
the other, and all sculptured. Each is divided into numbers of
lozenges, or ovals, containing figures of men and women – some of
them defaced and entirely gone, others standing out in as bold relief
as when the chisel finished them, in all but colour. Dark they are,
dark is all that is ancient of this venerable building, symbolical of the
times when it was founded, of the men who worshipped there –
dark, and dumb like Fate, yet saying unutterable things. There may
have been perhaps at first eighty of these sculptured arches. Nor is
the vault within left plain. On either hand, high above, are the
apostles – six upon each side, with an angel over them, while above
the inner door is the Saviour and two supporting seraphs. Beneath,
upon the right hand, is a large niche, said to have contained the holy
water in days gone by. The visitor feels inclined, gazing around this
ancient porch, to concur with the old sexton who shows the building
– himself an ancient who has occupied the post these fifty years past –
who, as he turns back the lock with his gigantic key, itself a relic of
the past, observes, 'It is the finest carved porch in the kingdom.'

On entering the doorway the church does not, as might have been
expected, burst upon the sight – the porch has not yet been entirely
left behind. Here will be noticed an inscription which, since (as the
old sexton will inform a stranger) it has been mutilated, or rather
altered, may be worth giving, with a view to prevent future mistakes:

Vnderneath this Stone Resteth ye Body of William Rabence of ye Abbey
gent. who ended this life Novm 5. 1700.

Some mischievous person or persons scooped out tails to the
noughts with their knives, making the date 1799 – all but a century
out. The voice here sounds hollow and sepulchral, re-echoed as it is
by the vaulting roof. Another door leads beneath the present gallery
and organ loft, at the west end of the church. Beneath it is dark and
gloomy. The gallery is supported by modern pillars. Here is the
font, an ancient piece of stonework, leaded within. On the left,
against the wall, hang two boards, with the following inscriptions,
the first of which explains the present condition of the church, the
latter relates to an almshouse.

The accommodation in this church was enlarged in the year 1823, by which means 341 additional sittings have been obtained, and in consequence of a grant from the society for promoting the enlargement and building of churches and chapels, 300 of that number are hereby declared free and unappropriated for ever, and are in addition to 60 previously provided.

GEORGE BISSET Vicar
R. PLAYER, JOHN PLAYER, Churchwardens

The other, which is in ancient characters and considerably abbreviated, runs thus:

Robert Jennor, of Widhil, in the county of Wilts, Esq., about the year 1622, did erect an almhouse for eight poor people of the town of Malmesburie, and endowed it with 40s p. an. for ever to be payd out of his manor and lordship of Widhil.

Mr Henry Grayle, one of the capital burgesses of Malmesburi, dy'd April 6th, 1661, and by will bequethed £10 p. an. for ever to be payd yearly out of his estate in Somerford Magna to ye Church Wardens and overseers of ye town of Malmesburie for ye apprenticing of poor children of ye said town.

Mr Edmund Wayte, one of ye capital burgesses of Malmesburie, dy'd in June, 1661, and by will bequeathed 40s. to ye poor of Malmesburie; 20s. to ye poor of Burton Hill, and 20s. to ye poor of West Port yearly to be payd out of Canopp's Mill into ye hands of ye Churchwardens of ye respective places and by them to be distributed on each Good Friday for ever.

The above endowment of an almshouse has long been lost, the building itself down, and the site seized and sold by the parish.

Stepping out from beneath this dark gallery, the body of the church is immediately entered. The roof arches over at a height of some sixty feet – a modern house might be built beneath it, chimneys and all, and never reach it – and the opposite wall beneath which is the communion table is nearly one hundred feet distant. The effect of this vastness is indescribable. On either hand huge pillars – eight in all – support the gigantic structure; and, although they are sixteen feet to the capitals, appear but dwarfs from the largeness of their diameter – five feet three inches – and on account of the general scale of the building. Like the sturdy stems of aged oaks upholding their wide spreading heads are these massive pillars; from which spring arches one to the other. From these arches again spring others, over these last are the second tier of windows, six on each side. They were originally nine, ere either end of the abbey fell in ruins. On the right hand high up, about midway down the wall, is a strange-looking house – if it might be so called -- projecting over the church, something like an enormous stone box pew hoisted up and affixed to the wall. It is called the abbot's seat, and tradition relates that it was from here he delivered the benediction. It would certainly afford him a view of the whole body of the remaining abbey church. The question that immediately suggests itself is, how on earth did he get into it? There appears at first sight no gallery, but a closer inspection reveals just beneath the second tier what looks like a succession of narrow arched tunnels running completely round the building inside, which a certain young lady once compared to rabbit holes. For what purpose these tunnels were constructed is not immediately evident. They would afford the monks an opportunity of passing around the church without disturbing service, or perhaps were found useful in making repairs. From the body of the church they, from their great and dizzy height, appear too small to admit a man, but we have been assured by one who has traversed them that a six-footer would have no difficulty in passing through in an upright posture. Unless those portions of these galleries now open were in olden times closed up, it must have required a steady nerve and firm foot to walk through them, on account of their narrowness, and the dizziness necessarily consequent upon so great a height.

At the extremity of the centre aisle over the communion table is suspended an immense painting, the gift of Lord Suffolk, representing the raising of Lazarus. It is said to measure twelve feet by ten. The wall beneath it is ancient, but behind and above it is comparatively modern. One third way down the centre aisle stands the desk from which the burial service is read, itself standing upon monuments of the departed. It faces the west end of the church, where is a high arched window comparatively modern. The gallery there contains an organ also modern, at least in comparison with the abbey itself. The word modern as applied to this building must be used in a very wide sense. At the extremity of the church towards the east are two chapels, at least such was their ancient use. They are fenced off as it were from the main body of the building by some ancient stone walls and iron bars. That upon the right hand contains a marble monument in memory of Lady Marshall, who died in 1625. The inscription runs thus.

> Stay gentle passenger and reade they doome,
> I am, thou must be, dead.

In assured hope of a joyful resurreccon, here rests deposited all that was mortall of the religious and virtuous Lady Dame Cyscely Marshall, daughter of the Honourable Sir Owen Hoptan, Knt. late lieftenant of the Towne Royal, the faithful, modist, and loyall wife of Sir George Marshall, Knt. Whether transcended in her more the ornaments that beautified a wife, a mother, a matrone, is still a question betwixte her all disconsolate husband, daughter, servants. Onely this is agreed upon all hands, such were her perfections in each state, that in vayne will any epitaph endeavour to delyneate them. What was her faith, hope, charity, temperance, piety, patience, may (to better purpose) be expected from the triump of an archangell in the day of Gods general retribuccion them from the faynte, and flagging attribuccons of any particular penn. To close all, with her close thies two spirituale ejaculacons. Miserere niei Deus, et domine recipe animam miam! (Have mercy upon me God, receive my soul O Lord!) were the wings, whereon the last breath of this turtle mounted towards heaven. To whose sweete memory her sad mate hath devoted this poor monument, which, – 'Oh let no prophane hand violate'.
Emigravit 23 Apryll. *Anno Salat* 1625.

The following is an extract from the register which may be very properly introduced here:

John Bridle reputed to be a gypsie, deceased September 21, 1657 at John Perynis house upon the Ffosse in Shipton parish in Gloucestershire; and was buried in King Athelstons chapel by [near] King Athelston, and the Lady Marshall, within the abbey church at Malmesbury. This buriall was September 23, 1657. Howbeit, he was taken up again by the means of Thomas Ivye esq. who then lived in the abbie, and by the desires and endeavoures of others out of the said chapell was removed into the churchyarde, and then was reburied neere the east side of the church poorch, October 7, 1657 in the presence of Thomas Ivye of the abbie esq., Pleadwell of Mudgell Esq., Rich. Whitmore of Slaughter, in the countie of Glocester, and Dr. Qui of Malmesbury with very many others.

On the left hand of this monument is an inscription in Latin dated

1712, old style, 1713 new. Immediately without this chapel, fixed upon a pillar, is a marble monument with the following inscription:

Sacred to the memory of Thomas and Edward Luce, sons of Thomas Luce, Esq., of this borough, and Susan his wife. Thomas was born at Malmesbury on the 13th of August, 1824, and died on the 22nd October, 1845, at Bombay.

Mentioning that he was a midshipman in the Indian navy, the inscription proceeds:

His brother officers erected a tomb over his remains in the Colaba Cemetery at Bombay in token of their estimation of his amiable qualities and of their sorrow for his loss.

Edward was born at Malmesbury on the 5th Feb., 1831, and was killed by a cannon ball at the bombardment of Sebastopol on the 11th April, 1855, a lieutenant in the Royal Artillery. Lord Raglan's despatch said of him 'The Royal Artillery have to lament the death of Lieutenant Luce, who was a zealous officer of much promise.' In every stage of his short life he was conspicuous for gentleness of demeanour, exemplary conduct and a deep sense of religion. His grave is at the foot of Inkerman.

The chapel upon the right hand is used for parish meetings. Upon this side is the pulpit, which is carved and has a carved canopy over it. At the foot of the pulpit stairs is King Athelstan's monument. He is not even supposed to be buried here, the monument having been brought in here from another part of the edifice to save it from destruction; and is moreover placed in such a position as instantly to demonstrate that the monks had no share in its arrangement, the head being towards the west. The monument is of an oblong form and over four feet in height. Upon it rests a stone figure of the 'Stout King Athelstan' laid out in state. He is clad in his robes with ornamented sandals and large sleeves. The countenance is much mutilated, but the general contour of the head gives it a sturdy appearance. If this be a truthful representation, Athelstan was a king every inch of him. A canopy forms the extremity of the monument over his head, which is crowned. His hair is most luxuriant, rolling down upon his neck and shoulders. The beard descends slightly upon the breast, and the upper lip is covered with a moustache. The arms are broken off, and it is impossible to say whether they were or were not crossed over his breast, as is so often in similar monuments. Upon each side of the shoulders are two seated figures of a small size, so much mutilated that at present it seems impossible to determine what they represent. The feet rest against the figure of a lion, in the attitude of watchfulness. On the whole the monument is in a very fair state of preservation. Over it there is an inscription dated 1793, close by one of 1734 – ancient in themselves, but of yesterday in comparison with the date of the death of Athelstan which took place in 941, over nine centuries ago.

The communion table is as usual railed off. The railing partly conceals an ancient monument against the wall dated 1699. On either side of the table are old chairs, carved, of a very ancient and rather uncomfortable stiff-backed appearance. Immediately behind the table is the monogram I.H.S. Above this the wall, which as far as the lower side of the picture here suspended is ancient, is covered with strange carvings of dogs and griffins and other figures of small size, and some of them mutilated. The reading desk is on the left side of the communion table if looked at while passing up the aisle, on the right standing facing the organ. Over it is a monument to Elizabeth Warneford dated 1631. The Warnefords once held the manor of Malmesbury. Within the chapel upon this side of the church – now used as a vestry-room, or place for the clergyman to change his gown – are preserved two ancient bosses which have been dug up near the abbey. One of them displays the wounds of Christ: the heart in the centre, the hands and feet disposed around, and pierced. Here also upon a table are preserved some remnants of the ancient mosaic pavement of the church. It will be noticed that many of the monuments instead of being of stone are of copper, displaying the ghostly death's head, cross bones, pickaxe and spade – especially down the north aisles. It is through this left-hand chapel – at the extremity of the north aisle – that exit may be gained to the eastern part of the yard. Within the vestry-room is the following curious inscription, said to be of a captain of the garrison of Malmesbury in the time of the civil wars:

Near this place lyeth the body of Thomas Stumpe, gent., who departed this life the 6th day of April, Anno-Dom. 1698. Ætalis Suæ 79.

O Death how cruel is thy Dart
To strike ye Captaine to ye Heart.
Too good He was here to remaine
Jehovah tooke Him for to traine,
In grave his body to remaine
Till Christ himself doth come againe!

The Stumpe family seem to have long held a respectable position in Malmesbury. Near this inscription is a copper plate affixed to the wall upon which are these words: 'The gift of Thomas Stumpe, of Malmesbury Abbey, gent., 1689.'

At the eastern extremity of the abbey church, exposed to the storms of heaven, stands a magnificent arch some sixty feet in height. The stonework upon its summit is in ruins and ready to fall. There is a circular hole through it, said to have been made by a ball from a cannon when Cromwell besieged the town. There were originally two of these arches, as is evident from the remains. It was at this end of the building that the cross aisle was, the abbey being built in the form of a cross; that part which is still used as the parish church formed the tree of the cross. A large portion of the western wall of this cross aisle still remains, much covered with ivy and other plants; of ivy a kind of tree grows upon it. Along this wall too is visible the before-mentioned gallery. To the east of this arch is an ancient building known as the Abbots' House, or Abbey House; where it is considered that the abbots resided. It is a strange old gabled structure, rising up exactly at the edge of the hill upon which Malmesbury is built. It is now in the occupation of Dr Jennings. The windows facing the Newnton river are arched. A great part of the roof of one of the gables has been taken off and glass substituted, in order to make a greenhouse or conservatory.

Passing round the abbey to the west end, which is also in ruins, there stands a cannon said to have been taken at Sebastopol. It was at this end of the abbey that the castle of Malmesbury stood, which was razed by permission of King John that the abbey might be extended. The Bell Inn now stands upon its site, which was well chosen; this being the narrowest part of the hill upon which Malmesbury is built, hence it could be defended upon both sides. The abbey churchyard is on the south side. Here are two curious inscriptions upon tombstones. The following is commemorative of the death of a servant killed by a tiger in 1703, which had been in an exhibition, and which she had teased.

> In bloom of youth she's snatched from hence,
> She had not time to make defence;
> For tyger fierce snatched life away,
> And now she lies in bed of clay,
> Until the resurrection day.

The next is said to have been written by Oldham the poet, on Dr. Abia Qui, who died in 1675:

> He, by whose charter thousands held their breath,
> Lies here, the capture of triumphant Death;
> If drugs or matchless skill could death reclaim,
> His life had been immortal as his fame.

The best view that can be obtained of the abbey, the abbots' house, and of Malmesbury, is by passing down the hill towards the River Newnton, on the north side of the abbey. Here on the left stands what is called the Abbots' Mill. It is still used as a mill. The upper stones are gained by a bridge from the hill, it being built at the foot. The building is evidently very ancient, and is much hidden by ivy. At the foot of the hill a bridge crosses the river and a path will take the stranger up the opposite hill into a field known as the Worthys, whence the abbey itself and Malmesbury can be seen to best advantage. The abbey is most impressive at night, when the sounds of the industrious toilers of the town are silent, and the stars look down dimly through the pall-like clouds upon the vast mausoleum. It is tenanted no longer save by the dead. At night the olden times seem to return, and though a shudder might ensue the cowled form of a monk might be met without surprise. It is an abbey such as might have suggested the lines of Byron.

> Beware, beware of the Black Friar
>   That sitteth by Norman's stone,
> For he mutters his prayers to the midnight air,
>   And his mass of the days that are gone.
> When the Lord of the Hill, Amundeville,
>   Made Norman Church his prey,

Though he came in his right, with King Henry's might,
   To turn church land to lay,
One monk remained, unchased, unchained,
   And he did not seem formed of clay.
For he's seen in the church, and he's seen in the porch,
   But he is not seen by day.
Amundeville he is lord by day,
   But the monk he is lord by night,
Nor wine nor wassal could raise a vassal
   To question that friar's right.

Such is the present condition of Malmesbury. The abbey cannot be described, it must be seen. Thus have we traced its rise, its progress and its fall, and now farewell to the merrie monks of Malmesbury.

Appendix

By way of an appendix to the *History of Malmesbury*, we publish the following interesting document descriptive of the assault upon, and capture of Malmesbury by the Parliamentary troops. The document is interesting as showing the mode of making war in those days:

Eben-ezer, a full and exact Relation of the several remarkable and victorious Proceedings of the ever renowned Colonell Massie, Governour of Gloucester from May 7th, to May 25, 1644, in which time he took these severall considerable garrisons of the enemies in Gloucestershire and Wiltshire, namely, Westbury, Little Deane, Newnam, Beverstow Castle, Malmesbury and Chippenham, with the Summons sent by Col. Massie to Col. Howard, sonne to the Earl of Berkshire, Governour of Malmesbury; And his answer thereunto, and the names of the Officers and Commanders taken there.

June 4, 1644
Imprimatur, JOHN WHITE

London: Printed for T. W. and are to be sold in the Old Baily, 1644.

A True Relation of Several happy and wonderful victories lately given unto Col. Massie, Govenour of Gloucester, from May 7, 1644 untill the 25 of the same Month.

On Tuesday, the 7th of May, the Governour marched out of Gloucester with about nine hundred foot, and his owne regiment of horse, and Col. Purefoy's regiment of horse, two pieces of ordnance, and other carriage fit for the march, with purpose to remove the enemies garrisons at Westbury, Little Deane, and Newnam, all strongly fortified, and well provided with men, armes, and ammunition; all which it pleased God miraculously to deliver into his hands. For he first assaulting the garrison at Westbury (which was Mr Colchester's house, and the Church) he got to the Church, and with granadoes and pistoll shot, the which he sent in at the Windowes, he presently made the enemy to forsake the church, and to runne to the house; which being discerned by the governour's force, the church was

quickly possessed by them; which made the enemy forsake all their out-
workes and to cry for quarter. There were slain of the enemy about twenty,
and about three score taken prisoners in that garrison, with their armes and
ammunition. Whilest the foot was at this garrison at Westbury, Colonel
Massie commanded some of the horse to march to Little Deane, were the
enemy had also fortified a house to face them, who, falling suddenly into
the towne, took divers of them in the towne, and there killed Lieutenant-
Colonel Congre, governour of Newnham; and the horse only with their
carbines, swords, and pistols, suddenly surprised the garrison itselfe
(although fortified) there were neere forty prisoners taken, and that night
Colonel Massie quartered at Westbury and Deane, and the next day drew
up to Newnham, where presently he beat the enemy out of the towne into
their workes, which were double fortified and very strong, having a very
small compasse to make good, and there being but one place possible to fall
on the enemy, who, having there foure small pieces of ordnance and good
store of provision and ammunition. Yet it pleased God to give the souldiers
such courage and resolution that they fiercely stormed the workes, and
made the enemy to forsake them, and to runne into the church, where the
governour's forces rushed in upon them pell-mell with much violence,
which enforced them to cry out for quarter; which one Tipper an old
servant to Sir J. Winter and an arch papist perceiving and being not willing
to take quarter, gave fire to a barrell of powder intending to destroy himself
and all the rest, which occasioned the putting of more to the sword than
otherwise had been, the governour being much enraged to see any of his
men scorched with powder. In this garrison was taken good store of
provisions of all sorts, 4 guns, one great wall-piece of 8 foot long, good
store of granadoes, and some fireworks, 8 barrels of powder, 60 skeines of
fine match, with good store of great shot for the guns, about 150 prisoners,
whereof 3 were captaines, and one Captain Butler was slaine with the butt
end of a musket, and so was old Tipper (that traitor to the rules of war) with
about 20 others; there were taken about 20 others; there were taken also
about 40 horses. The prisoners were instantly conveyed to Gloucester with
safety, and the governour quartered that night at Newnam and Little
Deane. But the wonderfull and extraordinary providence of God was in
this, that in the taking of three fortified garrisons in two daies, and all by
storme, the governour lost never a man, only some few were scorched with
the treachery of the papists powder-plot, and one had this arme shot off
with cannon-bullet, but none of the wounds mortal.

After the taking of the said three several garrisons, the governour of
Gloucester marched with his said forces to Lidney, where Sir John Winter's

fortifications and provisions being found too strong for such forces as the
governour had with him, the governour drew off his wearied men, and
caused three iron mills of Sir John Winter's, with his provision of coales to
be destroyed, burned, the same being very beneficiall to the said Sir John
Winter, and most usefull to him and the popish party for provisions of
warlike engines against the parliament's army and the kingdome. While
those able actions of the governour were performed in Gloucestershire,
Colonel Mynn with his regiments of horse and foote forsooke Rosse, in
Herefordshire and entered some into Hereford, and some into Monmoth
for their better security; whereupon the worthy Governour with his said
forces of foot and horse, marched into Herefordshire, possessed himself of
arms, tooke Wilton bridge, being a draw bridge on the river Wye, and took
the house or castle neere unto with one and thirty prisoners and some
horses, and then sent part of his horse, viz., Colonel Purefoy's regiment of
horse, towards Monmoth to give an alarm there, and the other part, viz. his
owne regiment of horse towards Hereford to performe the like, which
caused the great jesuitical papists and arch traytor, the L. Herbert, to gather
his forces of horse and foot into Monmoth to joyne with the forces thereof
Colonel Minns, and sent all their horse from Monmoth towards Wilton
bridge, but they were encountered by the way by the horse sent by the
governour towards Monmoth, who charged them bravely, slew 5 or 6 of
them, and the rest being neere the towne of Monmoth sheltered themselves
there. In the meanetime the governour being now quietly possessed of all
that part of Herefordshire, summons the county to come in, and to take the
covenant, and to pay contributions unto him, where he found willing
obedience by the greatest part of the yeomanry of that county, and was
resolved to have besieged Hereford, which would have yielded unto him in
very short time, as is since informed, had not other important occasions
called him from thence to performe a greater service in God's name. While
the governour was thus employed in Herefordshire, he received advertise-
ment that 7 of his souldiers had taken Colonel Oglethorpe, governour of
Beverston Castle, and six others of his troopers, and brought them to
Gloucester, and that a captain of his was going away into other service of the
parliament; whereupon he coming to Gloucester May 21 in the evening,
dispatched the business he came about, and finding them by examination of
some of the said prisoners, that there were some distractions hapned upon
taking the governour of Beverston castle, touching the government thereof,
and the rather because the King had granted the same unto Sir Baynham
Trockmorton whilst the said Oglethorpe was governour, the said noble
governour of Gloucester resolved to take the opportunity to performe some

worthy exploits; and having then about 10 o'clock at night the said 21 of May received letters from the committee of the house of Commons nominated for the affairs of the garrison of Gloucester, he wrote severall letters unto them from Gloucester, which tooke up his time until two a clocke in the morning, and then posted backe into Herefordshire, twelve miles from Gloucester the same day, Wednesday, May 22, and there drew his said forces of horse and foot into one body at Rosse, and then presently caused his horse to march by Gloucester appointing them to be the next day at the rendezvouz within 3 miles of Beverston castle, 15 miles from Gloucester southward; and also the same day caused his foot to march somewhat a neerer way towards Beverston castle, over the river Severne unto Frampton, being at least 16 miles, and were constrained to march all Wednesday night to meet the horse at the rendezvouz appointed, as aforesaid; and from thence marched to Beverston castle on the Thursday, where they first surprised about 60 horse depasturing under the castle walls, and guarded with about 6 musketiers, who flying gave the alarm to the castle, which the noble governour suddenly surrounded with his horse, and the same night drew up his foot and artilery, and then sending to summon the castle, and writing also to the lieutenant-colonell and other officers there some plausible letters, and offering faire quarter and true performance, the castle was surrendered unto him about 12 o'clock the same night by accord, only to give them quarter, liberty, and their wearing apparell. In which castle they had 50 muskets, 4 barrels of powder, and other provision; the command whereof was presently delivered unto Captaine Read, a faithfull man in the service of the parliament. The noble governour having thus settled a garrison for the parliament in Beverston castle, continued his march the next morning towards Malmesbury, in Wiltshire, and the same day sent this ensuing summons written with this own hand unto the governour of Malmesbury, viz.:

To the Governour or Commander in Chiefe of the Garrison of Malmesbury.
    You are hereby summoned, that you within one halfe houre after the coming of this to your hands, surrender the same, with all the armes, ammuntion, provision, and other things of service and use whatsoever unto Colonell Massie, governour of Gloucester for the use, and on behalfe of the King and his Parliament now sitting at Westminster. And he doth hereby engage himselfe by all the ties of honour, that you, your officers, and soldiers shall not only enjoy your lives, and be received under the protection of good usage and quarter, but also all such as shall desire imployment with us, under my

command, shall find entertainment according to their qualities, or depart whither they please and if you shall refuse this proffer of mercy, then you are to expect no other but what fire and sword shall bring upon you.

    24th of May 1644   EDWARD MASSEY

Within half an hour Colonel Howard sent out the following reply:

Sir, – I have received your summons, and without any unsavoury language do return you this answer – That we will maintain this town for the King and Parliament now sitting at Oxford, in defence of those rights which that pretended Parliament at Westminster have abused and robbed our nation of. For the action particular, viz., that upon denial we must expect the extremity of fire and sword, we make this answer – That those extremities I believe are as likely to fall on those that assault the town as on those that defend it. For that point of serving you – the truth is, we are all too proud.

                                           Your Servant

    24 May 1644   HENRY HOWARD

Upon the receipt of this resolute reply, Massey found it necessary to send back an order to Tetbury to bring on the foot and artillery without delay. In two or three hours, the former having arrived, he lost no time in taking possession of the houses at the foot of the town bulwarks. The place was perceived to be very strongly situated, having an exceedingly precipitous embankment all round, and this again being based by a double graff. The natural advantages indeed had rendered the garrison too indifferent as to the defenses of the one single avenue by which the town could be entered, this being neither supplied with drawbridge nor foss, but simply by a turnpike and a chain which ran across the street; which caused that worthy commander, Colonel Massie, to double his care and diligence to storme it, with all vigour, courage, and expedition; but it was late in the evening before he could draw up his horse, foot, and artillery before the said towne: and these two difficulties happened unto him the same time: the one was his souldiers' want of sleep, having continued their constant watch, and continuall duty for severall days and nights together, without intermission: the other was, the great storme of raine that fell the same evening, and continued all the night ensuing, whereby Colonell Purefoy's regiment of horse were constrained to forsake the field, and seeke out some shelter for themselves and their horses; but the unwearied gouvernour, with his foot, and some three or foure troupes of horse of his own regiment, gave the alarum to the enemy all that night, playing hard with his ordnance and musketiers, during which time he himselfe took great paines in making blines, and in taking such houses as might best preserve his men, and resolved to storme it early the next morning, and accordingly about sun-rising May 25, he drew out a strong party of musketiers against the turnpike and chaine, who very gallantly assaulted the enemy, and beat them from their ordnance and guards: some others of the musketiers assaulting the enemy in their works (at one and the same time) with scaling ladders, beat the enemy from their works, and with great courage and resolution entred the same, wounded some, and the rest fled further into the towne: in all which it was hard to judge whether that worthy commander, by his personall action, or discreet direction, were of greater avail in taking the towne; but sure it is, the same added much courage to the captaines both of horse and foot; insomuch that Major Gray and Captaine Ayleworth with joynt courage, and brave horses well mann'd swiftly entred the towne, by leaping their horses over the chaine, and over the turnepike, and encountred the first enemy, by cutting off his arme with a sword, and shot the next in the head with a pistoll; and Captain Blunt, one of the captaines of foot, upon the discharge of the enemie's ordnance forced his entrance into the towne through the enemie's worke where the enemy plyed the ordnance, which he overturned upon his entrance, and made way for his souldiers to follow: and Captain White entered the towne in another place over the works, first mastering the same with his musketiers: but the first man that by force entered the enemie's works was a sergeant with 40 resolute musketiers, to whom the governour had promised five pounds, with other rewards to the 40 musketiers, if they would give the first assault, and performe it with courage, which they did accordingly, and the governour paid them liberally. It was a brave spectacle to see how unanimous both commanders and souldiers undertooke the enterprize, and with what undaunted spirits and carriage all of them in one minute of time performed the same, notwithstanding their hard marches, wante of sleep, and the unseasonable raine all that night. But let all glory and praise be given to the Lord of Hosts, by whom the worke was done in so little time, and without so much as a man hurt of the governour's souldiers in the storming of it; nor did they lose a man during their time of being there, except the governour's boy and one common souldier: our forces lay but twelve or thirteene horses before the same, ere they tooke it by assault: the governour of Malmesbury, and such other prisoners as were taken, are contained in the ensuing list:

A list of officers and souldiers taken at Malmesbury, May 25, 1644 at 4 of the clock in the morning.

Henry Howard, col. of foot
William Howard, liev. col.,
    sons to the Earl of Berkshire.
William Chester, major
William Markham, capt.
Gilbert Wheathill, capt.
John Brimsden, capt. lievt.

Lievtenants.

Richard Bleak
Edward Scott
William Roach.

Ensignes.

John Barrat
Robert Bates
Richard Cage
—— Browning.

Quartermasters.

James Bower
—— Morely
Laurence Short.

Serjeants.

Henry Dixon
Richard Fletcher
Robert Baily
William Fenton

Corporalls

Thomas Hadley
Henry Painter
John Poole
John Peerce
John Chappell.

Gilbert Harris, drummer.
Wm. Weeks, chyrurgion.
John Clark, capt. of horse.
Private Soulders, 148.

Gentlemen that bare armes
John Freame
William Norris
John Bridges.

The rest of the officers and souldiers by running thorow the river made their escape.

  2 Iron faulcons
  2 Iron hamberguns
  2 Barrells of powder
152 Skaines of match
900 Weight of shot
150 Muskets, or thereabouts.

JASON ANSPACH

PRISONERS OF DARKNESS

SEASON 1   BOOK 6

GALAXY'S EDGE

JOIN THE LEGION

LEGION

FOR UPDATES ABOUT NEW RELEASES, EXCLUSIVE PROMOTIONS, AND SALES, VISIT INTHELEGION.COM AND SIGN UP FOR OUR VIP MAILING LIST. GRAB A SPOT IN THE NEAREST COMBAT SLED AND GET OVER THERE TO RECEIVE YOUR FREE COPY OF "TIN MAN", A GALAXY'S EDGE SHORT STORY AVAILABLE ONLY TO MAILNG LIST SUBSCRIBERS.

INTHELEGION.COM

That was Option Three. Let the Legion go Legion on the galaxy.

X did not shudder when he considered the death toll. Galaxy-wide, it would be phenomenal.

And what if the Legion didn't surrender power as it was supposed to at that point?

Well, thought X, sipping tea once more. There was that to consider.

And without meaning to, he had answered Question Three. Which was... Which way would he, X, go?

Save the Republic?

Ally with this Sullus?

Release the Legion?

It all depended on who showed up at the farm in the next two hours. It was amazing to think that such grand alterations in the galactic scheme of things had to be decided on the "weather" any given situation presented. In his mind there were no grand schemes, only long games.

He tapped the intercom.

The front girl answered. "Yes?"

"Have Carn bring the shuttle in. I need to run up to the farm."

Pause.

"Shall I accompany you, sir?"

"Won't be necessary. Just need to check on something. We'll be back in the evening."

"All right then," said the girl cheerily enough. "Take a coat, sir, the storm's broken up that way. Heavy rain for the rest of the afternoon."

"I shall," replied X. Then he drained his cup and went to meet the shuttle.

It was an uneasy feeling that wouldn't leave X that caused him to put the sniper team the Carnivale kept on constant ready out in the woods beyond the landing pad in the field next to the farm. The Carnivale used the farm for training. Nothing up to legionnaire standards, but for purposes of spycraft it was enough. Device training. Explosives. Sidearms. Knifework. Code school. Hand-to-hand with an emphasis on strangulations. All of that was taught within the three ancient stone buildings, erected most likely after the first explorers settled on Utopion who cared how long ago.

The farmhouse had a small staff led by Sergeant Major Avers, an old tail man who'd served in the Legion and taught tracking, following, and strangulations. He ran the old place just right for X's taste, and of course it would be nice to see the old fox and nip at a bit of scotch while they waited for the *Forresaw* to appear.

It was raining quite heavily up at the farm. The shuttle dropped off X and lifted off, leaving the tiny pad clear for the *Forresaw* to arrive. In the quiet that followed the departure of the transport shuttle, X listened to the rain falling beyond the landing site. He scanned the trees only occasionally, knowing that there was a sniper and a spotter out there waiting to do what they did.

Already.

Waiting.

And still, X had no idea why he'd ordered the team there. Just that uneasy feeling, an unquiet ghost wandering the old house he called his mind.

He wrapped himself tighter in his coat and made his way to the main house. Sergeant Major Avers had a fire going in the old riverstone hearth.

X wondered how he was going to play out the next move in this long game. There was every chance there might be a double-cross here. Or even an arrest by the House of Reason for some wonderfully trumped-up charge like high treason. They could make it stick long enough to make sure he went to his first court date. But then they would get a look, from some anonymous courier, at some portion of the files he kept on all of them.

And he would be free again shortly thereafter.

He wondered how long he could play that game.

He opened the door to the large cottage and saw the sergeant major waiting in a high-backed chair. The older man smiled his rose-cheeked smile and clinked two tumblers together. For the rest of the afternoon, as they waited for the *Forresaw* to make planetfall, they had at the scotch and talked about old times, old friends, and nothing of Nether Ops.

In Nether Ops no one ever talked about Nether Ops, because Nether Ops didn't exist. Not even in your memories.

Toward dark, the rain let up and the *Forresaw* finally cleared approach traffic and made her way down onto the landing pad. They heard her big engines whining as she came in through the storm, repulsors fighting the embrace of greedy gravity, and then some low and barely caught note of gears coming out as the ship approached the pad. Through the cottage's lone window they saw the landing lights cut the field. It washed over the darkness inside the cottage.

Engines flared, and the ship was down.

"C'mon," said X to the sergeant major. "Let's go see what our strays are up to."

The sergeant major stood and groaned, putting his hand to his back.

"You worried, Chief?" he said to X rather casually in the quiet putting-on-coats moment that followed.

X turned. Was it that obvious? He'd gone to great lengths to seem rather blasé about the whole mess. When really, all the options and questions had been turning over and over again and again in his mind throughout the long afternoon of scotch-sipping.

X shook his head. Then asked, "Boys in the woods?"

The sergeant major nodded solemnly, no trace of the joviality of their drink on his stone-cold hard man's face. "Aye."

And then they were out into the early dark, seeing the looming *Forresaw*, glowering over the landing pad like some evil and unwanted bird come home to roost. The boarding ramp was already coming down, throwing a shaft of internal bright light out onto the pad.

That apparently peeved the sergeant major as he trudged along through the field behind the long loping strides of X, who, though bent, was tall. "They're supposed to cut to light discipline when we're doing business. They know that. I trained them to do that. Why don't they do that?"

Doing business is code for Nether Ops work.

X sees only Andien Broxin coming down the ramp. No ghost team. No little girl. And this makes him deeply uncomfortable.

He pats the holdout blaster in his coat pocket, because something is wrong. This has all gone wrong. He pats the tiny blaster as though he is searching for a pack of cigarettes, or a pen, or something not a blaster, because he is, after all, just an old man who once had all the close up and personal business of spying and killing.

The *Forresaw*'s engines have gone silent by the time X stops just twenty feet away from Captain Broxin at the bottom of the ramp.

His protégé.

His Judas?

"We were worried about you," he says. The fields all around them smell of fresh wet grass, and the woods are heady in their cold night-misted fragrances. X knows this moment. This moment of killing. Because everything is so real. So vibrant. So wish-you-were-anywhere-but-here.

It's a shame to kill the girl. She had potential. But everybody does at this level of the game.

And... you might as well know you're going to do a thing before you do it.

What she says next will determine everything for X. He's noticed she's strapped. Carrying her blaster.

The girl says nothing.

Uncertain, X tries, "Where is Hutch? The rest?"

Especially the little girl who was so important to this mission. Maydoon's little girl. Prisma Maydoon. The key to the Doomsday Fleet.

"Dead," says Broxin, and X is surprised at himself more than he is at the answer. Of course, there was the potential that all of them could have been killed. But he hadn't really considered it even as everything began to go strange in this long afternoon of mysterious ships suddenly appearing. The truth was, he'd been concentrating on the long game instead of thinking about the actual mission. Maybe he was getting old?

"Are you ready for my report?"

That's odd, thought X, and he didn't even bother to weigh it before he nodded and replied, "Let's have it."

Why didn't you catch that?

Because you wanted to know what this was all about so badly. So you just said *Let's be done with it and have at it*. That's what you did.

When really... what she'd said was very odd.

Are you ready for my report?

It seemed like the right thing to say but really wasn't. Nothing was ever so formal in a place that called strangling, snipers on rooftops, and regime change, "doing business."

Far too formal.

Like she'd been asking him to identify himself as her handler. Like a spotter. Or an informant. For someone else to give some order of arrest. Or...

The sergeant major was knocking fuddy old X to the ground because he'd seen her pull her weapon lightning quick. Seen it while X was lost in self-criticism and fixations on the long game of what this all meant for his sacred Galactic Republic he was still desperate to save with all the games he could play.

He felt the sergeant major on top of him, covering him, as Andien Broxin began to fire at X, closing on the two old men. X tried to reach for his weapon, but he was pinned to the wet grass and the weapon was in the pocket beneath him.

The sergeant major was firing back.

Firing at the advancing girl.

Firing and missing? Or hitting her and it wasn't doing much?

Then the sniper team opened fire from out in the woods. A shot from the N-18 hit Andien Broxin in the chest. Knocked her down.

X saw all this from the ground, the wet grass kissing his face.

And the girl who'd just been hit by a shot from a high-powered state-of-the-art sniper rifle... got up and ran back into the ship.

The sniper team tried to hit her, but she was moving far too fast.

Even though she should be dead.

A moment later the boarding ramp was up, and the sergeant major was dragging X back through the dark, screaming into his comm for the sniper team and whatever other assets the sergeant major had waiting around, telling them to take out the ship.

The sniper team could disable critical systems or just shoot the pilot.

They were firing, and the rain was falling harder. The sergeant major was breathing heavily, dragging X into the cottage. X felt distant. Not himself. As though possibly he'd been hit?

He didn't feel hit.

The sergeant major slammed the cottage door and pulled up a trap door in the floor. X remembered they'd had a bunker installed. Right here.

"In," bellowed the sergeant major. "Now!"

They weren't halfway down the ladder when the *Forresaw* exploded, leveling the farm.

01

Dark Ops Headquarters
Deep Space Supply Station 9
Galaxy's Edge

Major Ellek Owens hadn't been in ener-chain binders in... how long *had* it been? Owens tried to think back as he marched down the dilapidated corridors of the deep space supply station his Dark Ops HQ used as a base of operations.

Perhaps it was during the Legion's standard REES training—Resistance, Evasion, Escape, and Survival. A brutal course that denied its students their buckets and weapons, forcing them to live off the land as long as possible, evading patrolling bots and Legion instructors. Owens had managed to remain loose for three months in the wilderness of Pratna-Kao. Until the instructors had to call for him to come out through amplification towers and messenger bots.

Owens shook his head at the memory. When he'd revealed himself, smiling, to a pair of instructors traveling in an open-air repulsor sled along a mountain road, the two leej instructors smiled back, hopped out, and put him in ener-chains before laying on a beating and "graduating" him to the next phase of the program, where he sat in a makeshift prison complex with other captured leejes, forced to endure physical and psychological stresses designed to get him to abandon the Legion code and flip on his brothers. That was the only time in all of Owens's training that he thought he might actually die from the experience.

But that memory wasn't the last time he'd been in ener-chains. He recalled a Dark Ops training program that augmented the REES course. Only in this one, the joke was that the "R" stood for "restraints." In that course, the instructors taught their students how to disable all sorts of restraints—including the top-issue Republic models that were supposedly foolproof.

The red-bearded major looked at the two Republic Army soldiers marching in front of him. Each of the men held a Miif-7 blaster rifle at the two-handed carry position. It wouldn't be difficult for him to escape the ener-chains and take both men out. There were two more behind him, and they wouldn't be hard to neutralize, either.

But things in the Republic were tense. Owens knew that Kill Team Victory's mission to destroy the shipyards at Tarrago had been against the desires of the House of Reason, even though it was tactically the best move in the blossoming war against this Goth Sullus idiot. And Legion Commander Keller had warned him that if the mission was successful—and it had been a *huge* success—someone was going to take a political hit for it.

That someone was Owens.

"Hey! Basics! Where the hell are you going with Major Owens?"

The shout came from one of the Dark Ops leejes based on the station. Sergeant Jason Henderson. DO-360, "Trident."

The army escorts, clearly rattled by this, quickened their pace. Trident stepped directly in their path and crossed his arms, covering the Legion crest on his black

T-shirt. He stood a head taller than the Rep Army soldiers, and looked down on them with distaste. As though those standing before him were not quite men.

"I'm talking to you, *Basics*," he said with a sneer. "Where you taking Major Owens?"

Owens popped his gum loudly and smiled, his eyes hidden behind seemingly opaque black shades. "Better answer the man, boys. I would if I was you."

One of the two soldiers in the front sagged his shoulders in an exaggerated manner and dropped his head, as if to show that he wasn't looking for trouble and was put off by its arrival.

"Look, man," the soldier said, nodding as if trying to reach an accord through some unseen rhythm. "I'm only in the army because the Reason judge said it was this or penitential confinement. My lieutenant says to go grab your boy, I do what she says."

"He does what she says," Owens parroted. "Don't want to get your lieutenant mad at you. She'll ruin your life."

"That's what I'm saying," added one of the basics behind Owens. "Have us on waste disposal with orders to outclean the bots."

"The major came with us willingly," offered the other soldier in the front, his tone carrying a note of hope that the comment might help.

"No kidding he came willingly," Trident said, as though the statement was the dumbest thing he'd heard all day. "If he didn't want to, you'd all be in line for emergency cybernetics. He'd already be out of the ener-chains if he didn't want to be in them, skipworms."

The soldiers looked at Owens, who sheepishly nodded that this was correct. This was the perfect diversion before whatever tongue-lashing the House had in store for him. A reprieve from reality. One more good time with the boys.

That's what it would have to be.

He was going to have to face some punishment, like it or not. Owens knew that Keller would protect him, ultimately. The Legion wasn't going to lose a Dark Ops sector commander just because the House of Reason was too obtuse to recognize sound tactics. The ener-chains were probably by order of no one higher up than the soldier's lieutenant. An overzealous know-nothing who took herself far too seriously.

"Yo!" shouted another legionnaire. His dark complexion betrayed significant annoyance. "Why is there a basic parade in my hallway, dammit?"

The soldier who had chosen army over jail shifted his feet. "Maaan..." he mumbled to himself.

The newly arrived legionnaire wore a captain's fatigues and had a jaw so hard he could chew impervisteel and then blow bubbles. He joined Trident in blocking the corridor.

"What do my wondering eyes see?" asked the new arrival.

None of the soldiers escorting Owens said anything. This only seemed to make the captain angrier.

"Y'all basics don't answer captains when they ask you a question? What I gotta be? A general? I gotta summon General Rex from the grave? That it, basics?" shouted the captain so rapidly that the soldiers were able to do little more than flinch at his every word.

"No, sir," they answered in unison.

"'No, sir,' what?" the captain shot back. "No, you don't answer captains? Well, seeing as how I earned these two bars fighting through McCoy Cluster while you four were gettin' fat off commissary life, I take offense! Yes, I do! O-F-F-E-N-S-E. What's that spell?"

"Offense!" shouted back the soldiers.

"Damn right. Now answer my other question!"

"Sir, we answer captains, sir!" shouted one of the basics, a remnant of his essential training camp experience springing back to him.

"I hear you say that, but I still don't know why a basic parade is marching through this supply station!"

"Sir, we have orders to escort Major Owens to a shuttle docked at Bay D-3."

"Orders from who?" bellowed the captain. He pointed at his chest. "*I* didn't give you no orders like that. Major Owens? Did *you* order these men to parade you through these halls like a prisoner? Is that how you get your jollies, you sick, sick man?"

Owens laughed out loud and shook his head. "Let 'em go, Drayus. Gotta be done, and the sooner it is, the better."

"All right," Captain Drayus replied, stepping aside. "I'm good." He stared daggers at the soldiers all the same. "Y'all know there's a war on, right? You gonna need Major Owens in his place, or Dark Ops ain't gonna be able to keep the big bad dire wolf from gobbling y'all basics right up."

Trident chomped his teeth at the basics, then gave a wolfish smile.

Footfalls sounded from farther up the hallway as a Republic Army lieutenant power-walked toward the blockage. "There you four are! You were supposed to be at the bay ten minutes ago!"

"Here we go," mumbled the hapless basic in the front, sounding as though he was strongly questioning the wisdom of choosing the army over prison.

The lieutenant pushed her way into the midst of the group. She stood at least a foot shorter than everyone, with red hair pulled back into a tight bun, stowed neatly beneath her cap.

"This is Major Owens?" she asked, directing the question at no one in particular.

Owens disabled the ener-chains and held out his hand. "That's me, Lieutenant..." he read the name from her uniform, "... Pratell."

Pratell's eyes fumed. Her wrath fell on the soldiers under her command. "Get those ener-chains back on the major right *now!*"

The soldiers hesitated, as if looking to the legionnaires for approval prior to moving.

"Do I have to do this *myself?*" shrieked Pratell. She strode next to Owens, standing only as high as the burly legionnaire's chest. She pointed at the binders on the floor and ordered one of the soldiers to "Pick those up!"

Ener-chains in hands, she re-fastened them on Owens's wrists. For his part, the Dark Ops major was behaving with complete compliance, though the smirk behind his beard conveyed an amused contempt for the whole show. This seemed to kindle a deeper anger inside of Lieutenant Pratell. She hooked her hand into the crook of Owens's arm and yanked him as hard as she seemed able to.

Owens took a step, following her, then dug in his heels, causing her to come to a complete halt, no matter how hard she pulled on the legionnaire's granite-like arms.

"Hold up," Owens said, his voice full of severe concern.

The Republic soldiers escorting him looked at each other with worry in their eyes.

"My shades are all catawampus," Owens said. "Captain Drayus, would you straighten them out for me before we head off to the docking bay?"

"Sure thing, Major," Drayus answered, standing inches from Lieutenant Pratell as he faced Owens. Drayus straighted out the black shades and then took a step back to appraise. "Oh, yeah. You look iced, Major. Parminthean."

Drayus looked down at Pratell, holding out his index finger like a scolding schoolteacher. "You're escorting a Republic hero, so you best treat 'im right. Major Owens saved the House of Reason once already, and his team just saved the Republic again at Tarrago."

Trident leaned against the wall, giving the Republic soldiers room to move past. "Not that you points have an interest in anything other than yourselves..."

"I'm not a point," hissed Pratell as she pulled Owens past the mocking legionnaires, her soldiers in tow. "I *earned* my way out of the edge."

Owens stood calmly outside the docking bay door as mechanic and tech crews blended among hovering maintenance bots to form a current of bustling activity in this busiest part of the space station.

"Comin' through," shouted a loadmaster in a green coverall jumpsuit. Behind him, a train of repulsor pallets carrying what looked like crates of aero-precision missiles and launchers moved toward one of the big loading stations that the destroyers and corvettes used for resupply. A pair of legionnaires in that horrible reflective armor followed the supply train.

Owens clenched his teeth. Dark Ops was a different world from the Legion, but they were kindred warriors. Each Dark Ops kill team member had served in the Legion at one time or another, and Owens didn't know of a single regular leej who was happy with just how degraded the Legion had become—other than the points, who didn't seem to notice. Yes, the Legion was still the galaxy's premier fighting force. But Republic "innovation" and cost-saving measures outfitted this current generation with armor that could barely stop a sport blaster. The reflective shine might look dazzling on parade grounds, but it was a liability on the battlefield. Hopefully Legion Commander Keller would make good on his promise to get the legionnaires back into the old gray model of armor. Stuff that had no problem stopping most small arms fire and didn't announce its presence like a beacon.

The supply train disappeared behind mammoth blast doors that irised shut behind them. Owens couldn't see through the docking station's many transparent impervisteel windows what ship was being loaded up, but the cargo made it plain that they were expecting to see action. And those leejes were going to die unnecessary deaths because of politicians who didn't care enough to send the equipment over that would keep them alive.

"Man, look at that," mumbled one of the basics guarding Owens.

A platoon of Republic Army soldiers in full combat kit were being led to the personnel access blast doors. Going to the same ship as the missiles.

"When's the last time you saw R-A going all out like that?"

"Heard they're massing to retake Tarrago."

"Thought that was the Legion's job," replied another soldier.

Owens lifted his ener-chained hands to stroke his beard. "My guess, boys, is that everyone in the galaxy with a blaster to their name is gonna end up using it before long. You four included."

This seemed to deflate the soldiers, who watched as their counterparts—men in whose position they could just as easily have been—walked up the docking ramp to be kicked out on rotation into a full-scale war zone.

Lieutenant Pratell had her hand up to her ear, obviously listening to something over her comm. She addressed Owens and her four soldiers. "We have clearance to enter the ship."

The docking bay door slid open, revealing a long, pressurized hall that connected the station to what appeared to be an armored transport shuttle. Owens had only been able to see a glimpse of the ship's nose and fins from inside the docking station, but that was probably what it was. A spacefaring fortress. Something that could take a licking from starfighters long enough to escape into hyperspace. Popular for dignitaries entering pirate-heavy space and for the transfer of high-value targets.

Owens had shuttled more than a few MCRs in these things, screaming away from pursuing Preyhunters until they could reach the safety of a waiting destroyer or the protective folds of hyperspace.

"Thought you said they were in a hurry for me," Owens remarked to Pratell as they walked the brightly lit corridor to the shuttle.

"What?"

"Just seems odd that after all that rushing, they'd make us wait outside for nearly ten minutes."

Pratell shrugged her shoulders. She seemed somewhat more soothed now that she'd regained control of Owens's transfer. "I couldn't say, Major. I'm stationed here with the rest of the Fifth Quartermasters Company."

"Quartermasters?" Owens said. "I figured you for a headquarter division type."

"You take your promotions out of the edge where you can get them, Major."

Pratell's tone still had an edge of offense waiting to be taken. Owens snapped his gum in reply. He was going to get a serious dressing-down. Maybe get busted down a rank. Still, he felt confident that he'd be back in his office coordinating with Victory Squad and the rest of his kill teams within a few hours' time.

The shuttle's dock-door hissed open, and Owens was ushered inside the spacecraft's large cargo hold.

He looked around, bewildered.

"What the... *hell*?"

All hope of quickly returning to work left him.

Owens knew he was inside an armored transport shuttle. He'd been escorted from a very real deep space supply station across an unassuming docking bridge, and through an airlock before reaching what—on every transport shuttle he'd ever been on—should be the cargo hold.

But this was no cargo hold.

The room looked more like a House of Reason courtroom, with a massive holoscreen taking up an entire wall. In front of the screen was a tribunal of five legionnaires—all full colonels or above—each one wearing his crisp blue dress uniform.

Owens scanned the five men for a familiar face. There was no one he knew personally, but at least three of the men he had seen before. They were points. He'd seen puff pieces on them in that awful "Life in the Legion" series that broadcast on the Republic's military holofeed. Pretty safe bet the other two were points as well. Never a good sign.

To his left and right were an honor guard of legionnaires, standing erect in their reflective armor. A banner bearing the emblem of the Republic hung from the ceiling of the cargo hold-turned-courtroom. Among the legionnaires, a flag with the Legion crest hung limply from a black graphite pole.

Owens took a step forward, examining the leejes in their armor. "Probably points, too," he muttered to himself. He was no longer feeling at ease. There was no comfort of home or familiarity as there had been just minutes prior in the space station. All of that had now been replaced with a gnawing at the pit of his stomach. The ship, the courtroom constructed in the hold of a transport shuttle... Owens had been ushered directly into a well-crafted political production of a trial.

No matter what happened, the word "guilty" would be involved. Of that, Owens was certain.

Legion Commander Keller had been told that there would be consequences if the kill team came through. Owens was about to face those consequences, and in a manner that was an affront to Legion protocol.

"Lieutenant Pratell, presenting the prisoners as ordered, sirs."

"Thank you, Lieutenant," said one of the points from behind his tribunal seat. "You and your soldiers are dismissed. Report to the forward crew compartments and prepare for travel."

Pratell hesitated. "Travel to where, sir?"

The point eyed Pratell coldly. "That will be all, Lieutenant."

Red-faced, Pratell led her men past the legionnaires and disappeared behind the whoosh of an automated doorway.

With all traces of the Republic Army gone, the man at the center of the tribunal—a Legion brigadier general—rose to his feet. The man had a well-kept mustache that showed the first autumnal shades of gray, as did the hairs of his temples. He was trim and looked healthy. He did not, however, look hard. Did not look rough. There was no fire in his eyes. He was hard in body, soft in spirit. A point officer if Owens had ever seen one.

"Major Owens," the general called, his voice amplified by hoverbots nearby. "Step toward the bar."

A spotlight shone down on a podium held rigid by fixed repulsors directly in front of the tribunal. Owens approached it, thankful for his shades in the blinding spotlight that bore down on him from above.

"So, you got a JAG for me, or am I representing myself here?" Owens asked, eying the tribunal in front of him. His voice echoed throughout the room, amplified by the hoverbots, same as his judge and jury. He waited a beat to let the reverberations die down. "Because if so, let me start by saying, for the record, that this is a bunch of hot garbage."

The tribunal sat, stone-faced.

"Anything else?" the general seated in the middle asked.

Owens knew that the smart move here was to keep quiet. To minimize whatever damage this laughable tribunal was set on doing, to make however much time he had to wait for Commander Keller to straighten things out bearable. To make whatever grief his wife and children—all of whom he hadn't seen in so, so long, except for holos—easier to endure. He knew these things, but refused to act upon them.

"Yes," Owens said, theatrically turning himself around to view the entirety of the room. "I also want to add that it's damn lonely being the only real leej in this room. I thought the point conventions were held on Utopion. Hotels still all booked up from Diversity Day?"

Several of the legionnaires in the room shifted uncomfortably, including at least half of the men at the tribunal table. The thing about points was, they hated being reminded of it. They served close enough to the Legion to know their own deficiency, and this often nurtured a hatred within them for the "true" Legion.

The general at the center of the tribunal twitched his lips, causing his mustache to bristle. "I feel that I've earned my Legion crest," he said gruffly. He motioned at a naval officer making his way toward Major Owens. "There's your counsel."

A middle-aged major dressed in white approached. The man had slicked-back hair and seemed tired, but also keen. As though wise of the galaxy.

"Piece of advice," the naval officer whispered to Owens. "Don't make a show. Go along with what's about to happen."

Crossing his arms, Owens asked, "What the hell's that supposed to mean?"

"It means—"

A flourish of bright lights swept across the hold, and a hoverbot zoomed down and fixed its camera on Owens's face. The major swatted at it like a fly, and the bot hummed its way higher, out of reach, but with its camera still trained on Owens.

"Major Owens," announced the general sitting at the tribunal's center, "after hearing the facts of the case, your personal testimony, and the testimony of your peers and the men directly under your command, and after spending the past several hours in deliberation, this tribunal is prepared to give its verdict."

"Testimony?" said Owens. "What testimony? No one's said a damn thing to me. I don't even know why I'm in here."

The general acted as though he hadn't heard the outburst. "Lieutenant Colonel Freth, would you please read for this tribunal the verdict?"

A smarmy-looking officer with a double chin and a baby face stood up and waited for a holocam to zip in and focus on him as he looked to read something from a datapad.

"Verdict?" shouted a bewildered Owens. He looked to his side and saw a holoscreen broadcasting a feed. He couldn't see himself on screen, but he did see the holocams switch from the tribunal to the House of Reason Security Council on Utopion, as though they were formally gathered to observe. What was happening?

The thought built mountains of worry in the Dark Ops leej's gut, followed by questions about his wife... his family. That this was a setup was obvious. But who else was in on it? Had Commander Keller...? No, that wasn't possible. Owens thoughts went again to his family. What would be done to them?

The naval attorney grabbed Owens by the tricep, not unkindly, and leaned in to whisper in his ear. "Nothing you say right now will be heard by anyone who is not in this room. This trial is on every holonews channel in the Republic, and all anyone will see or hear is what the House wants them to hear. The best thing you can do right now is to keep quiet. Don't rattle the tribunal, don't give the conspiracy nutjobs something to talk about. Take your lumps for the good of the Republic."

Owens tensed his arm, ready to grab the lawyer, snap his neck, and stomp a mudhole of fury into every point in the room until someone stopped him or he walked it dry.

The lawyer must have sensed this, because he hastily added, "You need to think about your family right now, Major."

Owens let his muscles slacken. He listened, stoically, as the verdict was read.

"In the case of the Galactic Republic versus Major Ellek Owens. Major Owens, you stand accused of attempts to destabilize the Galactic Republic, conspiracy to destabilize the Galactic Republic, contempt toward officials, willfully disobeying a superior commissioned officer, failure to obey orders, sedition, noncompliance with procedural rules, aiding the enemy, destruction of military property of the Galactic Republic, murder (five counts), maiming (two counts), and conduct unbecoming a Legion officer and gentleman."

The lieutenant colonel turned to the general at the center of the tribunal's table. "General Vex, this Legion tribunal finds the defendant guilty on all charges."

Owens gritted his teeth. Most of these charges would result in a mandatory expulsion from the Legion, at a minimum. Several charges carried with them the death penalty. He felt the JAG officer squeeze his arm, discreetly, as if to say, Remember your family.

The mustachioed general at the tribunal's middle, Vex, rose wearily from his place. He nodded at the lieutenant colonel. "Thank you, Lieutenant Colonel Freth. Major Owens, before I deliver your sentence, do you have anything more to say? I remind you that you remain under the Legion Oath."

Opening his mouth to speak—and to say what, he did not know—Owens caught a glimpse of the holoscreen broadcasting the trial. He saw himself standing where he was now, but from an earlier moment. The image of himself on the screen shook his head calmly.

Then this was all for show. The tribunal had no interest in hearing what he had to say.

Owens closed his mouth and waited for the reading of the sentence. The tragic, unjust, surreal sentence. A black culmination of a career of service to the Legion, for the Republic.

"As chief tribunal, I do hereby order that your commission be revoked, and that you be executed by nanite injection."

Executed.

His fate struck Owens like a blaster bolt to the solar plexus.

His attorney again squeezed his arm. Whatever complicity the man had in this farcical trial apparently was not enough to wipe away all of his compassion.

"A moment, General Vex."

The request intruded loudly through the speaker array in the hold-turned-studio. Owens searched for the speaker, whose voice was familiar, and noticed that the tribunals were staring at a screen in front of them. Looking once more at the holoscreen broadcasting his "trial," Owens widened his eyes at the sight of House of Reason delegate Orrin Kaar.

"Though I understand the reasoning of the tribunal's decision," Kaar said, "I would suggest that the sentence handed down is too extreme."

Owens felt some tension in his shoulders release, but he remained guarded. "Too extreme" might mean they'd let him keep his rank and then execute him. Still, Kaar's intervention was all he had going for him in this room full of points. Unless Commander Keller sent some real leejes in for him. But that would be akin to declaring emergency constitutional powers—and Owens had no illusions about his own importance. No one was going to break up the Galactic Republic's government solely for him.

"I had the opportunity to read over Major Owens's service files," Kaar continued, speaking evenly and with confidence. "It would seem that up until this colossal betrayal, the major served the Republic with distinction, though much of what he accomplished remains classified. His seditious acts in destroying the Kesselverks Shipyards should, in my view, be balanced against the good he once did for our great Republic. I daresay the major thought he was helping the Republic in so flagrantly disobeying orders? A reminder of the need for tighter discipline in the Legion."

"What would you suggest, Delegate Kaar?" asked General Vex.

Owens pressed his thumb into the knuckle of his index finger. He ground his teeth. The House of Reason wasn't supposed to have any oversight over the Legion's internal disciplinary processes. But with a room full of points—whose loyalty to the House and Senate was never questioned—it was really no surprise. The House and Senate had been growing in influence over the Legion for years. And, if you asked Owens, with a purpose of control. This looked to be the big play. This was the moment when the House would go on record as being the ultimate source of authority over the Legion.

Something that was never meant to be.

Something the House had always desired.

"I would recommend, General," Kaar said with a coolness that Owens found somehow... comforting, "that Major Owens not be executed. That he be instead given a life sentence of manual labor on the synth mines of Herbeer."

The synth mines. That was a one-way ticket. The gigantic planet Herbeer was uninhabitable on its surface, but some driven prospector content to live in a vacuum suit had discovered synth during a one-man mining operation. Synth could be turned into just about anything. Just press it hard enough against any other material, and it would take on the precise properties of that material, at the molecular level. It literally became that other material. That was what made it so valuable. And it had only been found on Herbeer.

On Herbeer, in the prison mines, from which no prisoner ever re-emerged.

Owens swallowed hard. He would never see his wife or his daughters again. He would never see the sun again.

02

Admiral Landoo slammed her fist down on the table and swore. She'd just received the report of the loss of the *Deseram* at Cordinal. The Republic was now down to three super-destroyers, spread out across the galaxy.

She was pushing a plan to retake Tarrago. No one knew if the orbital defense gun was even working. If it wasn't, a major raid could end this conflict now. But so far, the House of Reason had refused. They wouldn't even allow her to reposition any of the super-destroyer battle groups.

"Gathering a fleet of that size will leave much of the galaxy undefended," had been the official response. "We are still pursing diplomatic options as well a guaranteed conflict resolution option that is not in play yet."

The unofficial, and unspoken, part of the response had been: *What makes you think we would listen to you? You lost the Battle of Tarrago, Admiral Landoo.*

She still had command of the carrier *Freedom*, which was being re-armed at Bantaar Reef, the Republic's premier naval station. And in lieu of the super-destroyers and their escorts, she'd been requisitioning every corvette, frigate, and support ship she could get her hands on. Her ad hoc fleet was now at seventy-five ships, and over the last seventy-two hours they'd won three computer-simulated engagements against the mysterious battleships everyone was now calling "the Imperial Fleet."

Landoo did not snort derisively at this name, as so many of the senior Bantaar Reef admiralty, and their lackeys, had. She'd seen that fleet in action. They'd chewed through her front-line ships with minimal effort and overwhelmed the system defenses of Fortress Omicron just as easily.

But now, with her seventy-five ships, including her carrier and two auxiliary carriers, along with her knowledge of the Imperial Fleet's capabilities and tactics, she was confident she would prevail. Especially if the orbital defense gun was inactive. And hitting Tarrago now would restore the House of Reason's unquestioned power over the galaxy.

So why were they waiting?

Since Tarrago, the Empire and the Republic had faced off only in small raids and limited engagements. The Empire never committed to full-scale battle, instead appearing content to damage the Republic and run for the cover of Tarrago and an orbital defense gun that might or might not be working. It was attrition-style warfare, and she knew it.

Her command staff turned away from her frustration and rage as she pounded the tactical map. Losing that super-destroyer had been stupid and avoidable. The House of Reason had insisted the ship, and its battle group, be moved into position around Aegeia, within striking distance of Tarrago. As though its mere presence would check the enemy. Instead, one of the Imperial battleships had leapt out with a fighter strike force, complemented by the corvettes captured at the Tarrago shipyard, and attacked.

One super-destroyer. Two destroyers. Five corvettes and a support frigate. All destroyed. And enemy losses? Just a handful of fighters and a corvette used as a suicide ship. The corvette had hit the *Deseram* amidships and exploded—and the Imperial battleship, subsequently identified as the *Terror*, then plowed unchecked through the Republic support ships like a lion among sheep.

It had been a stupid move by the House of Reason, and it had resulted in the stupid deaths of many service members.

Of course, one of the crazy right-wing news networks was reporting that Aegeia was a major off-planet banking haven for many House of Reason dignitaries—and that the House of Reason's real motivation for positioning the super-destroyer there was to protect their own financial interests. Stacking the decks, shaving the cards, and loading the dice so that the odds were ever in their favor. As they always had.

But who knew what was true anymore.

Admiral Landoo had bought herself some time against the House of Reason by playing their own gender-diversity argument against them. In her first press conference after the Battle of Tarrago, she'd indicated that she hoped the House of Reason's view of her as a career naval officer, and her position of leadership in responding to this new threat known as the Empire, would in no way, shape, or form be impacted by her gender. She's subtly hinted that they might fire her not because she had failed, but because she was a *woman* who had failed.

She smiled grimly. Live by the sword, die by the sword.

Turning away from the darkness of the strategic overlays, she stared out at the wonder that was Bantaar Reef. A super-giant star had once burned here, before collapsing and reigniting as a powerful gas giant. The reef was what remained of the star's dead outer shell: a crescent-shaped debris ring that remained in low orbit about the swollen gas giant. Even though much of the ring was in outer space, the gas giant had formed a cloud, more like some nebulae, that provided an oxygen-rich atmosphere to the floating debris ring. The navy had quickly realized the value of having a zero-gee naval shipyard encased in oxygen. Repairs, refits, and construction could all be vastly increased without crews having to suit up for no-oxygen environments.

Shimmering cities now littered the reef, and Admiral Landoo saw her gathering fleet coming alongside the stores and munitions depots to rearm and refit. Frigates and corvettes gathered like schools of fish around the few destroyers she'd managed to acquire. And at the center of it all, encircled by her escort group, sat the *Freedom*. Though she'd been soundly beaten in two fighter engagements, the *Freedom* was still a deadly platform if she could hit with just the right amount of surprise. Admiral Landoo envisioned that surprise. She'd hit the orbital defense gun in the same manner in which the Empire had first attacked Tarrago.

She knew in her heart there would most likely be only one final engagement left. Like two deadly samurais meeting, this next battle would not be an exchange of cuts and parries. Each side would be delivering their death blow—and hoping that time, speed, and chance gave them the advantage.

Three dozen black and matte-gray tri-fighters came howling out of the darkness beyond the defense guns of Bantaar Reef. There was a brief moment of confusion, as general quarters hadn't even been sounded. The fighters were already inside the "lagoon," as the harbor of the crescent-shaped debris field was known, before return fire began.

Admiral Landoo watched it all from her vantage in strategic command headquarters, not believing what she was seeing. Tri-fighters, the strange wicked little fighters that had destroyed her last fleet, were suddenly racing to hit targets inside the heavily defended lagoon. But why? Once the Republic ships engaged their auto-turrets and interlocked fire via the *Freedom*'s coordinated fire control system in her advanced CIC section, three dozen fighters wouldn't stand a chance.

The call to battle stations erupted across the nets, comms, and speakers all across Bantaar Reef.

"What the hell is going on out there!" screamed Landoo as her command team tried to get a handle on the rapidly developing situation.

Two tri-fighters made a run on her carrier, blasters blazing. One of them managed to score a direct hit on the aft reactor. How much damage it did wouldn't be known until the reports came flooding in.

A flight of Lancers on patrol came roaring in, peeled off, and went after separate groups of tri-fighters. One of those tri-fighter groups hit the engines of a corvette with a torpedo of some sort. The explosion from the main engine compartment rippled up along the spine and blew the ship apart from stem to stern, sending debris into a nearby escort missile frigate group.

Then SSM munitions went up. The whole facility. Out there along the reef, rock and structure exploded out into the lagoon, slamming into other ships that had not managed to get their deflectors up in time.

At last the ship's batteries picked up the dancing tri-fighters and engaged at close range with turret fire. And just as quickly as it had begun, it was over. The fighters scattered and streaked away from the lagoon, leaving a few burning corvettes and damaged ships and facilities in their wake.

"Get me the watch officer at Base Sensor Array!" shouted Landoo as damage control reports began to come in from across the fleet.

When the final losses were tallied, they would prove to be small but quite meaningful. Key ships in the command and control structure of this new fleet had been damaged so badly they'd need months of refit. And the loss of ship-to-ship munitions—the heavy ship-killer torpedoes—was devastating. Much of Landoo's strategy had been to refit many of the smaller ships with the heavy SSMs, effectively turning them into one-shot platforms. Her strategy had been to follow a wave of these missiles with her main battle group and attempt to board the battleship using legionnaires.

Now the SSMs were a rare commodity.

And of course, the watch officer at Base Sensor Array had disappeared. A fleet-wide alert was put out, instructing all personnel to be on the lookout for the career officer who had not one black mark on his record.

But of course, he was never found.

03

The armored shuttle proved not only to be Major Owens's courtroom, but also his prison transport. Almost as soon as the tribunal acquiesced to Orrin Kaar's sentencing request, they were up and gone, leaving Owens under guard with the basics.

Owens had thought about overpowering the men and seizing control of the ship—he was relatively sure he could do it. He'd seen only two basics and Pratell since they'd set out, and he wouldn't be surprised if that, plus a pilot, was the extent of the crew. These shuttles didn't require much personnel, not for a simple prisoner transport. But if he did take over the ship... then what? Live out his life on the run, occasionally pinging Captain Ford for advice on how to navigate the treacherous slices of space on galaxy's edge?

No, Owens was a soldier. And, for now anyway, he would wait on the process. Allow Legion Commander Keller—who surely would have been taken off guard by what happened—to pull some strings and get things figured out. The initial panic of the sentence had passed, and Owens felt firmly in control of his emotions, and himself.

He waited out the jump through hyperspace in a satisfactory prison cell. The only opportunities for escape came when one of the two basics came to deliver him food and water. During those moments, instead of killing the guard and having his run of the ship, Owens made small talk. He spoke to his captors about their families and the nascent war. He laughed at bad jokes and discussed the contrasts of life as a Republic Army soldier versus that of a legionnaire. He told stories of how the Legion was before points. He openly lamented the state of the Legion of today, now that war was upon them.

The guards seemed to take a liking to him over the days it took to arrive at Herbeer. And when the armored shuttle approached planetary orbit, they both entered his holding cell.

"Hey, Major," said Mal, the older of the two basics, though not by much. "We've arrived in-system. Lieutenant Pratell sent us to see if you want to observe our entry into Herbeer. It's supposed to really be something..."

"Sure, why not?" Owens said, snorting his sinuses clear and lazily standing up to stretch. "Probably the last chance I'll get to see a sun. Synth mining is completely subterranean."

The basic looked down glumly. "Yeah."

Owens clapped the soldier on his arm. "Don't worry about it, Mal. Let's go see that view."

Mal led Owens to the main command hub. The basics had lost any pretense of alertness. Mal barely even touched the rifle slung over his shoulder, and they hadn't even thought to put ener-chains on Owens. They had made the mistake of growing too comfortable with their prisoner. He knew they thought of him now more as a friend than a captive.

It would be so easy to take command of the ship.

Instead, Owens followed the soldiers through the automated door to the command hub.

The hub was a rectangular room that sat above and to the rear of the shuttle's cockpit. It boasted a triple-layered transparent impervisteel forward window, with smaller triangular windows on the sides. This allowed the command crew, who often directed complicated space-to-space battles from armored shuttles such as this one, to have visuals no matter what. Holotransmissions and external viewers could be jammed fairly easily.

Lieutenant Pratell stood alone in the hub, facing the window, arms clasped behind her back, gazing down at the roiling auburn surface of Herbeer. She turned at the sound of the door opening, looking first at the basic escort and then at Owens. When her eyes went to the prisoner's unmanacled wrists, her brow hardened into a scowl. Owens waited for the tirade to begin, but instead the lieutenant turned back to face the planet.

"Have you ever seen Herbeer before, Major?" she asked.

Owens stepped up beside the lieutenant, standing shoulder to shoulder as they viewed the churning surface of the planet. It looked like a roiling, tumultuous cloud the color of Owens's beard. He wondered if they'd make him lose it—the beard—during processing. They might shave his entire head. He'd been to leej camp, that part wouldn't bother him. But he'd rather keep his beard.

"Major?" Pratell prompted again, gently.

"Mind was somewhere else," Owens said, shaking the thoughts from his head. "No. Seen a lot of hellholes, but not this one before."

"That's... understandable," Pratell managed. She paused and looked to be struggling with something internally. "For whatever it might be worth, I disagree with how your trial was handled. We all do."

Owens nodded. "Yeah, me too."

Quiet fell as the planet neared.

"How about you? You ever see Herbeer before?"

Pratell gave a fractional nod. "Two weeks ago, a stop while on my way to being stationed on the supply station."

"Picking up or dropping off?"

"Dropping off," Pratell said, the slightest edge in her voice. "My former commander at Fort Bantam."

"Bantam, huh?" Owens shrugged his shoulders forward and popped his neck. "And then off to a mid-core station. And now... you're back on the edge."

"For the time being," Pratell said, still staring out of the viewport as the planet grew larger.

Owens snickered to himself. "I've got the extended vacation package."

The sun peeked over the horizon of Herbeer, and a ray of sunlight flooded the command hub. The viewport darkened instantly, preventing those looking through it from being blinded.

"Looks like there's quite a storm raging on the surface," Pratell observed. The shuttle was now rapidly approaching the planet's atmosphere. Hemisphere-wide clouds of dust tumbled helter skelter, with white-blue streaks of lightning blinking everywhere like the flashing indicator lights of a starfighter cockpit.

"Think I'll just keep looking at the sun," Owens said, not removing his gaze from the massive orb inferno. "Might be a while 'til I see it again."

A singsong chime sounded, alerting all on board that the shuttle's captain was about to speak over general comms.

"We're two minutes to re-entry." The pilot's voice and inflection were as calm and professional as that of a commercial starliner captain. "All hands, secure persons and possessions for landing."

Pratell made her way to a command chair. As she lowered herself into the seat, she paused long enough to say, "Major Owens, you'd better get strapped in. I've sat through one of these Herbeer landings before."

"Yeah," Owens agreed. He stared at the sun until the last possible moment, until the *click* of Pratell's restraints spurred him to motion. He found a seat and fastened himself in, watching the orange flaming glow of re-entry begin to build around the main viewport window.

The shuttle bucked as it skipped its way into the atmosphere. Its engines whined in protest as they switched from smooth propulsion through space into the labored stress of atmosphere flight. These armored birds were *heavy*. Soon Owens felt like his ears were overwhelmed.

The ship passed from the upper atmosphere into the roiling surface storms that covered the entirety of the planet. Countless particles of sand-like glass and grit pelted the shuttle, scouring its armor like a chemical solvent. It sounded to Owens as though he were standing at the base of a colossal waterfall, or plunged to the bottom of a surging tidal wave tearing apart a coral reef.

Visibility went to zero. Through the viewport, it looked as if the shuttle were burrowing deep into a desert. The sun refracted inside the grains of ground glass to provide an amber light. Owens knew that they were on auto-pilot, following a slave recall signal down to a surface landing pad. But, Oba, it didn't seem like anything—even hypo-spectra signals—could find its way from sender to receiver through this. A part of Owens braced for the shuttle to just... nose into the planet's surface and go up in a spectacular ball of flames.

But the sensation of motion slowed, and though the noise drowned out the mechanical extrusion of landing struts, Owens could feel the massive armored shuttle settle onto a solid surface. First the two struts at the aft of the shuttle, then the single landing gear beneath the cockpit. The sound of the whirling storm continued to rage for a few seconds, and then Owens felt his stomach fly up into his chest—the sensation cf a sudden and unexpected drop.

Through the front viewport, the swirling storm gave way to smooth, concave walls. A brilliant light flashed as the shuttle descended on what had to be some sort of docking platform lift. It was quieter now, much quieter, and Owens could make out a resounding boom as something closed overhead—probably a valve to keep the storm out, for the glass sands had died down completely. Streams of sand still tumbled down in front of the viewport like a dry waterfall, but the grains were no longer whipped into a frenzy by the naked atmosphere.

The shuttle descended quickly, the blue lights and painted yellow lines on the walls of this express docking platform going by in a blur. The mine was deep beneath the surface. Eventually repulsors kicked in to slow the descent, and the platform settled down gently on the subterranean level that served as a hub for the synth mines themselves.

Abandon all hope, ye who enter.

Owens didn't actually see that written anywhere. The viewport showed a basic docking bay. Power and recharge cells, maintenance and mechanical bots, hover pallets, tugs, coupling hoses, and a customs bot instead of a Republic official or naval officer.

"Prepare Ellek..." Pratell paused. "Prepare the prisoner for transfer."

Owens released himself from his harness before the lieutenant or her soldiers did. It seemed that the reality of the situation—that they were escorting a Dark Ops legionnaire to serve a life sentence—hit the captors all at once. They tensed upon seeing Owens up and free, no doubt wondering if *this* would be the moment when he would attempt to take control of the situation. The soldiers got up awkwardly, holding their rifles as though the weapons felt uncomfortable in their hands. Pratell hurried to extricate herself from her seat.

Owens simply stood by patiently. There was nothing to be gained by seizing control of the ship at this point, far beneath the raging glass-storms of Herbeer's surface.

"You'd probably better put some ener-chains on me," Owens announced.

Pratell nodded at one of her soldiers, who shouldered his weapon to apply the restraints.

"Thank you for that, Major," said Pratell.

Owens shrugged. "Rather not get shot by some over-anxious guard who sees me coming out of the shuttle unrestrained."

Owens was frog-marched through the ship and down its ramp. Two black-uniformed guards waited at the bottom of the ramp, each of them carrying disagreeable-looking shotguns. Owens was marched to a halt in front of them. He looked up at the ship and raised both eyebrows appreciatively at the way it shone. Every last bit of paint had been scoured clean by the glass-sand storm. There was no Republic emblem, no identification numbers, no black and yellow warning stripes—nothing. Just unvarnished impervisteel, sand-blasted clean. If an organic was left to Herbeer's planetary storms... it wouldn't be pretty.

"Republic prisoner transfer of one Major Ellek Owens," Pratell told the guards.

"Yes, ma'am," came the reply. The guard nodded to a small room just off the docking platform. "You can take care of your paperwork over there. We'll process the prisoner from here."

There were no spoken goodbyes. Owens simply followed the directives of his new guards, leaving the basics he'd come to know behind him.

There was a layer of ground glass, almost a dusting, around the docking platform, and it crunched beneath Owens's boots as he was led to a long corridor. Around him, dome-like cleaning bots systematically sucked the area clean. As the guards took Owens further down the corridor, the glass dust receded, and the walk grew quiet except for the jangle of cuffs hanging from the guards' belts.

They stopped in front of a moving walkway. Owens noted that it moved only in one direction—farther down the corridor, which seemed to disappear into a curtain of blackness.

Owens took a deep breath. There was a slight gush of air from the inky beyond. It smelled subterranean. Moist and stale.

"Step on," one of the guards ordered.

"Too long a walk?" asked Owens as he complied, taking a step and then standing in place as the walkway moved him farther down the corridor.

The guards stepped on a beat later. "Not really. But this way, you stay still. Which is important, because if you move a muscle, you're dead."

"And," added the second guard, "you won't be able to see your hand in front of your face in a few seconds. Fewer broken noses this way."

"But don't worry," the first guard said in a patronizingly soothing tone, "we can still see *you* just fine."

The people mover carried Owens into darkness. The guards weren't kidding—he couldn't see a thing. His shades were still on, of course, but removing them wouldn't have made a difference. The only sound was the soft whir of the moving walkway. It carried on straight for what seemed a quarter of kilometer, as best as Owens could reckon based on their speed before the light faded from the corridor. The flow of cavern breeze caressed his beard, then abruptly blew on the left side of his face before blowing from the front again. He surmised that they'd taken a right-hand turn and forked off into another passage. There were more turns. Owens worked to create a mental map of where he'd gone so far.

"Not much farther," said one of the guards.

Owens repressed a half-dozen smart aleck replies and continued to mentally calculate distance and direction. And then he felt something soft but firm brush against his face. Whatever it was knocked his glasses off. He heard them clatter onto the floor.

"Easy, pal," warned one of the guards. "Don't get jumpy."

Another soft tendril of something brushed against Owens. This time across the back of his neck. He resisted the urge to swat whatever this was away. Something told him these guards would be all too quick to pull their triggers if he made any abrupt moves.

"Your shades are about a meter behind you and to the right," a guard said. "They're riding along with us on the people mover. We're about to stop. When we do, you can bend down and get them."

Owens ground his molars. Was this a trap?

The people mover came to a stop, nothing too sudden, but enough for Owens to take a step to steady himself.

"Pick 'em up or leave 'em," chided a guard.

Owens decided he'd rather have them. If the guards were looking for an excuse to kill him, they'd find one. He might as well die in style. He bent down and groped in the darkness with two outstretched hands.

A brittle plasteen crunch sounded as someone stamped a foot down just inches away from where Owens was reaching around.

Of all the rotten, no good—

A flood of lights came on, causing Owens to blink in pain. His vision returned, and he saw the blue stump of a bare foot standing on top of his ruined shades.

Seven-hundred-credit shades.

Owens visually followed the stump up an armored leg and to a broad torso. He saw dangling, icicle-blue tendrils resting on the being's chest and then locked eyes with an ugly, scowling Gomarii. The creature's head was thick, with a broad forehead and two jet-black eyes. Somewhere behind the tangle of arm-like tendrils that hung from its face down to its chest was a round maw covered with pointed teeth.

What were Gomarii, a notorious species of slavers, doing on a Republic prison planet? A multitude of potential answers sprang to Owens's mind. None of them gave him happy feelings.

"Welcome to the synth mines of Herbeer, *Legionnaire*," announced a guard. "You're fed when you work enough. Cause trouble and you'll *wish* you didn't live to regret it. Oh... and stay out of the abandoned shafts unless you'd like to become dinner."

Owens held his breath as the two guards and the Gomarii pealed with grotesque laughter.

The Indelible VI
Hyperspace

"I don't know... can you play it one more time?"

Ravi looked up from his console and regarded Captain Chhun for a moment. "I have played this message four times consecutively. I am not sure what you are looking to find."

Chhun shook his head, examining a still frame of Andien Broxin on the holoscreen. "I don't know... I've worked with her more than a few times. I'm just not getting why she'd do this."

Ravi twitched his mustache. "Yes, well, watch it quickly. I do not believe Captain Keel will be wanting to see the woman's face again." The navigator shook a finger. "Abducting a captain's crew—even when he doesn't particularly care for them—is very offensive."

Chhun nodded. "Thanks."

The holoscreen sprang back to life. Andien Broxin stood still for a moment, as if waiting for her cue to begin, unaware that the feed had already started recording.

"Captain Chhun, Captain Ford... I'm sorry about this." Andien looked from her left to right. Something boomed in the background. "I need members of this crew for classified reasons. They'll be safe. I promise. Trust me. Do not follow."

Ravi paused the image before it looped again. He looked back to Chhun expectantly. "Well?"

Chhun chewed his lip. This was bad. It was obvious to him that Wraith had gotten a little... *squirrelly* from his time on the edge. He was still more than capable while on mission, but there was something different about him now. Like he'd become too much of his alias. Too much time spent as a smuggler and bounty hunter, always looking out for the menace that had now revealed himself as Goth Sullus.

And at the same time, always having to look out for himself.

It would take some work to get Ford readjusted to life in Dark Ops. And the last thing Wraith needed was something like *this*. It didn't help that Ford's navigator had suddenly reappeared and insisted on referring to Ford as "Captain Keel."

Wraith needed to get his head straight, and Chhun hoped to help guide that process. At least until they could settle down on the *Mercutio*, or wherever Major Owens intended to have them stationed.

The *Six*'s cockpit door slid open, and Ford stormed inside. He had gotten out of his armor and was wearing his spacer's clothing. "Pored over every inch of the ship and I can't find a clue about what happened."

Ravi and Chhun exchanged a look.

Keel looked at the still image of Andien. "Ravi, take that down. I don't wanna see her face."

Ravi quickly powered down the display before Keel put a blaster bolt through the holoscreen.

"Listen," Chhun said, holding his hands up diplomatically. "I don't know what Andien was up to, but she's good people, Ford. You know that. She's helped us out while you were on Victory Squad, and she kept helping after you..." Chhun almost said "left," but stopped himself, "... after you went undercover."

"How about *you* listen, pal?" Ford poked a finger at Chhun's chest. "She stole *my* crew. Some of them I even like. And I learned enough about Nether Ops out on the edge to know that if they're involved—if they want one of my crew—it's not a good thing. It never is."

Chhun made no attempt to argue about the merits of Nether Ops. Apart from Andien, he'd be fine if that entire outfit went up in flames. "So what do you suggest we do? Chase her down? Ford, she said to trust her, not follow."

Ford gave a look as if all the secrets of heaven and earth had opened to him. "*Oh*? She said *that*? Well, in that case..."

The captain pushed past Chhun and dropped himself into his chair. "Ravi, we need to track them down. Take a look at exit signatures out of Tarrago—I know, too many ships to track with the size of the battle that was going on. Look anyway. And then do some... math stuff and try to give me the odds for the most likely stop after they left. They probably had to report on mission success, so that would mean dumping out of hyperspace in a system that still has its comm relays up. Which one?"

Usually, Ravi's fingers would be flying over his console, bringing up probabilities even while Keel spoke. Instead, the navigator sat still and patiently listened. This didn't escape Keel's notice.

"Hey," Keel urged. "Get a move on."

Ravi continued to sit in silence.

Keel opened his mouth to speak again, then caught the navigator's eyes. Ravi shot a quick glance at Chhun, as if to indicate he had something to say—but was reluctant to do so with present company.

"Oh," Keel said, rubbing his chin into the web of his palm. "You can say whatever needs saying in front of Chhun. He's okay."

Chhun shifted in place.

Ravi gave the legionnaire one final look, then turned his attention back to his captain. "I wish to say that a search is not necessary. I know where they were headed. I was with them, secretly, until I decided the time was right to involve you again, Captain."

Keel's bewilderment soon turned anger. He shot daggers at Ravi. "And what, exactly, was it that finally made you *decide* to include me in the affairs of this ship and crew, Ravi? Thanks for that, by the way. After all, I'm just the captain of the *Indelible VI*."

Ravi let the comment pass. "I initially had hope that the team of Miss Broxin would be capable of completing their mission—which *is* important. Observing them left me with a different impression." Ravi held out both hands. "They are not that good at killing. Nor are they sufficiently capable of staying alive. Not as good as you, in my calculations. And this mission will certainly require both."

"This mission..." Chhun said. "It's still ongoing?"

Ravi nodded. "Yes. They are traveling through hyperspace to Echo Comm Node Station in the Antilles system."

"So that's where we'll find them?" Keel asked.

"That is where you will get on their trail." Ravi blinked as if confirming some calculation. "There is almost no chance they will still be on the station by the time we arrive. And you should expect a heightened military presence."

"Great." Keel leaned back in his seat. "Well, I guess that's our next course, Ravi."

Chhun cleared his throat, causing Keel to look up.

"I could use the help of a kill team," Keel said. "Your team up to helping me get back my crew? You know, seeing how this happened because we helped you blow up that shipyard..."

Chhun held his arms out somewhat helplessly. "I mean... I'd have to get it cleared. Major Owens might understand. And we still need to get Sticks to a Republic med bay. As good as what you've got on board, he's going to need some long-term care."

"Yeah." Keel's tone was dismissive. He waved off Chhun's words. "Don't do me any favors, pal."

"No, it's not like that," Chhun insisted. "I..." The legionnaire hesitated for several moments. "Of course. Yes, we'll help. Or at least, I'll help. We can deal with the paperwork after we get your crew back."

"Thanks." Keel stood up and clapped Chhun on the shoulder. "Ravi, what's the closest Republic destroyer showing on our sensors *not* getting blasted to scrap by Goth Sullus?"

Ravi read a battlenet report on the display in front of him. "It looks like the *Intrepid* is in the next system."

"Good," said Keel. "Good captain on that ship. Probably won't try to keep us around and try to punish us just for playing Good Lumirian. We'll get Sticks offloaded and then take off for Echo Station."

Keel strolled down from the ramp of the *Six*, tugging at a pair of brown flying gloves he'd worn to guide the ship into the Republic destroyer *Intrepid*. He was the last man off the ship.

A medical bot and two corpsmen had removed Sticks from the ship on a repulsor litter, despite the legionnaire's protests that he could walk (on one leg) if he had a couple of guys to lean against. Bear accompanied the wounded legionnaire to the medical bay. Chhun and the rest of his team were standing away from the ship, just next to a medical shuttle, talking.

"I have orders to refuel and supply your ship, Captain Keel," a deck technician informed Keel.

The captain nodded his approval. "Don't skimp on the good stuff."

Keel looked at his surroundings. He'd spent the past seven years actively trying to *avoid* having his ship sitting under the control of the Republic. And now here he was. He felt a sense of nostalgia. Not just because every Republic destroyer pretty much looked like the next one, but because Keel had been stationed aboard *Intrepid* while serving on active duty with the Victory kill team. It was this ship from which he'd led numerous missions, serving together with Chhun, Masters, Exo, and Twenties. It was here that they'd drilled relentlessly to find the fastest, best way to infiltrate a Republic cruiser. And it was from this ship that they'd put that training to use, stopping the zhee-controlled *Pride of Ankalor* from jumping an unholy payload of explosives—the fruit of years of scheming by the MCR—into the House of Reason.

There were times when Keel wondered if the galaxy would have been a better place had his kill team failed in its mission.

Chhun jogged over to Keel. "Bring back any memories?"

"A few." Keel looked over to his long-time comrade and gave him a sardonic half-grin. "Not planning on sticking around long enough to jog anymore."

Chhun nodded. "Right. So, look, people are acting strange. Something's up, but no one's saying what. Captain Deynolds wants to meet with us—"

Keel rolled his eyes and gave an exasperated sigh. "So? *I* don't want to meet with *her*. We need to get going, Chhun."

"Ford..." Chhun began.

"Call me Keel."

"*Ford*," Chhun repeated. "I don't *know* you as Keel. And besides, Captain *Ford* understands that a legionnaire kill team can't just waltz off a ship when its team leader is ordered to a meeting. Deynolds knows we've got something hot on our hands, and you know she's not prone to wasting time when lives are on the line."

Keel kicked a toe against the destroyer's polished black deck. "Doesn't sound like you've got much of a choice."

"*Neither* of us do," Chhun said, moving in close to keep his voice low. "You're just as much in the Legion and subject to orders as I am. Or have you forgotten?"

Keel gave his old friend an unreadable expression, like a cabet player keeping his hand to himself. "Let's hurry up and get the meeting over with then."

"This way." Chhun began to walk toward a speedlift.

"I *know* how to get there," Keel barked after the legionnaire. He keyed his comm. "Ravi, keep the ship ready to go. Gotta deal with the red tape first."

"Yes, Captain," came the reply.

Keel jogged to catch up to Chhun, who was holding the speedlift door open for him. The two shot through the destroyer's decks, moving up and across toward their destination.

"Your friend isn't just a hologram," said Chhun.

Keel gave a half-shake of his head. "Doesn't seem like it."

"So, what is he?"

"Something else."

Chhun let out a sigh. "Yes, I know he's 'something else.' But what? He's jumping from a Nether Ops ship, traveling who-knows-where, and then back into a system with no comm access, just to give you a cryptic update on your crew..."

"Ravi's fine."

"I just want to know what I'm getting myself—and my men—into."

"Relax," Keel said, folding his arms. "Ravi's one of the good guys. I've known for a while he's not *just* a hologram. Too many clues to ignore. But he's always done right by me. He'll tell me what's going on when the time is right. Or when I tell him to."

"That doesn't bother you?"

Keel rolled his neck. "You stop worrying about other people's secrets when you're trying to keep your own."

The speedlift came to a stop, and its door swooshed open. Waiting on the other side was Captain Deynolds.

"Captain," Chhun said, staying put inside the speedlift. "Wasn't expecting to find you waiting here for us."

Deynolds motioned for them to exit. "There is a *major* situation happening right now, and I don't mean just the attack at Tarrago."

"So what couldn't wait for a courtesy officer to bring us to you?" Keel asked.

Deynolds didn't address the question, instead saying, "Welcome back to the Republic, Captain Ford."

The trio strode toward the *Intrepid*'s secure conference room.

"It seems," Deynolds said, looking Keel up and down, "you were a good study. You look like every smuggler captain I've ever encountered while patrolling the edge."

"Thanks." Keel hitched a thumb toward his chest. "And for the record, *they* look like *me*."

Deynolds seemed on the verge of letting a smile twist a corner of her mouth upward. "Well, for this, you need to be Captain Ford. We're about to have a meeting with Legion Commander Keller and members of the House of Reason Security Council. I have orders from Commander Keller regarding this meeting."

"Okay," said Chhun.

"Neither of you are to protest or argue over what you are about to hear."

"And what," Chhun asked, "are we about to hear?"

Deynolds sighed. "It's going to come as a surprise. And it'll be better that way. Just go along with Commander Keller and understand that there's more to be said among the four of us after this meeting is through."

"Sounds honest," Keel quipped.

This time Deynolds didn't hint at a smile.

They arrived at the doors to the bridge-level command conference room, Deynolds typed in an access code, and the doors swooshed open. Already projected inside the room were Legion Commander Keller and members of the Security Council. Including Delegate Orrin Kaar himself.

Keel and Chhun each took a breath and stepped inside.

04

Imperial Assault Task Force
Jasilaar System

Imperial assault frigate *Wolf* jumped into the Jasilaar gas giant ring at just after 0300 local system time. Republic intel was starting to put the pieces together that the Dark Legion favored this hour of the morning for their hit-and-run raids, but as of yet the word hadn't gotten passed down generally.

The *Wolf* was one of the brand-new fast production ships the Empire was cranking out from their captured Kesselverks Shipyards on Tarrago Prime. Thanks to automation—and a galactic populace that was starting to throw in with the newly formed Empire—they had produced three of the fast-attack frigates in short order. They were no-frills and built to fight. Longish from stem to stern, narrow and high-decked, the ships looked extremely deadly and ready for the business of combat, skinned in matte charcoal gray with the barest of Imperial markings.

The *Wolf* was transporting a task force assigned a very specific mission, a mission critical to the Empire. A company of dark legionnaires would move against the brand-new gas mining facility on Jasilaar Nine, the largest of the multi-colored gas giants that orbited the local star. Colonel Marius Reez had been charged with leading the mission.

Reez's advancement in the Empire's ranks had been rapid. In the Battle of Tarrago, he'd fought for the Empire as a captain at first, and proved himself a capable operator who got the mission done when others got killed. He was a member of the First Battalion Third Regiment during the desperate assault on the marine barracks, and when the battalion commander was killed by the mortar fire that stalled the final assault, Reez took charge. He led a small group of shock troopers through heavy fire in order to secure the barracks in room-to-room fighting. In the smoky aftermath, the day after hostilities had ceased on Tarrago, General Nero himself arrived by Grav-APC and personally promoted the senior-most surviving officer of the operation.

Since that time, now-Colonel Reez had led three successful raids against Republic assets and had brought his men back with a minimum of casualties. And that was the important criterion by which all Dark Legion officers were currently being judged. Because there just weren't a lot of shock troopers. In fact, there were very few compared to the nearly inexhaustible supply the Galactic Republic possessed, ranging from legionnaires to marines to Repub Navy and a variety of other paramilitary and specialty organizations.

This was the chief weakness of the newly formed Empire: it had no deep bench. Ship losses couldn't be replaced until the shipyards were running at max output, and that required more off-world resources, which required captured freighters, which required troops to go out and capture those assets. Dark legionnaires were the highest-value asset in the fleet, as they were the hardest to train and replace. The riff-raff and flotsam of a disillusioned galaxy were flooding through the battle lines to reach Tarrago and join up, but the system required to test, vet, train, and transform them into hardened killers couldn't spin up quickly enough.

Reez stood before his men, who were stacked in the hangar bays, ready to assault the station, as the menacing *Wolf* approached the gas mining facility, weapons armed. The plan was for the ship to hard dock alongside the big gas mining freighter docks, and for the shock troops to first take that section of the floating city before moving inward and capturing the main command and control areas that governed power and security for the sprawling complex that hung just above Jasilaar Nine's violent and turbulent atmosphere.

Unlike the past three raids, this was a full-scale asset capture. No hit-and-run. No smash their stuff and leave it burning as you jumped out of system. Right now, the Empire needed assets as badly as she needed shock troopers. Jasilaar Nine would become an Imperial mining facility, providing the raw materials needed to build the ships and equipment required for a rapidly escalating war.

"Captain says we got nothing, sir," announced the task force's intel officer over comm. He was stationed up in the frigate's ops center, where he could parse the sensor data and relay it to the commanders on the ground inside the station when the time for that came.

Reez waited. There would be more. Scout Drone Recon had indicated the facility had only recently been built and was still largely unoccupied. At best, the dark legionnaires should only meet a few techs completing the last of the shakedown tests.

"Negative on any military presence," continued the intel officer. "Intel confirms go for op start."

"Roger that," said the colonel. He gave a thumbs-up to his company commanders, and the troops began dispersing through the red-lit interior cargo hold of the assault frigate. In just moments the *Wolf* would come alongside the facility, the cargo doors would rise, and the shock troopers would storm the station.

The *Wolf*'s engines began to pulse as she slowed for docking contact, her massive engines reversing forward momentum. A deep hum and vibration passed through the ship, and not for the first time did Reez wonder if the frigate was as spaceworthy as it should be. Things were moving so fast, errors were bound to happen, and out here in the vast blackness of space, structure malfunctions were not easily recovered from. Deep space, despite all the technology, was still the most unforgiving of all environments.

Back in the Legion, he'd once been aboard a corvette that came apart in orbit after being hit by a surface-to-space missile in an MCR conflict. Reez had been just as stunned as everyone else running for the emergency escape pods as the ship came apart rather violently and quite rapidly. He'd received a medal as a result of that incident, for carrying a wounded crewmember off the ship. He was a sergeant at the time, and one of his privates had been caught by a blast door. Reez cut the man's arm off with a hull cutter, cuffed the wound, and carried the unconscious man to a lifeboat.

The Republic had always assured service members that ships were built to stand up to enemy fire; they didn't just come apart at the first blow. But that one certainly had. Reez read later that the defense contractor had been busted for using subpar impervisteel that hadn't met Repub Navy standards. He also read the contractor was some relative of a House of Reason inner council member. Nothing came of it.

"Still nothing," whispered the intel officer on S-comm. That was good, thought Reez. He liked things easy, but they seldom were. So he didn't plan for them to be.

Docking clamps fell into place. The *Wolf*'s, not the station's. Reez dialed in his S-comm for two channels: Command, and First Platoon. They'd be the first out onto the docks, and he wanted to hear it as it happened.

The platoon sergeant was hectoring his men. "... open space. But never mind that, you sociopathic poko herders. The docks have gravity plates, just like the ship. Move forward to position one and set up to cover Second Platoon. You see anything... engage. No questions, Satterly."

Reez knew the man the platoon sergeant was reminding general orders to. Reez knew all his men. He was that kind of commander. He was also the kind of commander who would have preferred to lead up front, but that was against Imperial SOP. There were fewer trained officers than shock troopers.

Of course, for Reez, a win was that everybody made it back and no one got killed.

The *Wolf*'s massive cargo doors, all along the lower decks' port side, rose into position, and a brilliant burning orange light flooded the holds, washing over the dark armor of the heavily armed shock troopers. Even from deep within the hangar, Reez could see the rising pinnacle of the facility's central hub in the distance. The docks' long spindly spider's arms stretched hundreds of yards from the distant main hab, and all of it floated high above the turbulent thousand-year storms wandering slowly across the breadth of the gas giant. It was both a terrible and beautiful thing to behold. Such super gas giants were resource rich, and this facility was capable of extracting and producing some of the most valuable raw compounds in the galaxy.

Pending success of this mission, captured Republic freighters would be docking here within the week and jumping back to Tarrago to deliver much-needed supplies to the factories, shipyards, and corporations already forming to support the newly established Empire. Soon the immense shipyards would be at max capability. Soon there would be more ships. And there were rumors that one of the first ships the Empire would produce was a dreadnought. A ship three times the size of their battleships.

With a ship like that, Utopion would fall, and something new would begin. Or at least that was the talk.

"Go! Go! Go!" shouted the platoon sergeant over comm, ordering his men to hit the docks. A long moment passed as troopers called out orders and sitreps. Though Reez couldn't see it directly, he followed his troops' opening movements on the tac display in his HUD.

First Platoon was in place, and Second Platoon was deploying forward. Passing First and heading toward a small docking control tower that oversaw gas transfer operations out along this particular arm of the docks. Reez had it in mind to make the small tower his command post until they reached the main hab, but he wanted to stay mobile and as close behind the forward platoons as possible.

Soon Third Platoon was out and moving to secure the spinal rail system that led back to the main hab from this docking arm. The rail system ran out to each of the eight docking spines, with bulk cargo rail cars occupying one side of the spine and light passenger cars occupying the other. The big cargo cars moved more slowly while the light passenger cars were supposed to zip along. Of course, all this was only reported intel, not actually known. There was a chance that this docking spine didn't even have rail access up yet. If that was the case, they would walk the tube into the main hab. At a run—in armor—that would take twenty minutes. If there were emplaced defenders, it would take much longer.

"Sniper teams in place," whispered Fourth Platoon's leader over comm. Fourth Platoon handled the special teams assets for the task force. Snipers, engineers, and anti-air. The other three platoons were straight CQB infantry.

"We got two cars up and ready, sir," said the lieutenant commanding Third Platoon.

"Do we have control?"

Pause.

"Roger on control, sir," came the lieutenant's voice over comm. "We can move downspine to main hab at this time."

Reez waited. He'd moved forward with Fourth's anti-armor section. They'd cleared the small docking tower and found that it wasn't operational yet. It looked as if construction had only recently been completed, and no computers or comm gear had yet been installed alongside the fresh white paint that covered the walls.

Reez turned to glance back at the deadly *Wolf* docked alongside the spine. It rose up several stories over the tower. *So far, so good,* he thought as he ran through his ops checkpoints once more. He knew them by heart, but it never hurt to check in.

Now came the part of the operation Reez had never fully liked. Now they would need to thread a chokepoint by loading all his men into the rail cars and moving them downspine as one element, with no cover beyond the guns of the *Wolf*. And the *Wolf*'s weapons, though powerful, were imprecise. Anything the assault frigate shot at had just as good a chance of hitting them as it did of hitting the enemy.

"Any changes?" Reez asked the intel officer aboard the *Wolf*.

"Negative, sir. In fact, we're not even getting any traffic from city docking and approach control. In other words, they know we're here, and they probably know who we are and what we're up to."

And what if they try to just scuttle the station with us on board? thought Reez. Except there were some things that didn't need to be said aloud. They'd been sent here to capture a gas mining facility, and of course that was inherently dangerous. You couldn't just not do things because people got killed doing them. That was the other side of being a soldier, no matter whether you served the Repub or the Empire. People were going to get killed once the shooting started.

Reez gave the order to deploy forward into the cars. He stayed with Fourth Platoon as they moved forward and boarded the second car. The signal was given, and both cars started slowly downspine.

Reez and everyone ignored the worst-case scenarios their minds conjured—chief of which was that someone would blow the emergency disconnect bolts on that docking spine and send them spinning off into space. Yes, they were in armor and had life support, but neither would protect them from the crushing gravity well just below the storm-tossed surface of the upper atmosphere. If Reez and his two hundred and eighty men were to fall into that atmosphere... then they were lost. There would be no rescue.

But that scenario did not unfold, and ten minutes later both rail cars reached the central terminal ring.

And that's when the company of dark legionnaires got ambushed by a reinforced battalion of Repub marines.

The Repub marines had the rail platforms covered with emplaced N-50s set up in what would one day be the mining city's shopping arcades, spacer cantinas, and tattoo parlors that always seemed to cluster about production cities' outer transportation rings. First Platoon vanished in a sudden electrical storm of high-cycle heavy blaster fire. They were the first off the rail cars, and they had ninety percent casualties inside thirty seconds.

The miracle, Reez thought a few moments later as he pushed his way forward past his armored men, was that one of the anti-armor teams now attached to Second Platoon reacted as quickly as they did. Without waiting for orders, they fired on the heavy blaster emplacement directly forward of their position. The anti-armor team's smoking missile trailed out like a Nytherian naga and smashed into the dark storefront where the heavy blaster team had set up. Its explosion knocked that team out, and perhaps killed them all outright. The platform was still in the targeting reticules of the other Repub marine N-50s, but the emplacement that had been able to fire directly into the cars themselves had just been taken out.

The Second Platoon leader had his men pop all their explosive ordnance and send it out onto the platform. A series of explosions rocked the outer ring, and suddenly the entire area was venting atmosphere—which didn't bother either side since both sides had come armored and armed for tyrannasquids. Second Platoon low-crawled out through the brief howling windstorm as Third provided cover from the inside of the cars, shock troopers holding out their compact assault blasters and spraying the terminal with fire.

Second Platoon gained the concourse and bounded up on the emplacements in teams, using fire and movement while lobbing more explosive over the barriers. They took losses, but nothing near as heavy as First. And of course, when you're being shot at... there's no other way but to do the thing that must be done. Whether it'll get you killed or not.

It was in such moments that Reez felt the most helpless—when the violence requires your men to act and react without your ability to protect them. In those desperate moments, the commander must merely wait for his men to succeed, or die. For the emplacement to be overrun, or not overrun.

But Reez did not wait. He dashed out onto the concourse and poured fire at the N-50. He saw the marine gunner swinging the powerful barrel over toward him just seconds before Second tossed in the last of their grenades. The gunner never completed his swing.

Blaster fire from another position filled the air. Third Platoon bought enough time for the snipers to take shots up close and personal and in full-effect CQB, in order to knock out the third and last of the marine heavy blaster teams.

As silence fell over the impromptu battlefield, Reez took stock of the scene. On the platform and in the lead rail car the medics were working to save whoever could be saved from First. There were a few. Their armor had saved them. But most had been drilled straight through by the high-intensity gain inherent in the universally deadly N-50 weapon system. They were dead now. Their war was over.

All around the Imperial assault task force, blast doors were irising and sealing off the damaged sections of the ring. As it turned out, this little automated reaction saved the task force from instant annihilation in the next few minutes. Two full companies of marines were coming up to sweep the kill zone the marines had planned, moving from opposite sides along the terminal ring, coming in to hit the flanks of the task force. But the blast doors stopped their advance.

Reez's platoon leaders were calling in blue sky reports on casualties and charge packs while Reez got his intel officer on comm.

"You got marines all over the ring," said the intel officer. "Captain Tancay says he can use the ship's turrets on the terminal ring to engage. Standing by for your fire mission request."

Captain Tancay was the commander of the *Wolf*.

"What will that do?" asked Reez. "As far as structural integrity to the facility?"

There was a long pause during which the intel officer left the comm open. Reez could hear the bridge chatter, electronic and actual, and beyond all this the marines using their hull plate cutters to get through the blast doors protecting the task force. He knew his first sergeant and the company CO were setting up defensive positions. Which wouldn't amount to much if they got hit from both sides at once.

"Ship's engineer says the outer ring is connected to the main hab. She'll hold if we fire on the marines from the *Wolf*. Your call, sir. Standing by."

Reez hesitated. He looked at how his men were set up. Because there was no oxygen in here they couldn't use the plasma throwers. And if both companies of marines came through at once and hit them from both sides... they'd all die.

And yes, there was that. Their personal deaths. But there was also the blow of their loss to the Empire. And for all his cynicism after getting busted out of the Legion on a bogus charge, he'd come to believe in this... this whatever it was. The Empire. Maybe not all the make-the-galaxy-a-better-place-rah-rah. But he believed.

And he had always believed in being a soldier and keeping his men alive. Whichever side he was on.

"Fire for effect," said Reez bluntly, then cut the comm link to the ship. Over command, he told the surviving platoon leaders and platoon sergeant to hang on. He was calling in fire and it was "danger close."

Republic Gas Mining Station
Jasilaar Nine

The tactical commander for the marine detachment watched in horror as the menacing ship, a ship that looked built for war in ways no Repub Navy ship ever had been in his memory, began to fire on the station. It didn't bring all its guns to bear, but two powerful turrets located along her port side opened up on the outer terminal ring.

Over comm, his officers were screaming at him for support. The ring was coming apart around them. He knew in his heart that those men and women were now falling out into the vastness of space, just above the atmosphere of the gas giant. And he knew they were lost. Atmo contact was less than two minutes. There was nothing that could be done. They hadn't planned for the assault ship to actually fire on the station once her troops were boarding.

It was a brutal loss. Three companies of Repub marines so far. But he had five more to burn.

The marine commander was a point in the worst sense of the word. It was more important for him to succeed than anything else. No matter what the cost. Or "who" the cost.

This ambush had fallen out of the sky like a gift for the Republic and his career. Some deep source, most likely from the shadowy world of Nether Ops, had alerted the Republic, at just the last second, that a strike team from this... *Empire*... was inbound for the newly constructed gas mining station at Jasilaar Nine.

"It'll be a lunkfish shoot," Admiral Stacs, a distant relative and ardent supporter of the marine commander's career, had assured him. "Do this right and we can get you confirmed for a promotion to general staff on Utopion. This will be a feather in your cap."

But at the moment, watching the evil-looking warship fire point-blank into the station he was aboard, this didn't seem too much like a feather in anyone's cap. He tried to ignore the casualty count in his HUD.

"Stage all five companies in position two. Main hab. Once they enter the central dome we'll engage them in a kill zone. Target the mall sprawl."

But there will be no "we" in this engagement, he thought, and he did not like this distant voice inside his head reminding him that he was not paying the ultimate sacrifice for his own advancement. He patted his sidearm. In time he'd have to go out there and lead something. Hopefully after they'd won. If just to get some footage for the award ceremony when they gave him a medal for running the ambush.

He turned to the station's chief engineer. "Are we experiencing any orbital decay whatsoever?" he snapped.

The man looked at him calmly. Almost serene, really. "This station is built to live close to the inherent danger of a gas giant like Jasilaar Nine. As long as our repulsor engines hold, we'll be fine. And frankly... they wouldn't do anything to them now. Not while they're aboard. They'd seal their fate with ours."

The marine commander thought about this. "And if the repulsor engines were to suddenly... go offline... how long?"

The engineer gave a grim, sour, smile. "Two minutes. Then we make hard contact, and unless you reach the lifeboats in the next five... and they can boost up to escape velocity in time... well then, you're going to find out what a super giant's gravity can do to a human body."

The marine commander dismissed the man. He didn't like anyone who was so blasé about death. Especially if it was his death.

Five minutes later both companies sent in to flank the task force had been destroyed entirely, taken down by the enemy ship's fire support capabilities. Now the shock troopers were cutting back into the station and taking the surrounding corridors that led into the main hab.

"Estimated strength?" barked the commander.

"Maybe two platoons. We got this, sir."

The man was right. The enemy's two platoons against his five companies did add up as a win for the Republic.

Still, the marine commander wasn't ready to rest on his laurels. He watched the tactical feeds nervously, glad he wasn't up front and having to fight for his life. Glad he was back in the headquarters they'd set up in the station control that ran and administered the massive floating city, surrounded by a company of his best marines.

He failed to notice the chief engineer slip through security, telling the beefy marines he needed to get down to engineering and make sure the repulsors were operating at peak.

Reez's two platoons managed to take out much of the five companies that faced them. He was surprised at the enemy's tactics. It was as though the marines' commander had expected the task force to move right out into the central mall of the open dome that rose up above the empty skyscrapers and main hab. And get ambushed again. Instead the shock troopers had shifted left and worked their way through the companies one at a time, storming building to building for cover. Blasters and explosives, backed by snipers that shifted positions and took out small unit commanders.

The marines tried to mass along one company's lines, but instead bunched up and got killed in bulk. This got bad when the anti-armor teams started firing into their barriers, getting three times the casualties they might have gotten if the marines hadn't gathered so densely.

Eventually one marine company was pulled back to the station's command and control facilities, apparently to reinforce the company already protecting their CO. Reez recognized this for typical point thinking. He surmised he was facing some point who'd been promoted without regard to past performance or ability. Most likely, the man was right now falling back to his ship and ordering a general retreat.

Forward in the thick of the fighting, working with his men to breach and clear, Reez helped his shock troopers tear through another series of defenses. First using fraggers, then bangers, then assaulting through with blasters on pray and spray, covered by sniper fire. Yes, they'd taken losses, but more than half the company would survive. An hour of this, and what was left was mop-up.

Reez had just knelt behind a blasted barrier when he got the call from the ship's intel officer.

"Something's up, sir."

Reez didn't like the tone in the man's voice.

Then the whole station went dark. One minute all was lit by the bright centers of the main hab and the ambient subdued glow of the corners and shops, all of which had somehow managed to remain on during the battle—and the next moment everything was a shadowy blue darkness.

And something was missing.

Some feeling he'd been sensing beneath his feet the entire time.

The constant and near undetectable vibration of the station...

It was gone.

He was beginning to float. Gravity decking was offline. Or were they...

"You're falling, sir!" shouted the intel officer over comm. "Someone's cut the power to the main repulsors. In fact, the whole station's dead. You're in free fall. Get back to the ship or find a lifeboat and get off the station *now*, or you'll hit atmo!"

The station began to roll over onto its side, sending Reez and the other troopers sliding across the highly polished decking. And even as he was tumbling, Reez was captivated by the surreal sight of this deserted downtown metropolis rapidly tilting over... and then flipping all the way upside down. Above the dome, which had once looked out on the universe, all was now swallowed by the—

"*Wolf* is disconnecting, sir!" shouted the intel officer frantically over comm. Then he was babbling something about how to survive. Except Reez was already tumbling up off the decking, and above him—below him—the gas giant known as Jasilaar Nine, a red swirling maelstrom of angry gases and titanic storms, was swallowing the top of the dome into its depths.

Reez flailed his arms, reaching for something to grab on to. As his fingers found some jutting bit of glass and impervisteel, his blaster fell from his grip and tumbled off into the chaos of a world gone topsy-turvy. His men were screaming for their lives as they fell past him.

Because there was no getting out of this. That was abundantly clear from the start. This was the long fall into the big crush, as some had called it.

The station began to burn up as more of it entered atmo. The spiny docking arms tore away in tantrums of physics and metal fatigue. The *Wolf* only barely disconnected and just managed to haul itself up and away before another docking arm that had spun around came loose and almost smashed into her. If it had connected it would have sliced the warship in two.

But it was the loss of the shock trooper company that would be felt the most by the Empire. The loss of a ship would have been just a hard blow on the heels of a catastrophe. At this stage in the game, equipment was replaceable; trained men were not.

The central dome of the mining city shattered, and the station fell more quickly into the gas giant's well, as though it were being sucked down into a never-ending eternal damnation. Gas swirled about the darkness.

Reez knew they were reaching the end when the hull began to groan about them in deep titanic bellows. The groans were joined by crumpling can noises and monstrous-sounding hollow booms as bulkheads buckled and collapsed in the relentless embrace of gravity.

The shock troopers' armor was rated for extreme gravity.

This was not a good thing.

What had once been a gift, a mercy, the ability to survive where man should not, now became a curse as the atmosphere of Jasilaar Nine swallowed the station and dragged it down to its innermost depths. Because it only gave the troopers more time to witness the destruction around them—to see their own inevitable fate. To anticipate it.

Buildings imploded with terrific bangs that penetrated armor with their noise and concussion. It was like being in the middle of an artillery storm. Explosions lit up the clutching darkness, igniting the gases in brief yet brilliant fireworks displays. And in those last terrible seconds, as even beneath his armor he began to surrender to the terrific crush of gravity, Reez searched for his men in the dark. Strained to find them.

He found none.

Then the extreme gravity of the gas giant simply crushed him to death in a slow and final instant.

The bodies and the station would continue the long fall for miles, would continue to be pushed down into places where even electrons screamed. And who really knows what goes on down there at the heart of these crushing stellar slow-burning furnaces? For all that is known of the known galaxies, in the end, so much is not known. Because it can't be. Because... how can it be?

Who could know it all?

Aboard the *Wolf*, a stunned silence had fallen over the bridge. The intel officer glanced at the captain, who stared in horror at the surface of the angry gas giant. Where there had once been a state-of-the-art newly built gas mining facility that would be added to the crown of the Empire... now there was nothing. Where there had been two hundred and eighty trained shock troopers, so dear to an Empire facing manpower shortages... there was now only death. Silence.

All had been lost.

Only one escape pod had managed to break away from the station. But that had been early on. Coming from the engineering decks. It had jumped away to hyper-space seconds later.

05

MCR Fleet
Muratawa System

An old Ravacaggi heavy cruiser dropped out of hyper-space inside Muratawa space. She had thirteen escorts, ranging from heavy freighters that had been Q modified to carry weapons and heavy armor, to actual mass-production corvettes from the latter days of the Savage Wars. Corvettes like these were supposed to have been broken down in the various salvage worlds out along the Dentu Arm, but here they were, fully crewed by the MCR, armed and bearing down on a Republic super-destroyer battle group guarding Muratawa.

MCR fleet admiral Jona Crimm was a newcomer to the old rebellion. No one quite knew what his pre-MCR history was, other than he'd somehow been a part of the Repub Navy. Once, certainly. But so had everyone in the MCR naval forces. Either they'd served in the Repub Navy or some local navy, somewhere you could acquire enough shipboard skills to crew and fight in toe-to-toe combat against any given Republic vessel.

Though that rarely happened.

Crimm had risen rapidly through the byzantine structure of the MCR Navy. He'd led daring convoy raids against overwhelming odds. Overseen tactical insertions and rebel resupplies deep within the most active mid-core worlds. He'd even taken out a Repub corvette in the Battle of Smerst VIII. Or at least, that's what the MCR called it. The Republic, and mainly the House of Reason, hadn't bothered to dignify the loss of a single corvette by calling the engagement a battle.

But despite his career successes, Jona Crimm felt he was an average man. Nothing more and nothing less. And the truth was, no one in the MCR cared where he came from any more than they wanted anyone to care where *they* came from. It just didn't matter in the MCR's grand scheme of things. The only thing that mattered in the on-going rebellion was what you did.

And now was a time for doing.

The truth was, before this Goth Sullus... before this *Empire*... the House of Reason—via their war dogs of Legion and Navy—had tightened their stranglehold on the galaxy to the point that even the MCR had to admit that they had become little more than a nuisance. Their rebel organization had seen more losses, more defeats, and more lack of relevance than at any time in their defiant history. The MCR had been defeated, though few admitted it, even to themselves. It was just too hard to realize you were dead when you were dead. Where did you go after that? What was your next act?

But Goth Sullus had disturbed everything for everyone. He'd changed the game. And suddenly the MCR had momentum again. Momentum enough to send an MCR force, a precious and rare commodity, against a Repub super-destroyer battle group.

Five state-of-the-art Republic ships...

The super-destroyer *Imminent*.

The two destroyers *Narganz* and *Pegasus*.

Two corvettes, *Antive V* and *Admiral Kamoda*.

And a support frigate, the *Sussa*.

Against...

The ancient Ravacaggi heavy cruiser *Defiant*.

Four ships from various local navies that classified as battle frigates: *Resistor*, *Anarchist*, *Revenge*, and *Winged Victory*.

The super-ore hauler *Triumphant*, which had been converted into a carrier.

And seven freighters that all might have met heavy to light corvette standards.

Randa's Gamble.

Dagger.

Lutao Makdama.

Patriot.

Payback.

Dart.

And *Skelly's Last Bullet*.

At any other time in the decades-long conflict, an MCR ragtag fleet such as this would have stood no chance against a Republic super-destroyer battle group.

But the MCR was being led by a man who was rapidly proving to be a legend.

The commodore, as Crimm was officially ranked, brought the fleet out of hyperspace in relatively good formation. Which, even by modern fleet standards, was still a navigational feat. With good position and alignment for attack, the carrier began launch operations. Within minutes it had seven squadrons of various fighter types up and hurtling toward the super-destroyer.

The Repub battle group admiral went to active guns but held back on launching cover squadrons. TACAN AI calculated that the super-destroyer's Aegis point defense system would easily handle the incoming fighters. The Repub admiral decided that if the MCR felt they were losing and decided to flee, he'd use the fighters to get in among their ramshackle ships and disable their engines to prevent escape.

SOP engagement resolution. Perfectly by the book.

Before a shot had been fired, the admiral in charge of the Repub battle group was already writing his own meritorious action commendation.

PDC guns were hot as the first wave came in over the outer pickets. The Aegis point defense system went live and activated guns. Quietly, in the CIC aboard *Imminent,* the admiral and his tactical staff waited for the kill count on the TAC displays to spring to life with rising numbers. All across the fleet could be heard the thunderous barrages of point-blank defense fire, but kills were coming in only one and two at a time. This was well below performance estimates.

They'd been assured that an inviolable net of protective fire would vaporize any fighter-based swarm attack within seconds. This was not happening.

"Loose comet," stated the CIC officer in charge of sensors. He said this off-handedly. Even carelessly. As though this was nothing to be concerned about if one happened to be ensconced within the secure craftsmanship of a Repub super-destroyer. When he called three more "loose comets" within a minute, the admiral in charge of the battle group shifted nervously. This was unexpected.

"*Pegasus* reports deflectors collapsing."

The silence that fell over the CIC spoke volumes about the state of uncertainty.

The admiral cleared his throat as the four loose comets streaked in toward the defensive perimeter that ringed the massive super-destroyer.

"Will we—" he began.

"Yes," interrupted the CIC officer in charge of electronic warfare. The response had been a little too quick. A little too testy. As though he took even the merest suggestion of failure to stop the incoming SSMs as a personal slight. "Of course we'll have them down." He added a brief, "sir."

But they didn't.

Four loose comets didn't streak in past the perimeter. Instead they hit the picket destroyer *Pegasus* over the course of fifteen seconds. It was either mere luck, or an incredible display of naval acquisition targeting and gunnery.

SSMs generally had to dodge heavy volumes of incoming PDC fire as they approached target, especially in the last moments before striking. SSMs were wonderful at violating armor and doing incredible amounts of internal damage, but due to their erratic nature, precision targeting—or targeting, period—had always been something that eluded weapon developers.

But in this instance, the MCR managed to land all four SSMs directly on the aft engine compartments of the *Pegasus*. The ship blistered internally and exploded, killing sixteen hundred crew instantly.

Every ship in the Republic battle group heeled over and away from the blast as repulsors and engines fought to maintain course and heading. Deflectors surged and even collapsed as what remained of the *Pegasus* turned into a spreading debris and vapor field inside the defensive perimeter.

With the loss of the *Pegasus*, the Republic's newly developed Aegis Mark VII Integrated Point Defense Cannon System failed an integration reorientation and target shift alignment recalc as it refused to accept the loss of a major warship. The combined targeting communication collapsed long enough for inbound MCR fighters to concentrate fire on the temporarily defenseless ships.

A hodgepodge of MCR fighters taken from local navies and old surplus fighters from the Republic Navy swarmed the destroyer *Narganz*. Her deflectors collapsed in moments, but the ship was built to stand up to heavy fire. Once the loss of the Aegis system was fully realized, the commander pulled her from the battle group's defense grid and switched over to gunnery commander's discretion. *Antive* and *Admiral Kamoda* pulled back to defend the support frigate *Sussa*, while the main super-destroyer launched all fighters to get cover up.

Three minutes in to the engagement, the *Narganz* lost motive power. Even as the Repub battle group commander ordered a jump calculation be plotted, a thing he could not possibly have considered a remote possibility in the five minutes prior to the start of the battle, knowing he would have to leave a major warship behind, not to mention having lost another one already, things were going from bad to worse. The metrics of devastation were overwhelming and increasing.

It was under these trying circumstances that the first officer of the *Imminent* became concerned that the battle group admiral might be having trouble making effective tactical choices. The man had gone pale and was sweating profusely—and instead of shifting forces to meet the incoming threats, he merely stared in horror at the tactical displays, rubbing his left arm as all three Raptor wings of the fighter complement carried by *Imminent* streaked away to join the chaos of battle enveloping the *Narganz*. The first officer asked the chief medical officer to report to the bridge for a rapid fitness assessment. The first officer wasn't just going to mutiny without following the proper guidelines for doing so—even if it cost them lives and the opportunity to flee.

Casualties were mounting on the *Narganz*. Several decks were holed, and an out-of-control fire raged on hangar deck three. The MCR fighters had shot up engineering, making close passes across the hull and knocking out reactor control. Internal explosions had damaged starboard life support, and several turret batteries had been taken out by ship-to-ship fire. And as the MCR fleet closed to turret and blaster cannon range, they began pounding away at the *Narganz*'s forward deflectors.

Dagger was the first to punch through the defensive screens. It raked the *Narganz*'s forward command structure with rapid bursts of intense auto-turret fire. While no internal hits were scored, systems and automation functions went down. The massive destroyer was now blind as well as immobile. But the turret gunners of the capital ship continued to fight on in a desperate attempt to save their lives.

The three state-of-the-art Raptor wings swept in over the burning destroyer. They broke off into teams and decimated the MCR fighter groups that had been launched over the ancient super-ore carrier-turned-freighter *Triumphant*. Most of the old fighters, being turn-and-burn rocket sleds, fared badly against the agile Republic interceptors. In moments the gunners were free to target the incoming MCR smaller ships as the main Ravacaggi battle cruiser came lumbering behind their screen, hurling powerful blasts from her main guns.

A concentrated volley of gunnery fire, directed by the fire control officer in command of the turrets along the spine of the wounded *Narganz*, struck the *Resistor*. Deflectors collapsed, and immediate internal systems targeting was available to the gunners aboard the burning destroyer. In the next volley the *Narganz* savaged the *Resistor* across her starboard side. Crew quarters and gunnery decks ruptured.

The MCR crew, badly trained and poor at damage control, did little to contain a developing cascade breach that collapsed a central bulkhead and disconnected much of the ship from her main power supply conduits. Many of the crew had failed to suit up for extended vacuum operation and were caught without air as blast doors and force fields refused to contain the spreading damage now decimating the ship from within. Effectively, the *Resistor* was dead in the middle. Only aft engineering and command-and-control forward remained under power. Some turrets were still firing on local batteries, but the ship was out of action for what remained of the battle.

This knockout blow did little to slow the fury of *Revenge* and *Winged Victory*, which raced through the fighter swarms, protected by PDC blaster turrets, and fired another salvo of SSMs into the *Narganz* at close range. Both torpedoes struck the ship's spine, once again avoiding PDC fire and re-routed interceptors. The *Narganz* cracked in half. Lifeboats and escape pods jettisoned thirty seconds later as the "abandon ship" order was given.

The Republic battle group commander collapsed to the deck of CIC, suffering a massive heart attack. This freed the first officer from the bothersome procedural constraints regarding mutiny. He took command and immediately ordered jump control to begin their calculations for a general retreat. Thirty seconds later a message from jump control indicated that the mass of the super-destroyer was too great to attempt a jump with such a crowded star field, but *Antive* and *Admiral Kamoda*, along with the *Sussa*, had active jump windows and were released for escape.

All three ships leapt away, leaving the *Imminent* to her fate.

The first officer of the *Imminent*, now in command, ordered an atmospheric descent maneuver in order to protect the ship from incoming fire. Fighter groups were ordered to cover the retreat. The first officer's thinking was that SSMs were atmo reentry incapable. Getting beneath the atmosphere with deflectors at full would at least protect the ship from the ship-killer missiles.

The *Imminent* was still a force to be reckoned with, and she proved that in the next few minutes. As she reversed thrusters and dropped back into the atmosphere of Murakawa, she targeted all fire on the closing *Winged Victory*. The first shots from her powerful guns smashed the forward deflectors of the MCR ship. The second volley targeted the command section, and *Imminent*'s powerful energy bolts slammed into the hawkish forward bridge of the repurposed Gomarii war cruiser, destroying it.

With no one to control it, the *Winged Victory*, which was at max intercept speed and executing an atmospheric descent at the time, spiraled into the planet below. Her deflectors ablated the heat damage caused by atmospheric re-entry, but nothing could stop her from spinning in like a rock. Four minutes later she would crater into a wide desert at almost max cruise power. The hole would be almost half a mile deep, and little would be left of *Winged Victory* beyond a micro-particle debris field.

Jona Crimm pulled the rest of the fleet back above the atmosphere and executed his second-to-last trick of the battle. His plan had always been to force the *Imminent* down into the gravity well of Murakawa and use this dangerous environment against the bigger, more powerful ship. Crimm knew that his fleet, even with the advanced SSMs, or lucky targeting, wouldn't be able to take out the mighty *Imminent* on their own. Now it was time for gravity to help out.

MCR recon teams had been lying in wait on the outskirts of a small fishing village along Murakawa's Great Southern Sea. As soon as the *Imminent* began her descent, the teams were launched to their new target locations. Former Republic supply shuttles, purchased off the black market, made their way out into the desert wastes, twenty-eight thousand feet beneath the spot where the *Imminent* was holding position. Up above, the atmosphere did indeed prevent the MCR from using their new voodoo SSMs, but it didn't stop the ragtag fleet from bombarding the *Imminent*'s ventral deflectors with turret and blaster cannon fire. The power of these attacks was dampened, but not eliminated, by the fire's passage through the atmosphere.

The *Imminent*'s sensor officer reported the presence of the shuttles crossing the landscape beneath the hovering warship, but the first officer decided the local Legion commander was preparing for a rescue operation and chose not to react to this. He pulled the fighter wings close in about the super-destroyer in order to protect the ship from another fighter attack.

Ten minutes later, five prototype man-portable surface-to-ship missiles launched from several spots along the desert floor. The *Imminent*'s sensors relayed the new data to the bridge, though it would be unclear in the aftermath whether the first officer ever knew the warship was targeted. The first officer would be killed in the crash of the *Imminent*, and post-battle investigators would hypothesize that he might have felt these SSMs were sent by the Legion to target the encircling MCR fleet.

All five missiles smashed into the *Imminent*'s repulsor stabilizer array system. Though the repulsors were still able to maintain thirty percent lift, it was insufficient. *Imminent*'s incredible mass dragged her plunging down toward the desert below. The abandon ship order was given at fifteen thousand feet, and just over twenty-five percent of the crew were able to escape the doomed ship before its destruction. At ten thousand feet, the bridge crew were able to set up a limited descent profile and effect a crash landing onto the desert floor. The ship hit nose first, killing the bridge crew as it carved a scorched black slash into the baked rock and blasted sand before coming to rest in three pieces among the drifting dunes. The hull wings had broken away from the central spine and main engineering.

When the titanic wave of dust and sand that had been flung into the air cleared, what was left of the fractured and burning Repub super-destroyer looked like the ancient skeleton of some leviathan from a lost age that bore no resemblances to the times and struggles of the galaxy in its current state.

The Battle of Murakawa would be called just that. Despite the House of Reason's attempts to downplay and even cover up the catastrophic loss of an entire super-destroyer battle group, news of the defeat was soon leaked. Footage obtained three days later showed the still-burning *Imminent* buried in the sand, its crew struggling away from the wreck, trekking out and across the burning sands to reach a safe evacuation distance. As the footage zooms in on the straggling survivors, in the background one of the stricken ship's internal magazines goes up in a sudden thunderclap of noise and camera movement. The ensuing shrieks of horror and disbelief make the surreal tragedy much more real than the House of Reason might want it to be.

The MCR Fleet leapt away from the battle shortly after the engagement, returning to their zones of control deep within the mid-core worlds. But just before the ancient Ravacaggi cruiser executed her jump, a small shuttle left her main hangar deck and jumped away in a completely different stellar direction. This shuttle carried Jona Crimm, architect of the Victory at Murakawa.

06

Republic Destroyer Intrepid
Mid-Core

"Captain Cohen Chhun, reporting as ordered."

Chhun stood ramrod straight, his bearing perfect and military. Keel made a mental note to tighten up and do the same. He found that standing at a smart attention came naturally. As easy as drifting into a docking bay while on repulsors. It just... happened.

"Captain Aeson Ford, reporting as ordered," Keel said, ticking one thing off his mental checklist as he spoke. He'd figured goofing up and calling himself by his alias would be the first hurdle, so he had been repeating to himself that his name—his *real* name—was Ford, and not Keel.

The two stood in the conference room, Captain Deynolds behind them, waiting for a reply either from their Legion Commander or one of the delegates whose image was projected straight from Utopion. It was tough to figure out just who was running this meeting, but based on Deynolds's briefing on the way, both men sensed it would be the House of Reason.

"Have a seat," offered the holographic rendition of Legion Commander Keller, broadcast seamlessly from his place in a similar conference room aboard the super-destroyer *Mercutio*.

Keel and Chhun sat, as did Captain Deynolds.

Keller continued. "Joining us today are three members of the House Security Council. Delegates Orrin Kaar, Aletha A'lill'n, and Valon Uprecht."

"Delegates," mumbled Chhun and Ford in unison, each giving a perfunctory nod.

"Captains," answered Delegate Kaar, who wore the affable smile of a politician forever in good favor. "I appreciate you both joining us. We weren't sure when you'd resurface following your mission at Tarrago."

Chhun hesitated, unsure what to say.

But Ford—Keel—was used to talking. And as he spoke, no trace of his roguish double life as a smuggler and bounty hunter could be heard. He was all precision. Full Legion. As fresh as though he'd just arrived from Officer Training Academy. "We were fortunate that *Intrepid* was just a short jump away. Exfiltrating from Tarrago was difficult."

Kaar's smile faded somewhat. "I'd rather imagine so." His eyes drifted down to some sort of display beneath him. "I had the pleasure to review the service records of your kill team, Captain Chhun."

"Yes, sir," Chhun answered.

"And for the life of me," Kaar continued, "I cannot comprehend why you have not yet been awarded the Order of the Centurion. Distinguished service on Kublar of all places, a seemingly never-ending parade of successful missions in Dark Ops, a commendation for your part in halting the *Pride of Ankalor*... you certainly *deserve* the award."

"Thank you, sir," answered Chhun, his voice steady, indicating neither pleasure nor apathy.

"Unlike the regular Legion, Dark Ops legionnaires typically aren't awarded the Order," Keller said, his face showing a dissatisfaction that *this* had somehow become the topic of conversation. "At least, not until retirement."

"Or death," interjected Delegate Uprecht. "But it seems a shame to forgo the honoring of the Republic's heroes until it is... too late for them to be appreciated."

"We don't serve to be appreciated, sir," Chhun said.

"Well said," agreed Kaar, his warm smile returning. "Such is a truth for all who serve the Republic—my colleagues and, I daresay, myself being no exception." The delegate tapped his chin. "Captain Ford... your service record, while impressive as any I've seen, lacks the continual *thrills* of Captain Chhun's."

Keller shifted in his chair. Ford's time out on the edge, grifting and fighting against MCR, criminals, and the Republic alike, was gray territory at best. It was kept a close secret from the House and Senate in any event. Now likely wasn't the time to shine a light on what the Legion was up to.

"No, sir," Ford answered plainly. "After Kublar and the *Pride* operation, I was reassigned to a small task force charged with reducing piracy in the edge-mid hyperspace trade routes."

"Is it wrong," asked Delegate A'lill'n, "for me to wonder how then you would have been assigned to the mission on Tarrago?"

"No, ma'am," answered Ford. "The mission was launched in haste. I just happened to be in a position to provide the necessary support to Captain Chhun's kill team."

"Captain Ford," Delegate Kaar said, his voice effusing warmth. "Before we go any further, I should like to clarify that in my estimation, you *also* deserve to receive the Order of the Centurion."

"Thank you, sir."

"Having served on Kublar, I imagine you both knew Admiral Silas Devers."

"Yes, sir," Chhun replied.

Almost was able to shoot him the head, Ford thought to himself.

"Then it will come as a blow to you to learn that Admiral Devers was killed in action, defending Tarrago from invasion."

"That's... unfortunate news," Keel managed.

It was the best news he'd heard that day.

"It is indeed," Kaar said, his voice betraying a tremor of emotion. "The Republic *needs* heroes in times such as these. I fear a darkness is upon us, the likes of which hasn't been seen since the Savage Wars. I shall endeavor to do all in my power to see that you both are given the recognition you've earned, so that the Republic can feel at ease, knowing that the men who served under Admiral Devers at Kublar still live on to fight."

"Thank you, sir," said Ford, quick to respond how he imagined any officer in his position would.

"Thank you, sir," echoed Chhun.

The hologram of Kaar sank back in its seat, just as the real Kaar did in his office in Utopion. "Think nothing of it. But first, we must attend to some less pleasant business. Captains, were you aware that your mission to destroy the shipyards at Tarrago was an unauthorized operation, carried contrary to the direct orders from the House of Reason and Legion Commander Keller?"

Chhun felt his face grow hot. He clamped his jaws down tight. This was always the way it was with the House and points: someone was being set up to take a fall. Chhun guessed it was him.

Ford, however, was alert and ready to play. He allowed himself a brief expression of shock. "Sir?"

"It was the intention of the House of Reason to retake Tarrago, keeping the shipyards in production for the good of the Republic." Kaar folded his hands into a steeple and pressed them to his lips, staring at the two legionnaires. "That... is no longer an option... thanks to your *successful* mission."

"Sir..." Ford did his best to look taken aback, alarmed. He locked eyes with Chhun and, without winking, tried to say, *Trust me*. Then he looked down at the table. "Sir, we had no idea that this mission was anything but a Dark Ops raid authorized through appropriate channels."

"Captains," began Delegate Utrecht, "who authorized this mission? Who was your point of contact?"

Ford looked over to Commander Keller, as if seeking permission to answer. Keller nodded once. "Major Ellek Owens was my sole point of contact."

"And you, Captain Chhun?" asked Delegate A'lill'n.

"The same."

Chhun looked like he was going to lose his lunch. Ford hoped he could hold it together. Something was up, and the legionnaire-turned-smuggler had a feeling that *this* was the part Captain Deynolds wanted them to play along with.

"Captain Deynolds?" Delegate Kaar asked, his tone suggesting more of a summons than a question.

Deynolds slid two datapads onto the conference table, putting one in front of each of the legionnaires.

"What's before you," said Kaar, "is a sworn statement indicating that Major Owens solely arranged and authorized your mission. If this is true, your signatures and bio-stamps are requested. Major Owens is to stand trial for treason against the Republic, and your personal presence will not be required if you are willing to supply the Republic with this affidavit. In keeping with House law, as you are victims yourself—being sent on a mission against your government unbeknown to you—Major Owens's defense will be denied the right to cross-examine or question your testimonies."

Both men held the datapads in their hands. It was Keller who nudged them to bring the meeting to its conclusion. "Sign it if it's true, boys. No one is above the laws and constitution of this Republic."

Ford signed. Chhun followed with a weak scrawl of his own. The datapads recorded their bio-sigs and time-stamps, then chimed before their screens went dark. Captain Deynolds collected the pads, though the information had already been transmitted to Utopion.

"Thank you both for your service to the Republic," Kaar said, his congenial and warm tone mixed with a sense of gravity over the situation. "I will do my best to see that you are awarded the Order of the Centurion. I promise you that."

"Thank you, sir," Chhun and Ford answered in unison.

The three holographic delegates winked out, leaving the legionnaires to share the room with Captain Deynolds and the hologram of Keller.

"What in Oba's name was that about?" Chhun shouted. "Major Owens isn't guilty of anything."

"They set him up," Keel observed. "Happens all the time."

"I'm afraid that's correct," Keller said with a sigh. "This entire Tarrago situation looks awful for the Republic. It's Kublar on alpha-roids. The Seventh Fleet was whipped, and its poster child, Admiral Landoo, was shown to be completely incompetent. Not that anyone serving on the edge couldn't have told you that. Admiral Devers is dead, so there's another golden boy gone. The moon and its gun were taken... with no clue if there are any legionnaires left alive on that base. About all the Republic has going for it is the promise that the Legion is preparing to mount an invasion to retake the system."

Keel leaned back in his seat and laced his hands behind his head. "That kind of an operation's gonna cost you, Commander."

"I'm aware." Keller observed Keel with an icy gaze. "The shipyards were clearly Goth Sullus's primary objective. Any humanoid with half a brain stem can figure that out. *He* wasn't going to destroy them. And if the Republic could just retake the planet as easily as Kaar makes it seem, that leaves the question of why *we'd* blow them up. Sort of puts a damper on the notion that we're all set to march back in and put things back to normal. Unless..."

"Unless," picked up Captain Deynolds, "the shipyard's destruction can be made to appear the act of a rogue element inside the Legion. A traitor. Perhaps someone with previously unknown allegiances to the MCR or some other anti-Republic group."

Chhun shook his head. "And so we're just supposed to go along with that? Commander, all due respect, but that's garbage. The mission was the right thing to do. Tactically, if we hadn't destroyed the shipbuilding capabilities on Tarrago, Goth Sullus would be using our own destroyers against us. We *had* to deny him that ability. Major Owens shouldn't be on trial. He protected the Republic and saved Legion lives."

For a moment, Chhun wondered if he'd crossed a line. He'd spoken comfortably with the Legion commander on multiple occasions since the day he first was drafted into Dark Ops. But it wasn't like he'd asked for or had been given permission to speak this frankly. The commander had every right to bust his chops.

Chhun braced for a butt-chewing that didn't come.

"I don't agree with the decision of the House of Reason," Keller said, his voice weary. "Not at all. What I'm about to tell you... I need you to understand something. You'll become guilty of a number of Republic ordinances even by listening. That includes you, Captain Deynolds."

Deynolds stood firm, while Chhun nodded his approval for the commander to go ahead.

Keel shrugged his shoulders. "What's a few more charges?"

"Major Owens," Keller said, "already has had a trial—if you want to call it that. It just hasn't been broadcast to the rest of the galaxy yet. Your testimonies will be part of an evidence package that will be included in a press release. He was found guilty by an illegal court formed by Legion appointees, some of whom hold ranks as high as general, though I'd never even heard of them until I saw their information on the after report. They found him guilty and 'mercifully' sentenced him to a life term on the synth mines of Herbeer."

"Why would they do that?" Captain Deynolds asked, flabbergasted at the utter betrayal and violation of not only Legion custom and law, but actual *Republic* law. This wasn't supposed to happen.

"It's my belief," Keller said in a grave voice, "that the House of Reason is making a move toward seizing full control of the Legion."

For a moment, the room fell silent.

Then Keel let out a sardonic laugh. "Ha *ha*." He leaned forward in his chair, shaking his head as he smiled. "I'm sorry, Commander, but this has been a long time coming. You'd have to be a fool not to have seen the writing on the wall."

Chhun glared at his friend, then looked back to the holographic image of the Legion commander. "Sir, I assume you have orders?"

"I do," said Keller. He looked to Keel. "And you're correct, Captain Ford. The House of Reason has hardly kept its intentions a secret. But the Legion... has contingencies. For now, I hope they're not needed. But what *is* needed is to get to Major Owens out of that hellhole and back where he belongs. I'll explain to the House of Reason that in our own *legal* opinion, their efforts mandated a mistrial, and the Legion will take things from there. But Captain Chhun, that's *after* your team gets inside—quietly—and removes the major from Herbeer. I'll leave the preparations to you. Consider any asset requests approved. Captain Deynolds has the necessary authorization codes to get you whatever you need."

"Yes, sir," Chhun said, his spirits picking up.

"You can transmit your debrief on the Tarrago mission as time allows. This takes priority." Keller's hologram rose from the table, an indication that the meeting was coming to a close. "And, Captain Chhun..."

"Sir?"

"I have the paperwork authorizing your Order of the Centurion award ready to go the moment you deactivate from Dark Ops. I want you to know that."

"Thank you, sir," Chhun said. He paused and added, "I never did anything that the rest of my leejes wouldn't have done."

"I know, son. I know."

Wraith had been unusually silent ever since the meeting ended. Chhun had tried to work with him in the speedlift in an attempt to put together a cursory plan, but had gotten only monosyllabic, one-word answers in return for his efforts. He figured maybe it had to do with Keller's closing remarks. The Legion commander had singled out him, Chhun, specifically for the Order of the Centurion, when Wraith had been just as crucial on Kublar and again in stopping the *Ankalor*.

So Wraith had gone back to his ship, while Chhun looked into supplying his team.

What difference should a medal make between friends?

Chhun already knew the answer to that question. He'd heard it from the few men he'd met who'd actually been awarded the Order while still living. Most received it posthumously, earning the Legion's highest battlefield honor with their dying breath.

"Your brothers see you differently," he'd been told by one old leej who'd served in the tumultuous times after the Savage Wars. "Like... you *asked* for the distinction. Wanted the attention. Like you're better than they are." Chhun remembered the old man's eyes welling up with tears as he spoke. "I didn't ask. I'm *not* better. The ones who died... they were the better men."

It was easy to see how that would be the case. One minute you're just another leej, the next, you're some kind of near-sacred deity. That you could no longer even function inside the Legion after receiving the award was the reality. Who's going to bust a guy's ass when the Legion commander *himself* is required to salute you on sight? So guys just quietly filed their termination papers and tried to find meaning in the civilian world.

It didn't happen often—to get the award while still serving. Chhun didn't want it to happen to him. He didn't want to be forced to leave the Legion. Ever. It was his life. He was married to the Legion, and in the Legion he hoped to die.

For a moment, he wondered if Exo had ever felt the same way. He should look Exo up. Before this new war really got going. While there still might be some time to make calls... and catch up. To talk about something other than mission planning. To engage in something other than the banal conversation that passes between men who think constantly of the potential for death to take them, but refuse to give those thoughts the power of being spoken aloud.

It would have to be later, though. For now, he'd gathered Masters, and the two were on their way to find Wraith aboard the *Indelible VI*. Hopefully he'd had a chance to cool off, and they could go over the best way to rescue Major Owens from the notoriously hostile planet of Herbeer.

"What are all those crates?" Masters asked, pointing to a stack of cargo that was being sorted and loaded up the ramp and into the hold of the *Six*.

It appeared that Wraith was down-stacking cases of det-cord and other explosives.

Chhun didn't quite feel comfortable with any single person having access to the amount of weaponry and ordnance Wraith *already* had on the ship. His armory was ridiculous. Now it looked like he was not only replacing what had been used on Tarrago, but expanding it.

"Looks like he's fixing to start his own Legion with all that stuff. C'mon, let's go. He was in a pretty foul mood earlier. Hopefully it passed."

"Oh," said Masters. "Thanks so much for bringing me along in that case."

Chhun held out a hand against Masters's chest, halting the legionnaire's progress. "Ford... *changed* out there. Between the two of us, I don't know that he's fully reconciled himself to being back in the Legion. I think the man he became to complete his mission is battling with the man he was. Do you understand?"

"Not at all."

Chhun sighed.

"I get it, yeah," said Masters, playfully slapping Chhun on his shoulder. "So... is this like good cop, bad cop? I think I'm a better good cop—better looking at least—and you're pretty good at being a jerk when you want to, so..."

"Let's just see how it goes."

Chhun walked up to Wraith, who had just hoisted a heavy-looking rectangular crate and was making his way up the *Six*'s ramp. "Need a hand with that?"

Wraith paused to examine Chhun and Masters. "Sure," he said. "Why not?"

Chhun motioned for Masters to take hold of one of the crate's sides.

"What, me?" protested Masters, even as he jogged up the ramp. "If I ever become an officer I'm never doing anything for myself ever again." He grabbed the handle and struggled to hold up the heavy crate. "Oba, this is heavy. What's in here?"

"Credit chits, platinum bars, and silvene ingots mostly," said Wraith matter-of-factly.

"There's gotta be a small fortune inside this thing," Masters said through grunts, walking up the ship's ramp with Wraith, who didn't seem to be straining much.

"Nothing small about it, kid."

Chhun followed the men inside. As they lowered the crate onto the deck with a thud, he said, "Quite an arsenal you requisitioned, Wraith."

Wraith, still stooped over the crate, looked up from beneath his brows. "Comes in handy out there. Besides, you heard Keller, we got the green light to get whatever we need."

"And you... *need* two crates of anti-personnel mines?"

Wraith stood up and wiped some transit grime off his hands. "I might."

Raising his hand timidly, like a schoolchild seeking to ask a question, Masters said, "I'm sorry, I missed the part where the Legion commander said we could have whatever we wanted. Can I get one of those crates full of money?"

"You'd be a fool not to," said Wraith as he moved back toward the ramp.

Chhun positioned himself between Wraith and the exit. "He said we could have what we needed for the mission."

Wraith stopped inches from Chhun's face and smiled. "Yeah. For the mission." He walked around the legionnaire and took a step down the ramp.

"Wraith!" Chhun called, causing his old friend to stop in his tracks. He softened his voice. "We don't need that much boom—or money—for an infiltration and rescue op."

Masters rubbed the back of his head sheepishly as Wraith slowly turned around on the ramp.

"Ah," Wraith said, his voice rich and patronizing. "I think I see the confusion. I need this much for *my* mission. Your little rescue mission? Not my problem."

"What are you saying?" asked Chhun, as though he hadn't heard the man.

"I'm saying," Wraith said, again arresting his own progress down the ramp, "that once I get this loaded on board the *Six*, Ravi and I are spacing out of here. Now if you'll excuse me..." He took another step down the ramp.

"You know, you could have some sailors load this up for you," Masters quipped.

It was a joke. Keel knew it was a joke. But he wasn't in the mood for joking. "That's a great idea, Masters. So go find some and have them get started."

Masters shifted in place uncomfortably. "I—I was just... kidding."

"Yeah, well, I'm not. So get going."

"Ford..." Chhun attempted to intercede.

"Ford nothing. Call me Keel. And Masters... get *going*." Keel felt his face grow hot. When he saw Masters hesitate, he said, "I'm still a captain in the Legion, right?"

"Yeah, but..."

"So go get some spacers to load up my ship, *Sergeant* Masters." Keel paused to let the words sink in before adding, "That's an order."

Masters looked from Wraith to Chhun, but the leader of his kill team had his gaze fixed on Captain Ford. "Yeah, sure," Masters said, and then hustled past Wraith down the ramp.

With Masters gone, Chhun said, "What's the matter with you?"

Ford pressed both palms into his chest. "*Me*? I'm as good as gurling."

"No," Chhun insisted, "you're not. You've been struggling with something since the moment you picked us up."

"That's your imagination," Ford said, waving the comment off.

"Is it? Because the Captain Ford I remember *never* treated NCOs as if he were a point."

"Listen, I don't have time for this. You may have forgotten that I've got a kidnapped crew, but *I* haven't." Ford held out his arm to indicate that it was time for Chhun to leave his ship.

"That's what this is about?" said Chhun. "Look, I'm still in to help you out—we all are—but we need to take care of our own first. Major Owens is going through who-knows-what on Herbeer. You don't turn your back on a fellow leej—especially one in need."

"I never turned my back on anyone!" Wraith jabbed a finger at Chhun. "Owens'll still be on Herbeer when we get my crew back. It's not like he's going anywhere. I've been on my own for *seven* years, Chhun. Seven years! The only 'brother leejes' I ran across were the ones looking to take my ship or put a blaster bolt in my back. You know how many leej kids I made take a dirt nap thanks to the points commanding them? Go on... take a guess."

Chhun remained silent. This, he didn't want to hear.

"Thirty-eight," Wraith said. "Thirty-eight legionnaires dead in their shiny, ridiculous armor. And that's only what I know of for sure. Ravi could give you a reliable estimate to the tenth decimal if you want an idea of indirect casualties."

Chhun held up both hands. "Look, I know it was rough out there—"

"You think so?" Keel said, amused at the very idea. "Because I think you and every other leej in Dark Ops has no idea—Owens included. I had to let good people die and bad people live. I watched pirates plunder and murder aboard commercial starliners, and then watched it happen again because of the ineptitude of the points tasked with hunting them down. Sometimes, if some scumbag got really bad, and the authorities couldn't—wouldn't—stop 'em, I'd just tail them from the cantina, follow them as they took a shortcut through a back alley, and put a blaster bolt into their head. I learned how to swindle, lie, and double-cross with the best of them, *and* I learned how not to let it happen to me. And I'm not going to go against all that and let some dame from Nether Ops get away with kidnapping *my* crew just because the Legion would rather me kill someone else first. I'm coming for Broxin and her little speed-team of wannabe Dark Ops, and I'm going to kill each and every one of them. *Slowly*, if anything happened to my team. Even Prisma, the kid. And I don't even like her."

A silence fell between the two men.

Ravi stepped into the hold. He spoke in a soft voice. "Captain, the ship is prepared to launch, and I have clearance pre-arranged from docking bay control. The ship will take I am thinking another ten minutes to fully load its cargo."

"What's still out there?" Keel asked, not removing his gaze from Chhun.

"Four crates of Republic Navy ration packs, one case of aero-precision rockets—the extra launcher is already loaded..." Ravi seemed to be scanning some unseen list, communicating directly with the *Six*'s internal manifests. "Tech upgrades for your helmet and all blaster packs are on board. About half of the requested bot parts and replacement parts for the *Indelible VI* are unloaded."

"How 'bout the replacement concussion missiles and blaster turret charge spikers?"

Ravi's azure turban seemed to sparkle under the lights of the ship. "These were the first items loaded."

Keel finally broke off his stare. "Fine. Let's leave the rest and get out of here. We've got enough to grab what's left at a night market or a spaceport if we need to."

"Yes, Captain," Ravi said. He disappeared in the direction of the cockpit.

"So I guess that's it?" Chhun said once the navigator was gone.

"Pretty much," answered Keel.

"You're leaving the Legion?"

"Looks that way."

Chhun let out a sigh. "I have a responsibility—"

"Look," Keel interrupted, "spare me the—"

"I have a responsibility," repeated Chhun, drowning out the smuggler's protests, "... to the Legion. To Dark Ops. And to Major Owens. I'm going to get him out of those synth mines. And when I do... I'm going to look you up. And if you still need help finding your crew," Chhun paused, "then you've got it."

Nothing seemed to move for a moment. Time stood still.

Then Keel gave a half smile and an almost imperceptible nod. "Thanks."

Masters reappeared at the base of the ramp. "Okay, I found some star-hoppers to load up the cargo. *And,* I just want to say that even though Mommy and Daddy fight, I know that you still love me."

"We're taking off without the rest of the cargo," Keel said.

"Oh, okay," Masters answered, without missing a beat. "I was hoping I was wasting my time the entire time I was hunting down sailors out there."

"Masters," Keel said, "sorry about treating you like that. You're a good legionnaire. Always have been."

"Well, that's true," said Masters. He sobered up, seemingly aware of the finality of the moment. "Don't worry about it. Stress, right?"

"Stressful times," Chhun agreed. "Let's get going, Masters. We still need to figure out a way to get down into the mines without being detected. Lots of work to do."

Masters seemed to take the hint. Wraith wouldn't be joining them. He nodded, then disappeared down the ramp. Chhun moved to follow.

"Take care of yourself, Chhun," Keel called after him.

"Always do," replied the legionnaire as he made his way down the ramp. "KTF, Captain... Keel."

"KTF," Keel replied.

Chhun watched from the gleaming black floor of the docking bay as the *Indelible VI* rose up off the deck by its repulsors. He could see Keel and Ravi in the cockpit until the ship slowly made an about face, orienting itself toward the large shield array that served as the entrance to and exit from *Intrepid's* docking bay.

The modified freighter hovered slowly forward to the illuminated trench in the docking bay that warned personnel not to cross—the engines-free zone. The *Six*'s twin engines then flashed a gorgeous light blue, and the ship rocketed out of the hangar bay, banking "down" and out of sight with a flawless corkscrew roll.

"So..." asked Masters, "what do we do now?"

Chhun pushed his tongue against the corner of his mouth. "Same thing we did the last time he left. Complete our mission."

07

The Grand Pavilion of the Zhee Tribes
The Near Wastes of Ankalor

The Grand Pavilion of the Mighty Khan was indeed grand in delivering the expectations of opulence and excess. Jebba Monteau knew he was seeing something few in the galaxy-spanning Republic would ever see.

But Jebba Monteau bore, with great stoicism and pride, advanced degrees in Zhee Studies, and was considered one of the foremost protégés of the great zhee apologist who advised the most-worthies of the select councils of the House of Reason. Plus, he was good-looking, tall, thin, and scholarly in precisely that way that all the entertainments liked to cast the right leading man professor-type. Types with the right ideas that must be acted out seriously and with a certain gravitas in their contrived social justice playlets, performed by extroverted movie stars who would be entirely unsuited to the realities of introverted academia. This was why Jebba was cast by the House of Reason, or rather recruited. It was his job to sell an idea, and an offer, to the zhee.

Now, it was one thing to study the zhee. The richness of their ancient culture. The enigmatic nature of their power structures, and struggle. The nobility and almost backward nature of their patriarchal and, unfortunately, blatantly racist culture. That was all fine and good in the lecture halls. It was another thing to go out to one of their worlds and engage with them in real life.

That was a deadly thing indeed.

It was a smelly thing in practice.

It was a thing one might not come back from, in truth.

In fact, during his doctoral studies on zhee inheritance rights, Jebba had been part of a diplomatic mission out to Ankalor—guarded by a Repub marine embassy detachment of course—in which one of the female students had been kidnapped, despite assurances by the city's Grand Wutti that they would be safe deep inside the fetid zhee slums. It turned out there were three Grand Wuttis that year, and they were having a little power struggle they hadn't bothered to inform anyone about. They'd found the dead Tennar graduate student three days later, raped and mutilated. The zhee were dancing, trance-like, in the streets surrounding the scene of the murder, waving their *kankari* knives and mumbling their blasphemies.

It was one thing to study the zhee.

It was another thing to meet them.

And of course, the Grand Pavilion on Ankalor at Mahlumba, this year, this hottest of sweaty years when the stink of the zhee made the fear and anger a thing you could reach out and touch, was indeed all those things... and it was grand.

Mooma, the zhee diplomatic contact, was ever turning back to Jebba as he led him through the outer courts of the Grand Pavilion. He would raise his baleful donkey eyes with delight every time some new exotic and forbidden pleasure was revealed in some richly carpeted inner sanctum of the Grand Pavilion.

His pride was quite evident at the Court of Ten Thousand Concubines. A place where the most beautiful females from every species the zhee favored with their near-insatiable lust lay waiting, draped in Tantor silk and drugged to the eyeballs on gilamine, waiting to be used by the Grand Khan of Eternal Battle for whatever delights he might imagine.

But their ultimate destination was far more impressive to Jebba. The Paradise of Fountains. They found this place after threading vast chasms of tapestry-laden "walls" deep within the Grand Pavilion.

Jebba looked up into the heights of the tent. Far overhead, strange and exotic birds flitted among the golden support beams. Below them, in silver filigreed "trees," bunches of fat grapes the size of a baby's head waited to be cut by a silver blade and fed to any of the lounging zhee headmen most favored by the Grand Khan Who Will Lead Us to the Slaughter that year. And the fountains themselves spouted milky white surges of *ruhrak*, the fermented drink of the zhee.

Jebba noted with awe the ornately mosaicked tiles beneath the pooling *ruhrak*. Tiles the color of the universe were inlaid with the zhee's ancient astrogation charts in filigreed and scrolled silver and gold. The zhee had once been learned astrogators, advanced even by the state of the many starfaring races humanity had discovered. Once, they might have discovered the entire galaxy on their own. But they had abandoned that possibility of hope and exploration in favor of something more satisfying—to them. Something in zhee history had made them turn away from that lost age of learning, seeking instead warfare, bloodshed, and mayhem. Ever carving out their slice of the worlds in whatever back yard of someone else's they found themselves grazing in.

But as Jebba gazed at the wondrous mosaics, he couldn't help but think that deep inside their art, those ancient yearnings still revealed themselves, lying there like they might be taken up when all the matters of bloodshed, war, endless revenge, and lust were finally sated.

A corpulent zhee headman extended a silver pitcher down into the bubbly murk of the fountain Jebba and Mooma stopped beside. Some unseen musician, blinded as per custom, as Jebba most certainly knew, delicately worked at a disembodied string of notes on his haunting flute. The Hitherene bone pipe. The silver pitcher, carved with images of slaughter, was proffered to the human as though some great honor were being extended. And of course, it was. Indeed, this was a great honor.

Jebba took it, held it to his forehead—a thing that was commanded by zhee protocols—and when he had received the customary barest of nods and the baleful donkey look of contempt from the permitting zhee, Jebba drank, ignoring the sour pungency of the beverage that assaulted his nose, slaked his thirst, and bent his mind.

It burned like liquid fire in one instant. It cooled like polar ice in the next. And then—as one epicurean described it, after managing to taste an illegally smuggled vintage and before ultimately paying with his life, courtesy of a zhee assassin squad, for daring to tell the galaxy—then it was like slipping into the warm bath of shock just before dying.

The hours that passed seemed like a summer's dream of something pleasant and satisfyingly murderous.

The zhee, who now switched over to their ancient language, which Jebba had learned over many long years, gathered around the drunken-stoned human representative of the Galactic Republic and mummed-hawed their promises of galaxy-wide destruction. Reminding themselves and the dreaming listener of all the murder and mayhem and greatness they'd been achieving before humanity arrived on the scene with their magical little hyperdrive. Yes, yes, the zhee intoned at that drawing of their silver, shiny, almost hypnotically damascened blades to the drug-stupefied delight of the human, yes, given time they would have conquered all the star systems, eaten all the races, all of this at sublight speed, for sublight speed was where the magic of time, speed, and mayhem reached an art form worthy of their lineage.

It was in that moment, as they touched him and assured him he was ever a friend to the mighty zhee, that he was most acutely aware, in a distant sort of way, that he would die soon, because it would be an easy thing for them to frenzy all around him and, with him under the influence of the fermented *ruhrak*, stab him a thousand times.

The zhee rituals called that particular hell "Paradise by a Thousand Cuts." When done perfectly, the victim survived the first nine hundred and ninety-nine, and lived. It was the perfection of the thousandth strike that indicated the level of mastery of the murderer. And of course, that took practice, and so there were all the lives that had served merely as practice for the zhee.

Lives ended so that the zhee might master perfection.

If this was done right, then a zhee was authorized to wear the crimson turban as opposed to the ordinary hoods of the common zhee. Hoods that covered and concealed their donkey faces in some sort of secret shame they had ever carried with them along the star roads of endless conflict.

Jebba noticed now, somewhat absently, that every zhee surrounding him was wearing the turban. The red turban that indicated mastery of Paradise by a Thousand Cuts.

It was in that moment he was, as has been said, distantly aware that he was about to die. Experiencing this most fabled of zhee feats for himself, finally.

Side by side, dawning horror and keen desire danced and circled about each other in a push-pull waltz that only stars and stellar bodies understood.

It was one thing to study the zhee.

It was another to meet them.

In time the delirium of the *ruhrak* faded while some distant zither played on and on, as hypnotizing as the insects that buzzed about the courts, mixing with all the pleasant and unpleasant smells. Calling Jebba back to the waking death the zhee called life.

Mooma lifted him to his feet and led him on past other halls and forbidden courts. Past the Temple of Wives, where the donkey-faced beauties of the Grand Warlord of the All-Conquered Slave Races could never be gazed upon by unclean eyes. That sight was forbidden unto the penalty of death. And if the eyes were not the large, coal-dark baleful eyes of the zhee, then of course they were unclean.

Of course.

Mooma averted even his own long zhee muzzle from the direction of the promised hidden beauties lying imprisoned in silken shrines.

In time they came to the Courts of Enlightenment, and it was here that Jebba tasted the thick dark coffee of the zhee inner home worlds. Steam and heat mixed with the bright polish of brass as delicate bone china cups were brought forth while the *kaffa* machines howled in demonic hisses, screeching out the pain required to brew the dark delight.

"Zhee were the first bring *kaffa* to the galaxy."

Jebba nodded. So wise. So true. Never mind all the evidence to the contrary. Never mind the truth. The zhee were most-favored in the symposiums of the House of Reason, and of course they must be treated as the rich and diverse culture-bringers they were made out to be. The zhee were like some Prometheus bringing the fire of knowledge contained within the thick dark syrup they called *kaffa*.

Some revisionists said it was actually lost and fabled Earth that first brewed this magic concoction. But of course, those were just crackpots writing their lies in the obscurity of unverified publishing. Madmen who'd never attained tenure at all the greatest and most noble universities.

Mooma leaned close over their brews.

Mooma is different from all the rest of the zhee. Even Jebba knows this. Jebba thinks of the zhee diplomatic functionary as a kind of citizen of the galaxy, much like himself. More scholar than holy warrior fanatic. Unlike the murderous zealots, male, female and child, of the many tribes of the wandering zhee nations.

To take life is the privilege of zhee, as the old proverb goes.

So wise. So much to learn from this.

The dark brew awakens Jebba's mind, reminding him of all his scholarly learnings he has accrued in order to be called wise in the ways of zhee. He ruminates on the wonder of even being inside the Grand Pavilion, an experience known to few even among the zhee, and to fewer still of the Galactic Republic.

"What is it that you bring his Immensity of Purpose and Bloodshed?" snorts Mooma in that deep swallowed huffy voice all zhee have. As though they are chewing and have terrible sinus-laden head colds.

Jebba smiles, buying time, and thinks how to maneuver within the confines of the culture to which he has devoted his life's work. Because, of course, this is yet another way in which one can die among the zhee.

Even the zhee do not trust the zhee. Another proverb.

The inner machinations of the zhee are Eastern and Byzantine in the extremist sense. They make other cultures look naïve and child-like when it comes to intrigue, backstabbing, and generations of mistrust. The zhee life is struggle. Even if they must struggle against one another when there is no one else to struggle against. And so what Mooma is asking is in no way innocent. It is no mere exchange of information. It is a play for advantage. A seeking for room in which to maneuver. And who knows whom Mooma truly serves? The zhee have four gods. And all their gods are trying constantly to slaughter one another.

So it goes with the zhee.

"I have my nose," intones Jebba over the delicate bone cup. He closes his eyes, pleased that he has applied the right proverb at the right moment to effect what he perceives to be a deft escape. And tactical, too. A sense of elite satisfaction in being able to speak the language at its deepest root warmly reassures Jebba that he is a player.

The zhee merely stares at him. Betraying none of his disgust or contempt that a mere slave species would dare to use the utterings of the Prophet.

And yet the game is to probe and to know.

And the game is still a-hoof, even though the first cut has failed.

Mooma feints, conceals, and waits to strike another time. Like any zhee might.

"Of course," murmur-rumbles Mooma. "Of course, my friend. Only the Grand Butcher of the Galaxy may know of your most generous offer. It is just... it is just that obviously you will become a great friend among the *zhee-aroi*..." Mooma has honored the human by using the zhee name used only among the zhee. It is like dangling a piece of stupid bait on a hook in front of a snakefish. Pride will make the snakefish inhale its hood and strike out at the barbed trap. To Mooma, Jebba is the stupid snakefish. Mooma is hoping pride will make the stupid *hooma*, as the zhee call humans, do the same as the snakefish.

Jebba is flattered in the extreme that "*zhee-aroi*" has been used in his presence. It is like being invited into a secret club one has known about and waited so long to be invited into.

Of course, Jebba's mind is also playing chess as far ahead as he can possibly make the moves, knowing that a mistake here leads him closer to death than he's ever been. But like so many gamblers, he's become more than a little bit addicted by a few easy victories, and allows himself to disbelieve the maxim that the house always wins. And he cannot help but to think, briefly, of next year, when he teaches back at Hallgate on Utopion—the top tier of the elite colleges and where the House of Reason send their young to receive the most proper of educations—and to fantasize about how this little tale will dazzle the students. How it will captivate the beauties among them whom he has selected for his own delight-filled tutoring. He always has two or three a semester.

It's as good for them as it is for him, he has oft told himself in the farewells of end-of-the-semester breaking-offs.

"I just want our friendship to precede the great honor you are about to receive," huff-whispers the zhee, leaning in close over the brass-topped tables. Other zhee recline on rich-tufted leather couches, arguing and plotting their endless murders of succession and promises to one day feast on the smoking entrails of the slave races of the galaxy.

"I am flattered and honored," replies Jebba properly. "But the gem I bring is for the Mighty Khan alone. And of course he decides whether the gem is a gem, or even if the truth is the truth." Jebba bows his head, and so must Mooma at this most sacred of prophetic murmurings.

Damn this *hooma*, thinks the zhee.

"And what if it is not a gem?" continues Jebba after the refrain. "What if the truth I tell you is not the truth that is desired by him I should not name?"

The zhee stares at him. Whether cautiously or balefully, neither can be known to the human due to the zhee's strange anatomy.

"Where would you be then, my pack-friend?" lectures Jebba, like he's holding forth before a classroom of children.

Mooma, of course, knows the wisdom of this. And hates the *hooma* even more for reminding him of it.

The zhee reaches out a hairy paw and strokes Jebba's hairless arm beneath the rolled-up white cotton shirt. Jebba has that "ever-seeking-knowledge adventurer" look all the *hooma* seem to think is required of them.

White shirts and khaki pants. As though they are always on safari.

"You are indeed the best of my friends..." says Mooma. "To the zhee, and to this simple pony."

A gong that must be eight stories tall sounds once across the many secret rooms that lie beneath the Grand Pavilion. When they see it, or rather, when Jebba sees it for the first time, he will see that the massive brass gong is indeed eight stories tall, and that its twin lies beside it, guarding the Doors of Heaven that are thick tapestries, woven in enigmatic circle mazes like star systems never known, guarding the entrance to Grand Audience, an audience with the one Jebba has come to offer a gift to on behalf of the Galactic Republic, but really the House of Reason because that's all that really counts in the big grand scheme of favor and tribute.

"We have been summoned," whispers Mooma reverently, and even Jebba smells the sudden stink of fear the zhee cannot help themselves from making in such terrible moments. "Let us go."

The stories-tall thick curtains were drawn aside as Mooma and Jebba approached the inner sanctum. They'd had to pass through a series of security checkpoints where zhee platoons, armed with compact yet powerful Dantarri blasters, held them at gunpoint while prior clearances were cross-checked. Jebba had no doubt that heavy weapons teams waited just beyond the curtains nearby, ready, willing, and eager to charge in and blast everyone with high-cycle fire in order to protect the Grand Khan from the vaguest hint of an assassination attempt.

Jebba knew this but... he'd made it this far. Surely all would go well and every dream of avarice would be realized.

Surely.

Jebba knew he was being vetted yet again, for the umpteenth time since he'd been sent on this secret diplomatic mission by the highest of the high of the worthies of the House of Reason. Knew that once more they were going through his credentials as an academic and student of Zhee Studies. Making sure he wasn't a trained assassin sent from the zhee's most hated of enemies inside Nether Ops. Going over his schooling at Highgate. His advanced work at Anders in xenocommunication. Matching the bio samples—samples they'd secretly collected long ago when all this had first begun—to the man standing in front of them. Yes, he'd been cleared by others, repeatedly, but it would be these zhees' hides if something went horribly wrong. And so the murderous clusters of heavily armed zhee stayed close to Mooma and Jebba, ready to hack, stab, trample, and probably shoot for good measure, if even one thing went just a little bit wrong.

Jebba's reason for being here meant no more to them than his life. If his purpose was important enough, the House could always send another envoy. Or so reasoned every zhee security commander all the way up the chain that led through all ten security checkpoints until they found themselves standing, finally, before the Doors to Heaven, the massive brass gongs of judgment looming eight stories high on either side.

The Doors to Heaven were not even doors, but heavy curtains, centuries old and now pulled aside, and Jebba was led into the presence of the Grand Khan of the zhee tribes.

The woven carpet passed down a length of golden columns. Each column was carved in the likeness of a previous Khan and inscribed with the scrollish writing of the zhee. The listings of triumphs. The tallies of the slaughtered. The conquests and the matings. The wisest of sayings stolen and recut for time.

Reading the zhee text was a struggle for even the best of galactic linguists. The common complaint was that the mind felt like it was unraveling when one read it. Maybe, some had dared hint, that was an insight to the workings of the zhee. So Jebba kept his mind away from the madness that lay carved into the solid gold, and instead chose to keep his head reverent and downcast as they approached the Ivory Throne That Ruled a Million Lesser Thrones.

Upon the magnificent and near-pagan throne sat the largest zhee Jebba had ever seen. The belly of the Grand Khan was swollen and well-fed. Powerful arms and legs told of the Khan's recent warrior past—because no one ever became Khan by any means peaceful.

Mooma fell to one knee, and so did Jebba, who'd been waiting for the opportunity to do so. The scholar knew well the traditions. The protocols. The pomp and the circumstance. As a scholar at the most elite university in the galaxy, as the master of all things known about the zhee, he felt he knew the ways of the zhee better than the zhee might know them themselves.

Such is the way of the learned who have never done. This was also a zhee proverb, but one that did not spring to Jebba's mind in this most glorious of moments.

"O great and savage Khan of the Eternal Houses..." began Mooma. "A thousand apologies for daring to tremble in your presence."

The Khan gave some huffy snort, signaling that the lesser zhee might continue.

"The scents on the winds have brought us the smell of victory. This lowly *hooma* brings a gem... that you might appraise its worth to all your loyal subjects."

Silence.

Jebba waited. He would need to speak. No one knew the message but him. And it had seemed, all along the long trail that had led to the throne room and this moment, ever since the events on Tarrago had begun to unfold, that everyone, every zhee, had tried to pry forth from him the secret he possessed.

He had held. Resisted. Waited them out.

Now it was time... if the Grand Khan desired to know what he'd been sent to offer.

It was in this moment that Jebba was most afraid. Because of course the zhee were all insane by galactic intelligence standards. Or at least, that's how the rest of all the civilizations perceived them. With their endless wars. With their seemingly maddening choices that led to nothing but conflict. In a galaxy full of aliens, they were the most alien of all aliens. It was as though they were aliens even to the rest of the aliens.

Jebba had long been working on a theory. A secret theory.

It lay in the back of his mind because he wasn't quite sure it would be the truth some wanted to hear. If it was...

then one day, toward the end of his career, he would publish it. And perhaps it would make him credits untold if it was done just right. Especially if it was done with the blessing of the zhee.

What was that theory?

The theory suggested that the zhee were the descendants of the Ancients. That they were the original aliens, enigmatic and unknown and therefore so contrarian to galactic civilization in its current format that they struggled to integrate.

Who knew how that would be received? On any given day it might get him labeled a racist, the worst thing you could be called in Republic culture, or a saint, depending on which way the winds were blowing in the House of Reason.

Whatever happened then, this meeting now would one day give him the street cred to make such a wild claim—and thereby cement his status as a legendary thinker. Of course, he would have all the evidence his claim needed, if he ever made it. Evidence that would show his narrative to be the truth.

Because what was truth?

Truth was nothing.

Narrative was king. Narrative was everything in the House of Reason. Because it was they, not this savage donkey, who decided what the truth was.

The House of Reason were the masters of that.

"Rise and speak, messenger," rumbled the Great Khan.

And Jebba did so, feeling his legs suddenly go weak, feeling as though all the times he'd rehearsed what he'd been sent to repeat weren't enough at this final moment of actually having to do it. But there was nothing to do but begin... so he began as best he could. Halting at first, then warming to the narrative once it began to flow.

"Oh greatest of the Khans who have known the darkness and the light between the star homes..."

This part was easy. That was an ancient greeting from the Subaruka Texts of the zhee poet Numastedies from over three thousand years ago. Using it would indicate Jebba's love for the zhee. The Great Khan would know this, and so all along Jebba had planned to open with this ancient yet beautiful line.

But to his hidden shock some warm smile of recognition and appreciation did not cross the donkey face of the great Khan. Not like Jebba had always imagined it might in all the dreams and practicing of this moment. He'd imagined it would, and that he, Jebba Monteau, would become a great friend, even a secret confidant, to the Great Khan.

Instead the Great Khan merely stared at him, waiting for the messenger to continue. Those baleful donkey eyes burned with dull contempt.

Jebba recovered from this setback and moved on.

"I have been sent by the House of Reason to offer, not a gift, but a challenge."

That part had been his personal adjustment to the script. And it had been a smart one. The House of Reason had wanted to call what they were offering a gift. But they had no idea that the zhee perceived gifts as a form of charity. And charity was especially contemptible if it came from the lesser races. The slave races, which were the second lowest of all categorizations in the zhee hierarchy of prey.

The lowest was food.

But of course, the zhee ate everyone.

So everyone, in the end, was a kind of food to them. Everyone was the lowest.

This was why it had been wise of Jebba to frame what was being offered as a challenge instead of charity. The zhee would respect the offer of challenge. They had to.

"Since the events, O Great Khan, known as the Battle of Tarrago, our weaknesses against this new foe have become painfully evident."

Even though the court that waited all around the Grand Khan remained silent, there always seemed to be a sort of subtle micro-chorus of hushy whispering. This was everywhere among the zhee, and it contributed to the theories that they might even have some rude form of a hive mind that fed their locust-like nature. Jebba wondered if it was a devolved form of psychic communication they'd once had during their time as the Ancients and masters of all the mysteries of the galaxy—now manifesting itself as a sort of constant and undetectable whisper even they did not understand the true nature of.

But at the mention of Tarrago and the confession that the Galactic Republic admitted its weakness against this new foe, a sudden silence erupted across the zhee. Like predators sensing the movement of prey in the bush.

For this was a stunning thing.

All the news networks, all the intelligence services, all the constant chatter and murmur indicated that the Republic was handling this disturbance rather deftly.

But to come here and admit in the court of the Grand Khan, a place where it was decided what the truth would be...

"The Republic asks that the Grand Khan save us from this threat. From this Goth Sullus. From his terrible war machine we cannot stand before due to our cowardice and lack of understanding of the beautiful art of war."

Silence.

Everyone was a coward according to the zhee. It was the only way one could approach the zhee on their terms. Because in the zhee mindset, there was only ever one way. And it was theirs. They would insist it be that way by persuasion, murder, or wholesale slaughter. There were races that no longer existed because they had not seen things the way the zhee insisted things be seen.

The Grand Khan stood abruptly. His hoofs rang out on the Tyrasian marble dais upon which his throne rested.

"And what of your fabled Legion?"

Jebba was an academic. He held the Legion in just as much contempt as the zhee did. What a place the galaxy would be without their kind, he'd often lamented at faculty parties. What an age of wonder and enlightenment would begin when the Legion was no longer an issue. Its protection no longer required. Like all academics, and every elite, and especially those of the House of Reason, the Legion was a necessary evil one dreamed of doing away with. Never mind the consequences.

And maybe, perhaps, the unexpected gift of Tarrago, if there was one, was that the moment for discarding the Legion might have finally come. Maybe it was time for the galaxy to learn to do what needed doing for itself. By itself. And once it did, the Legion would finally be revealed for the petty tyrant it was.

And the zhee... well, the zhee might just be the saviors who freed the galaxy from the iron shield of the legionnaires. And Jebba Monteau was there at the start. Close friend and confidant to the Grand Khan.

So it was that Jebba too quickly replied.

"The Legion has failed, Most Noble of Khans. It cannot stand before the forces of Goth Sullus. The House of Reason realizes this and sees this as the moment for the zhee to assume the role of galactic defender of the Republic."

At this the Grand Khan charged down the steps suddenly, snorting and huffing in terrible fury.

Jebba recoiled in horror, though not because he had any choice in the matter. Fight-or-flight had decided the matter without him, and he was not a fighter. So he withered beneath the Khan's sudden storm. He cowered beneath the glare of the War Chief of All the Tribes of the zhee.

"And how are we supposed to stand against three advanced warships and reports of a new 'Dark Legion,' as they are being called?" brayed the Khan. "How are we supposed to stand against these things when the House of Reason has kept us from building warships, buying the latest in arms for battle, or even using weapons of mass destruction at our pleasure?"

The zhee glared down at the pitiful human academic with utter contempt, even raising one hairy paw as though it might batter to death the weakling cowering beneath its terrible terror.

"With these?" howled the zhee warlord, and suddenly, faster than Jebba would have thought possible, the famed *kankari* knife was in paw. Except this knife was more ornate than any the academic had ever seen in all the various state-funded museums on the noble zhee history and cultural contributions the House of Reason had seen fit to establish for the students and tourists, subtly reminding them by contrived woven rugs and baskets that the zhee were anything but the murderous species they were in reality.

"No, no..." stammered the academic, suddenly aware that the script was no longer in play and that his own personal death was closer than it ever had been. "There are ships! Weapons! Armor! A base!" he blurted out in rapid-fire succession, some primal part of his brain reaching out for the actual truth with which to save himself.

The grand culture of the zhee was so much fiction; beneath it all they were nothing but craven killers craving the weapons to kill. Jebba knew that. Everyone knew it. And now, certain that he was about to die, Jebba found the truth of them and used it to save himself. Because he had come to offer them weapons on behalf of the House of Reason.

"I've come with these things. They're for you! They're waiting out there."

The Khan held his wicked and damascened knife aloft, as though ready to strike downward and plunge it into Jebba's redlining heart. "What things?" he howl-snorted. "You have brought no things. No weapons. No ships. Nothing but begging to save your miserable Galactic Republic."

The Khan gave a great and gusty spit, landing a sickly yellow mucus glob on the academic's finely tooled Barona leather shoes.

The terrible silence that followed dared Jebba to dispute the Khan's indictments. And of course, if Jebba did not, then what good was he? The fear-struck fool knew that in this moment of clarity the Khan's wrath was revealed, and the strand of his life was about to be severed.

"I am the messenger. I bring the news..." he fumbled. Then, pathetically, "The scents of battle are in my nose." These were the words of some ancient zhee poet he'd lectured on for a semester, instructing his doe-eyed students of the nobility and purity of the words of the ever-wise zhee. Now they felt hollow and empty in his mouth, and he knew they were merely the mewling of a craven worm attempting to save itself from the terrible reality it had always thought it was in control of.

He'd been foolish to come here.

The dream he'd held in reserve—of somehow becoming a valued and vaunted interlocutor between the Grand Pavilion and the House of Reason—was now laid bare as the fantasy of a precocious child who lived behind cloistered walls and played with fine toys.

He was that ignorant child.

A hushed murmur of zhee whispers began all about him, crossing the court like a sudden and violent wave rolling on shore. And for all his learnings, for all his preenings about being the master who knew the zhee more than anyone—an easy statement to make in a lecture hall—Jebba had no idea what this meant to his survival.

The Khan knelt on his thick haunches. His smell was ripe and acrid. His nostrils flared, and his large dark eyes burned like hot coals.

Closely, close to Jebba, he whispered, "Then what is the message, little *muffa*?"

Muffa was the zhee word for *child of a slave*. It also meant *worm* and *quick meal*.

"T-t-t-en," stuttered Jebba.

The zhee leaned in closer, its hot breaths coming in short snorts.

"Ten what?"

"B-b-ba-battle cruisers."

The zhee leaned back, its eyes suddenly wide.

"The Republic does not manufacture such a warship... anymore. Just your weakling 'super' destroyers and little messenger ships running about."

Jebba swallowed thickly and nodded. His mind raced to recover all the technical details he'd been sent to dazzle the zhee with.

"Th-th-these are n-n-new. Mass-production high-firep-p-power ships. Excellent speed for close engagement. Heavily armed... or-or-or so I have been assured."

The Khan made a face at this.

"But there's more... Oh-oh-oh greatest of all the Eternal Khans Who Conquer us lesser races. M-m-ma-master of the—"

The Kahn cut him off abruptly. "What is more? Military-grade equipment? Weapons of mass destruction? Biological? A planet killer?"

"Yes... y-yes. The Legion was going to receive the new N-20 battle rifle weapon system that's been in development for years. We've cut the funding and re-funded it for development for the zhee. It's a much better weapons system... as-as I understand it. Higher rate of fire. It... aims...targeting, I mean...it's better, but I must confess, my K-K-Khan I don't understand those things. War. Weapons. Tighter blast grouping was what—what they told me to say. But that's not all..."

"No!" shrieked the Khan. "That better not be all."

"Armor."

The zhee were incapable, or so it seemed, of developing any technology on their own. Their mullahs prevented them from using any weapons that were not sacred and holy, and anything considered new was often the opposite of sacred and holy. Hence very few zhee pursued the advanced sciences. But canonical loopholes within their texts allowed them to *buy* whatever they needed. The problem was that the market had never seen sufficient demand to develop an armor system that fitted the physicality of the zhee.

"Impossible!" snorted the Khan.

But Jebba nodded furiously, willing the zhee to believe him with all his heart. "It's true, oh greatest of—"

"Silence, *muffa*! Tell me of this armor! Now!"

Jebba responded to the spittle-laden demand by devolving into tears, mewling pathetically, and begging for his life.

In time the zhee Khan came and knelt. Close and intimate. Familiar even. He put a coarse-haired arm, massive and bulging, around the frightened academic.

"Tell me," he snort-whispered, his breath tangy with the smell of sour *ruhrak*. "Tell me everything that was offered, and this will end."

Jebba raised his tear-streaked face. The Khan brushed one of the tears away. The movement was incredibly gentle.

"B-b-better than... Legion armor. It f-f-flies."

"It flies!" whispered the Khan with delight. "As in... jump jets?"

Jebba nodded. He was suddenly hopeful as he considered the Khan's deep brown eyes. All about him the other zhee, hooded and turbaned, closed in to hear what was being said.

"And there's ma-ma-more," stuttered Jebba.

The Khan made a kind face, indicating that Jebba should go on.

"A base. Out beyond the wastes. They've built you a war base. T-t-t-training. Equipment. Tactical sensors. Cradles for the sh-sh-ships. P-pow-powerful defenses."

The Khan stood, rising above the uncontrollably shaking human, and Jebba stared up at him. Stared up hopefully, believing that he might survive. Because that was the end of the message. Save one last... nuance.

"The House of Reason has built and provided all this in secret," he began. His voice calm. All of this was memorized, and he had it by rote. This was the thing he'd come tell them. Been sent to deliver. And saying it now felt like a kind of absolution of crimes. He was done. He was no longer important. The zhee would hear it, be grateful, and turn to the task at hand. Jebba would be forgotten. He might even just slip away to safety. He would return to the halls of academia, and he would never leave again. He promised himself that desperately.

"They only ask," he continued, "that you destroy the... the..." He faltered. "The Empire... and save the House of Reason. If-if you do..." He thought about adding "Oh Great Khan of Whatever." But he didn't. "There will be more."

The Khan nodded.

There was delight in his eyes.

A fire roared within them as he turned and spread his arms. Suddenly he cried into the upper reaches of the tent. Hee-haw-shrieking the terrible blood-curdling zhee war cry. And then all the zhee followed him into the throes of ecstasy, howling murder with madness at the roof of the Grand Pavilion and the stars beyond.

As though promising the galaxy all the final destruction the zhee had ever promised it.

Jebba remained mercifully forgotten beneath all the madness.

For long moments this barbarian terror filled the entire court, echoing out and over all the surroundings courts, and passages, and secret gardens. And when it was over, a silence fell across them all as the Grand Khan stood, paws on hips, staring out and over his fevered subjects.

And then, as if suddenly experiencing some new thought, the Khan turned.

His eyes fell on Jebba with what only a zhee knew was special delight.

"You are done," he stated simply. Once more he knelt to the trembling Jebba. Those tremors now came only intermittently. "You have studied us?"

Jebba nodded.

"You love our rich culture?"

Jebba nodded again.

"Our ways?"

Jebba nodded. Maybe all those dreams of being the one the Khan trusted were suddenly possible again. He nodded desperately, gazing into the Khan's large dark eyes like a lover. Like a savior. Like a true believer.

"Then let me show you something... sacred to us."

The Khan's eyes fluttered as he drew out his silver damascened blade once more.

"This indeed is a great privilege for you, my little teacher. Now you will know us in our truest of forms."

And with that, the Khan began the Paradise of a Thousand Cuts. And of course, he was a master. Jebba survived, screaming and begging, but he survived all nine hundred and ninety-nine cuts in the hours it took.

It was the thousandth that was the kindest.

08

Synth Mines
Herbeer

Owens held a fortune in the palm of his hand. The value of the synth he'd just painstakingly rubbed and crumbled out of the sandstone walls was beyond anything else he'd ever physically held on to before—and he had wrapped his mitts around some pretty cutting-edge tech in his years in Dark Ops. He gently placed the black flakes—the consistency of gold leaf—into the tiny collection pouch on his belt.

He had collected about two grams, by his count. Assuming there wasn't too much crumbled sandstone riding along with his synth. Still another gram to go, and then he could report in and get a sleep reprieve. Six glorious hours before he was forced to get up and get back at it—usually by way of a vicious kick by a Gomarii or one of their black-hearted human colleagues.

Owens understood that the synth mines were a hellhole not because the Republic didn't know the extent of the conditions, but because they *wanted* it to be a place of suffering and hopelessness. Work until your hands feel like they'll bleed. Until you can no longer even make a fist. And if by some feat you manage to ball your hand up while sleeping, you'll have to work to pry it apart upon waking. It was a life of neuropathy driven by the constant finger-work required to remove the synth from the veins that ran through the sandstone. Only you could never go too fast or rub too hard, otherwise the synth's miraculous ability to replicate itself as whatever it is mixed with would kick in, ruining the synth by turning it into so much worthless sandstone.

Sand scrubbers, as the prisoners took to calling themselves, worked to make riches for others—and to avoid a taste of the energy-whips. If a Gomarii felt the urge, for any reason, or no reason at all, the blue energy whips would crack mercilessly. And they didn't take anything off of it, didn't go soft so a miner could still meet quota.

It was a miserable life.

Arching his back, Owens could *hear* bones popping as he stretched, hands on his hips and eyes looking up at the low ceiling dug out of the rock. He was covered in sweat. The mines ran from hot to cold with little rhyme or reason. He wore a stained olive tank top and tattered fatigue pants—the remnants of the same uniform he'd worn into the place. His Legion jacket had become one of the guards' prizes not long after his shades were destroyed. It hadn't bothered him much at the time. He'd expected to lose it when they issued his prison outfit. But the mines were run on the ultra-cheap. No prison uniforms. The clothes on your back would do just fine.

The very use of prisoners in the first place was part of the ultra-cheap mindset. It seemed clear that sophisticated bots could do a quicker job of mining the fragile and precious synth. But they would be more expensive—and less punitive. No, this was a place of starvation rations. You slept in the cave, relieved yourself in abandoned shafts where the veins of synth had dried up, and suffered through the temperature swings.

Most nights, Owens really would have liked to have that stolen jacket.

"Okay, one more gram to go. Back at it, Ellek."

He'd taken to talking to himself. It had only been a couple of weeks, but it seemed somehow necessary. A way to stay sharp until Keller arranged for his release, or— barring that—he was forced to make his bid to take over the place.

If it came down to it.

He began to rub the tips of his fingers softly against the sandstone, causing tiny crumbles of sand to sprinkle down onto his boots.

He missed his wife.

Squinting at the wall, shrouded by his own backlit shadow from the portable lights strung up behind him, he came upon a thicker-than-usual vein of synth. He rubbed with more intensity as the matte-black substance that seemed to absorb light grew and grew. This was by far the largest concentration he'd yet seen. He'd have no trouble getting his remaining gram with this vein. In fact, he reckoned he would have no trouble meeting his quotas for weeks with what was before him.

Of course, this was both good and bad. Good, because it would easily fill his quota for today—and, if he was patient, many days to come. This was the proverbial "honeypot" the older miners always seemed to dream about. It was bad because now he would need to guard this rich find from other miners looking for an easy three grams. As tedious as collecting the synth was, finding it was often the more difficult part.

Well, he would just keep working. He had the strength, still. He could hide the extra somewhere even though the rule was you turned in everything you had, even if you were over quota. Of course, there was no reward for additional production. And no one ever went over quota.

Owens would hide it and hope the Gomarii didn't perceive his secret through those weird, blue, tentacle-like appendages. They were able to read emotions, it was said. But more than that, those tendrils somehow gave the Gomarii an idea of the measure of a person. Were they fighters? Cowards? Proud? Quislings? Supposedly, that's what made the Gomarii such good slavers. They knew who would serve willingly, and they knew how to break those who would not. The tendrils revealed all.

"Revealed that I could kick their asses," Owens chuckled to himself.

In contrast with the way they dealt with other prisoners, the Gomarii apparently had a rule never to be around Owens with less than three people. The legionnaire figured they sensed how dangerous he was, sensed just what would happen if they pushed their crap too hard with him. Unless they had sufficient backup.

The joke would be on them. He could kill three guards in his sleep. He had, in fact, been doing just that. They were his favorite dreams.

From behind him, Owens heard the shuffling of footsteps. Whoever it was, they were trying to be quiet—and doing a good enough job of it, if going up against untrained ears. That wasn't Owens. He reached down and picked up a chunk of stone that filled his palm like a seamball. He took the rock with him everywhere, his great equalizer in a world without blasters. Except for the guards.

The footsteps halted, and Owens heard a somewhat ragged breathing still several meters behind him. It wasn't the sound of a Gomarii—absent was the electric crackle of their whips. A prisoner then.

So far, the gangs that vied for control of the mines—or at least what passed for control if you ignored the guards—hadn't bothered with Owens. There really wasn't much to fight for. There was so much space, so many shafts and caverns to mine, that you could wander for days without seeing another being. It was only the need for food and the fear of being caught alone by a guard that kept people close to the central complex that housed the guards. From what Owens had seen, the only time these gangs congregated was when they'd found a rich deposit of synth. In that case, wandering into the wrong shaft might cost you a beating, if not your life.

The stranger was still standing some ways behind Owens.

"Find your own vein," Owens said over his shoulder.

"Don't hafta." The voice was wizened, like that of an old man.

Owens turned around and saw an ancient-looking old coot holding up a bulging collection pouch, fastened loosely around his neck by a cord. The old man shook it back and forth as if he were ringing a service bell. "Got my quota for the next few years, right here."

If that bag *was* full of synth, it was an impressive feat. More than likely it was just a bag of silt. The old codger seemed a few grains short in the head. Something about the look in his eyes. Far away. Not in the here-and-now. But whether the synth was real or imagined, flaunting or proclaiming it was foolish. Owens knew that much. A dishonest or desperate man would have no qualms killing the geezer and taking his prize.

Owens was an honest man, and he'd rather kill himself before reaching the point of desperation or depravity where he'd consider murdering a man to make his own life easier.

"Well," Owens said, turning back to his work, "I'm still a gram short. So if you'll excuse me..."

Owens worked in silence, still aware of the old man's presence behind him. He resisted the urge to tell the old codger to scram, and focused on the work in front of him.

Eventually he heard the shuffling of another set of feet, followed by a predatory, heavy breathing.

He turned around. A massive drusic now stood just behind the old man, filling much of the tunnel. It didn't escape Owens's notice that the massive ape-like humanoid was equipped with a whip of the same type as the guards'.

The drusic let out a snuffle of air that sent dust particles flying.

"Hey, Orpe," said the old man.

"Crux," said the drusic, his voice so low that it sounded more like one monotone rumble. "Got your quota?"

"Same as always," Crux answered.

The drusic nodded at Owens. "How 'bout him?"

Crux smiled faintly. "A gram short, wasn't it, friend?"

"Yeah," answered Owens. He held the rock behind his back, squeezing it in the palm of his hand, assuring himself that it was still there. The old man—Crux—didn't seem concerned with the large alien, but Owens certainly was.

Wiping its nose off with the thick black fur of its trunk-like forearm, the drusic gave another snuffle. "He with you?"

Crux drew his mouth down into an appraising frown. "Nope."

The massive beast of a humanoid gave a growling chuckle and stepped forward, eclipsing the old man. It removed the whip from its side and said, "Let's have the two grams you already got."

"Sure." With such a large vein behind him, Owens readily agreed. He tossed his pouch at the feet of the drusic.

The alien seemed taken aback at how quickly Owens acquiesced. Did it not realize its own size and strength? Or did people just refuse to roll over down here in the mines, even if it might cost them a beating? Owens didn't care much... until the drusic began squinting at him.

"Move," the creature demanded.

Owens scratched his cheek. "Where? Little crowded in here."

"Lemme see that vein of synth you're standin' in front of."

Owens shook his head. "Nah. Take your two free grams and leave while you still can."

The drusic released a primal scream and cracked the whip, which charged electric blue and buzzed with energy. But it was a clumsy attempt at show. In these close quarters, Owens didn't think a whip would be of much use. Of course, a drusic rarely needed much help in a physical altercation. Its slabs of musculature did quite well in a fight.

Owens ignored the scream as if he hadn't heard it. "I said, you'd better quit while you're ahead."

The drusic charged at him.

Owens hurled his rock, striking the alien flush in the eye. With a ferocious howl, its palms clamping the wound, the would-be thief took a step backward.

Owens took advantage of the shift in balance, ignoring the gleaming and pearl-white incisors of the drusic's open maw, and hurled himself, shoulder first, into the alien's abdomen. The force knocked the air out of his foe.

He reached up between the drusic's legs and gripped its gonads tightly, causing it to howl again and drop to both knees, wracked with pain.

"I don't usually have to take down beings as large as you," Owens said softly into the ear cavity of the drusic. "But that doesn't mean I can't take you apart piece by piece. I know where all six of your testosterone-pumping balls are, and I can have you begging for death in minutes."

As if to emphasize the truth of this, Owens jabbed an elbow just under the drusic's breastbone, jarring past the relatively thin muscle to send shockwaves into the internal reproductive organ. Drusics were testosterone machines, but that came at a price.

Releasing the alien, Owens picked up his rock and bag of synth. He held out the bag to the drusic. "Take it and leave. And anyone else looking for an easy quota—you warn them about me."

Still grunting, eyes watery, the drusic paused. It looked up at Owens warily, as though it were being subjected to a test. Finally, it reached out with a great hairy paw and snatched the bag of synth.

Crux stood to the side as the big ape-man limped out of the mineshaft. He gave a dry, one-note laugh. "About how I expected."

"Whatever you say," grunted Owens. He returned to his place at the vein and started over again. It wouldn't take long to make up what he'd lost.

"You're down two grams now," said the old man.

"Looks like it."

"Wanna know how I got so much?" said the old man in an insistent wheeze, again holding out his own bulging pouch of synth.

"What, like some kind of mining tip?" Owens asked, attempting to sound cordial. He rubbed away more of the sandstone, trying to better expose the synth vein. His fingertips ached despite the calluses he'd built from so many trigger pulls. "Sure, old-timer."

"Not a mining tip" said the old man with a half-chuckle. "I didn't *mine* it. I *took* it from someone. We all did."

Owens hadn't yet discarded his rock, something he was thankful for upon hearing the word "we." He spun around, expecting to see a gang where the old man had once stood alone. But there was no else there beyond the geriatric prisoner.

Crux pointed a knobby finger at Owens. "That was a Legion crest on your back shoulder. Wasn't it?"

"Yeah," Owens said, scanning the area behind the man for signs of trouble. "What of it?"

"You were in the Legion?"

"Maybe I just liked to pretend."

The old man let out a cackle. "*Pretend* to be a life-taker and heartbreaker? Well, I can see the temptation. You didn't seem to be 'pretending' during the fight."

"Got lucky," Owens said. He wished his visitor would leave him in peace.

The old man laughed to himself. "Pretend. To be a legionnaire. The surest way to get every bone broken in your body is to get caught pretending to be Legion. We, uh, never took too kindly to that."

"We?"

Crux tucked his bag of synth back into his raggedy vest and held out a shriveled arm as though he were flexing his bicep. He pulled back on the loose skin to reveal a faded Legion crest. "I was Legion, too. Fought during the tail end of the Savage Wars, if you can believe it."

The man seemed positively ancient. Owens could believe it.

"So why are you in here?" Owens asked.

"Same as you and most every other leej in these mines," said the old man. He spat on the floor. "Because they don't want us out *there*."

Owens followed Crux through a labyrinth of abandoned mining tunnels. It was pitch black, and he hadn't seen any portable lights for at least ten minutes. It was even longer since he'd last seen a guard or miner. The twists and turns in this sheer blackness left him pretty well disoriented, no matter how much he tried to make a mental map.

Still, his training allowed him to surmise that they were moving northwest. He was sure of that much. He'd never lost his directional bearings, in spite of the lack of a sunrise or sunset. Knowing the approach of his shuttle, seeing the sun that one last time, and then *feeling* the pattern of the flight as it homed in... that was enough for him to keep north in his head. He hadn't lost it in all the days he'd been underground.

The pace was easy enough, thanks to traveling with a spindly-legged old man. But it was dark and unfamiliar. If the old geezer was bringing him all the way out this way just to kill him... it was likely that no one would ever find him.

Two things kept Owens from dwelling on that possibility, though he remained ready for it. First, to kill a legionnaire is easier said than done for even the fittest species, and the old man didn't appear to be in peak physical condition, even for his age. Second... something in Owens's gut told him to trust the old coot. That didn't mean he wasn't curious about how much farther the two would be traveling.

"Not much longer," the old man said, as if sensing the question at the tip of Owens's tongue. "Name's Crux, by the way."

"So I heard. I'm Ellek Owens."

"Nice to meet you," said the old man. "Watch out now, narrow passage."

They took a sharp right turn in the darkness. Owens had kept his hands stretched out, feeling along the walls, and now they seemed to be closing in around him. "How do you find your way through here?"

"Used to it. I got an ultrabeam, but I try not to use it. Fool thing nearly makes you go blind if you switch on after this long in the dark."

Owens wondered how the old man managed to keep that sort of contraband away from the guards. He didn't bother asking. Instead, he asked a question that was of more personal interest. He had studied the Savage Wars extensively, had even written a thesis on the Battle of Larkspur while at the Academy. "You said you were in the Savage? Tell me about it?"

"Yeah, I was in the Savage." Crux cackled softly. "I was younger then. Still, I was already an old man by the time General Rex came on the scene with his young men and brought the whole thing to a close. Served twenty-four years. Most of 'em in combat."

"That's a long time to fight."

"Coulda gone home. But the fight wasn't finished. So I kept on fighting until I couldn't any longer."

Owens smiled. There was no requirement to stay in the Legion for life, but it always warmed him to meet a leej who shared the urge to keep on fighting until he died. "That was a pretty rare occurrence back then, from what I've heard—fighting that long."

"Yeah," Crux agreed, absently, as if he were concentrating on something else. "Most of us got killed before we had a chance to fight so long. The smart ones did their three tours and went home, hoping the Savages didn't show up on their planets."

Owens grunted in agreement. The Legion fought the enemy on their turf, so their families wouldn't have to face the fight back home. That was the thing that had the galaxy buzzing the most right now. With the fall of Tarrago, the specter of real, in-your-face warfare was a frightening reality for the first time in two generations. War was something that was supposed to happen out on the edge, or maybe in the mid-core in small doses. Tarrago had changed all that.

The passage puffed a draft of stale air in Owens's face. There was something alien in the scent. A sort of musk, or a mix of urine and mold. What could cause that?

"Crux, you ever worry about coming across those... whatever those things are in the abandoned shafts? Guards warned me about them the first day."

The old man laughed. "That's just to keep you in line. We're the most dangerous thing in these tunnels. Leejes is always the most dangerous thing, wherever they are."

Owens let out a chuckle. That was true enough. Or at least it used to be. It was still the case in Dark Ops, but the influx of points and their lax standards had had an eroding effect on the rank and file of the Legion. It was concerning.

"We're just about there," the old man announced. "Now, the boys—even though they sent me to get you, they'll seem suspicious at first. But it's just them being cautious. Understand?"

"Sure, I understand," said Owens, but his mind was fixed on just who these "boys" might be—and whether he had jumped out of the runkar's arms only to land in its nest by agreeing to follow this old legionnaire into the distant darkness.

They turned again, and a faint glow of soft, yellow light played against the uneven walls. It was a weak light, Owens knew, but after complete and total darkness, it seemed to him as though he were staring directly into the sun.

"It stings," the old man said, no doubt feeling the effect himself. "But it gets better as you move along. By the time we go inside, your eyes will be adjusted. More or less."

Owens wiped away the wetness from his eyes. They had always been sensitive. The shades had helped with that. Or at least, that was his thought; his wife had maintained that the shades only exacerbated the situation. Either way, he wouldn't have minded having them now, as he trailed the shuffling Crux toward the bend in the tunnel that seemed to shield them from the source of the light.

Just before reaching the bend, Crux held up a hand. It was the old, ingrained signal for his patrol—in this case Owens—to stop.

Owens halted immediately, the sight of that upheld hand causing him to react in practically an instinctive manner.

"I'll go in first and announce our arrival," Crux said, what teeth he had left glimmering in the light as he grinned. He seemed to be perpetually winking, and the shadows on his face deepened the aged lines found there. "Like I said, boys might be a little jumpy around you."

"You said suspicious," Owens said.

That constant wink intensified. "Suspicion makes you jumpy."

Crux turned the corner. "Okay," he said to someone unseen. "I brought him."

"Send him in," replied a commanding voice.

Beckoned by the old man's curled finger, Owens turned the corner and shaded his eyes with his palm. He was facing a dead end, a small cavern, that contained only two things: a soft yellow light that still overpowered Owens's eyes, and twenty or so hard-looking men.

One of these men, a man of granite with a flat-top and a neatly trimmed mustache, pointed at Owens. "Search him, and if he tries anything... kill him."

Imperial Temporary Prisoner of War Interrogation and Detention Facility
Tarrago Prime

Tyrol Gogan drove his gauntleted fist into Thales's gut once more. For the umpteenth time, Thales wished he'd worked out more. Yes, since being captured he'd lost weight. But there was a part of him that knew if he'd done more core workouts he wouldn't be suffering as much during these beatings.

Sergeant Gogan of the shock troopers seemed to have sensed this and so had given this area the most attention in the beatings of late.

Thales lay on the floor of the warehouse gasping for air. The weather had turned cool on Tarrago since the defeat. He sucked at its crispness, knowing winter was coming on. It would be a hard and cruel winter if they weren't rescued, or exchanged, soon.

And that was unlikely.

Unlike many others, Major Thales of the Repub Naval Artillery didn't hold out much hope for a rescue. The truth was, he'd never had much faith in the Republic. He doubted any rescue operation was underway, nor any sort of negotiations for some kind of prisoner exchange. He doubted anything was going to change in his circumstances.

"Seriously..." wheezed Gogan, his bucket off, his face red and florid. "You're gonna need to talk, fat boy."

The two shock troopers behind Thales dragged him to his feet. Stood him upright. Steadied him.

Gogan hit him again. Savagely. Knocking him to the cracked concrete of the factory that now served as the camp's interrogation center.

Thales went lights out.

When he came to thirty seconds later, he was still lying on the cold concrete and Gogan was going on and on about other prisoners taken from Fortress Omicron. About how they were talking. Telling all their secrets to get the orbital defense gun working.

Thales resolved two things in his mind.

This was a lie.

And he would not talk.

Again, the two shock troopers dragged him to his feet. Everything felt distant, and he wasn't even sure he was making a conscious choice to stand. Only that his mind and his body were in a kind of loose diplomatic alliance to work together regardless of whether he contributed or not. The alliance felt very fragile.

"Just stand there, fat boy," sighed Gogan. Thales could tell he was winded. If only slightly. The man had pointed to a specific spot on which Thales was to stand. Thales marked the spot with the one eye that remained open.

Then he shifted ever so slightly, hopefully without notice, to a spot just to the right of the one he'd been ordered onto.

He'd read about that in one of his books. A book on escape and evasion written by some legionnaire hero who'd been taken captive. He'd read that you resisted in a hundred small ways just so your mind didn't break, because then you'd start telling them everything they wanted to know.

The Dark Legion, the Empire, whatever they were calling themselves, they wanted to know the secrets of the orbital defense gun. Very badly.

Which meant, to Thales, that it still didn't work.

Which meant...

"Cute," muttered Gogan. He struck Thales once more. Hard.

Thales went down, fading into a darkness that seemed like a hiding place. Hearing Gogan's voice from some distant place on the other side of the forest he found himself running through.

"Fine, fat boy. Tomorrow we hand you over to the pros. You want advanced interrogation... you got it. They know what they're doing. And believe me... it ain't gonna be a picnic."

But Thales was gone by then, and he only heard the words like some echo in a dream.

Somewhere not this place.

Not this reality.

Not this war.

09

**Imperial Temporary Prisoner of War Barracks
Tarrago Prime**

"It's gettin' bad, Cap'n."

Desaix stared out the window of the old office park that had been converted into a prisoner barracks. At the compound. The razor wire. The prefab towers and search-lights. The new dark legionnaires in their armor. Doubled. All of it was hasty. The real base was up the road.

After the Battle of Tarrago, they'd all been held in the massive brig facilities aboard the three high-tech battle-ships. Desaix had been interrogated, given the minimum information back, and then been transferred down to the surface. Once installed in the camp, they'd sat for a few days before being put to work on a crew constructing a road between the temporary barracks and the new base being built out beyond Tarrago Prime's outskirts.

An Imperial base.

The base was massive, well designed, and definitely gearing up to start training shock troopers en masse.

All captured personnel had been offered a chance to switch sides and join... the Empire.

What empire, thought Desaix.

But this was for real.

Some had joined.

Many had not.

Desaix was a captain in the Repub Navy. He may have been wild and reckless and occasionally disobedient, which he liked to think of as daring and bold, but he was all in for the Republic. He just wondered if he'd ever command a corvette again. The *Audacity* had been blown to pieces. As he was being ferried away to one of the big battleships in an Imperial shuttle, the shock troopers who'd captured them had scuttled his ship.

That moment had been like a knife right to his soul.

And yet the *Freedom* had jumped away.

The *Audacity* had at least bought enough time for the carrier to get clear of the defeat that was known as the Battle of Tarrago.

So, there had been that.

"I said, it's getting' bad, Cap'n."

Jory was right.

Jory Moncray had been a sensor operator on one of the big destroyers of the Seventh. He'd barely escaped the destruction by making it into a lifeboat, but it had failed to boot up to jump. Instead he'd been captured and so eventually ended up here in the temporary prisoner of war dorm.

But he was still a sensor operator.

He was still listening and reporting in to his commander.

He knew all the news there was to be known inside Camp Spirit.

"Camp Spirit" was the Empire's name for it. Their little joke. As though the only thing about *spirit* in this place was that it was being broken. Slowly. One long day at a time.

Still, there was a worse camp.

A small factory a mile and half away.

High value prisoners were taken there to be broken. What made them high value was the information they knew. A Repub corvette captain like Desaix was not considered high value. A credit a dozen, someone might have said. Desaix had seen two other corvette captains in the morning formations on other days.

Then one day there had just been him, and Desaix wondered if maybe the other two had flipped.

"Yup," said Desaix. He walked over to the little stove they kept inside the cold barracks, lifted a pot of tea, and poured a bit into the prison-issue canteen he'd been given, if just to hold it between his hands. If only to keep warm. Night was coming on.

He walked back to the window.

The early twilight was a deep blue. Stars were coming out above, and the air was cold and clear. Up above, a corvette, a Repub corvette in fact, dropped down out of the sky, activating her landing lights as she approached the brand-new base in the distance.

Ground searchlights from the defensive towers that ringed the new base came to life, caressing the falling ship.

Across the silent forest, Desaix heard the comforting hum of the ship's repulsors throttling up for landing.

Jory came to stand next to him. "Enough of us have flipped for them to crew that vessel."

Desaix said nothing, instead thinking... *Then they ain't us.*

"'Specially when you consider those two captains like yourself mayhap have flipped, sir. Unlike yourself."

Desaix took a small slurp of the tea.

A good captain, he reasoned to himself, would put together a resistance plan. Organize and escape as per training, and implement the plan when the time was right.

"We're leaving," said Desaix. He took another slow slurp of the tea.

Jory said nothing for a long moment.

"Just like that?"

"Just like that."

"When?"

"In about twenty minutes."

Then Desaix went over to the wall, levered out a loose panel, and pulled out a blaster.

The prisoner transfer sled pulled into Camp Spirit with just two prisoners in the back. One prisoner knew exactly where they were. The other had no clue. She'd only just recently been captured.

Atumna Fal had no idea where she was.

She'd been interrogated at the factory camp. Questioned, really. It was little more than a prolonged question-and-answer session. A Raptor fighter pilot, and a junior one at that, didn't have much anyone wanted. If she'd been a squadron leader, or a special weapons pilot... then maybe. But the questions she was asked covered only her actions during the battle and since. As though the interrogators were interested only in filling in the missing pieces for some permanent record no one would ever bother to read.

She gladly told them how many of their comrades she dusted during the massive fighter engagements over both fleets. She leaned in and told them everything with a zesty relish, hoping to provoke some anger within her interrogators, enjoying pushing the ice pick into the wound. But the Imperial interrogators hadn't seemed to mind. The questioning had gone on and on, covering and re-covering her movements during the battle and not really caring about much else.

They hadn't seemed interested in her time beneath the waters of Tarrago. Which she'd completely lied about, instead opting to paint a story of desperate escape and evasion in the weeks since the battle.

When at last they'd added their bureaucratic signoffs to her data files, they ener-chained her wrists and ankles and placed her on a bench inside the main admin section of the temporary headquarters inside the interrogation camp. Toward dark they loaded her, and another prisoner, onto a sled and drove off, not bothering to tell Atumna exactly where they were headed in the early twilight.

The other prisoner still wore the uniform of a Repub Artillery major. He'd been beaten soundly.

He opened one good eye and smiled at her in the half darkness of the rear container atop the sled.

"Major," said Autumna.

Thales started to laugh, then coughed up some blood onto the metal deck of the sled.

The two dark legionnaires driving didn't seem to care if he died.

After a moment he leaned close. "You still Navy?"

Atumna looked forward and then back, a worried look of desperation crossing her beautiful orange face. She raised a tentacle and covered her mouth on the side facing the dark legionnaires.

"Nothing can stop us," she whispered.

Thales lay back and smiled.

She'd given the correct E and E response.

He coughed some more.

Then, "Don't give in. They'll come for us. Republic's not done yet."

She didn't really believe him, and she was rather surprised when a few minutes later she was "rescued."

This was classic Desaix, though nobody who was part of his ad hoc escape plan knew it.

Desaix was a gambler. Always had been. He knew that the new base was ready. That more and more of these dark legionnaires were starting to come down planetside and begin to form and train a much larger military force. He guessed that in time the prisoners who had refused to join up with the Empire would either be shot or transferred out to the base for some kind of conscript work. The time for an escape attempt was now.

And not from the base itself. From working the road crew, he had learned that escaping from there was going to be nigh impossible. It was built like a big Legion base. Forty-foot-high walls just as thick. Squat heavy blaster towers. The latest in sensors and security. Add in the troops, and the training, and getting out would be rough.

But here, at Camp Spirit, the converted office park, there were weaknesses. There weren't enough shock troopers to keep everyone watched. Especially just after dark, as the night watch came on and immediately went to chow for some odd reason.

And every night the prisoner transfer sled came back from the factory right on time. Apparently the interrogators only worked but so long.

So the plan had been to take the sled by force. Take the sled and get clear of Tarrago Prime. Head off somewhere out there beyond the city. Find an old airfield and get his hands on a freighter. Then slip away, back to the Republic.

That had been the plan.

But tonight, a corvette had come in and put down at the new base.

Desaix knew corvette operations. Knew that the corvette would be open to the maintenance crews for the rest of the night. Most likely she'd brought something, or someone, or even many someones in. Maybe more of the dark legionnaires who would most likely be in-processing onto the new base. Grabbing gear and getting assigned quarters and duties.

Tonight might be the last night of chaos, the last chance to slip through the crack left between the construction of the base and its military occupation.

Except, thought Desaix, why slip away when you can fly?

A corvette just down was a corvette that could get ready for takeoff quickly. Standing there next to the window, he'd run through all the checklists he knew to figure out what it took to get the corvette underway. It wasn't much.

And if he could gain the bridge...

Well, he thought. He might *really* do something then.

When they saw the lights of the sled coming down the road they'd built between Camp Spirit and the new base, Desaix and Jory left the empty top floor of the prisoners' dorm.

On the second floor Jory leaned into the main prisoner bunk bay, a bay Desaix had held forth in keeping up the resistance when everyone hadn't been on some supervised work detail. There had been a few who'd seemed willing to stick when everyone else was considering the big flip—switching sides from the Republic over to this new Empire.

"We're leaving..." said Desaix, a twinkle in his eyes. His roguish good looks conveyed nothing but confidence in the cards he was playing. "Who's in? Right now."

No one said a word, and it didn't matter which of the prisoners knew. The escape was going down. There was no time for someone who was thinkin about going traitor to inform. You either threw all in, or you folded.

Only three slid off their bunks. The rest weren't ready. Or perhaps had made other plans.

Corporal Casso, a legionnaire from the security detail who'd protected the orbital defense gun, was the first to rise. He was joined by Jidoo Nadoori, a personnel admin specialist in the Repub marines, and gunner's mate Rocokizzi, from the *Audacity* herself.

"Finally," murmured Corporal Casso. Desaix handed him the blaster, but Casso pushed it away. "I'll get my own, sir."

Nadoori fell in without a word, but Desaix could see the look of fear on her face. He didn't know how much good an admin specialist would do in a fight to take a ship against a bunch of ex-leejes... but every warm body helped.

Rocokizzi just smiled that bashful smile he'd smiled every time the captain had come to inspect the guns of the *Audacity*. Like he was proud, with good reason, of his guns, and his ship.

Now he was smiling because he was proud of his captain.

That checked Desaix.

He wasn't just gambling with his pay here. Playing reckless in some officer's mess regular game. He was gambling with people's lives.

In the hall he stopped them, gathering them about him.

"No one dies tonight," he said, low and serious.

They all looked at him. Ready. Afraid. Hopeful. Or wait-and-see.

But that was the promise he'd just made them. And he intended to keep it.

There were only four shock troopers guarding the exit from the building that had become the main prisoner dorm. The rumor was that all the shock troopers, or the dark legionnaires, as people were calling them, were actual ex-legionnaires. Not the kind of person average people wanted to mess with—or, say, try to overpower and escape from. But Corporal Casso had informed Desaix that he believed many of those guarding the prisoners weren't actually leejes. They had the armor, and the weapons, but they weren't leejes. Maybe from other services. Maybe something else altogether. But Casso was inclined to try them once he got a chance.

Desaix had told him to wait until he ordered the corporal to take a chance. The dark-eyed, dark-haired corporal merely nodded.

Desaix had no doubt the man was capable. He just had no idea at what odds they might roll the dice. And gambling really is about the odds. Whether Desaix liked it or not.

Casso entered the watch room at the bottom of the building where the four shock troopers waited. They had their buckets off. Their weapons were on desks or leaned against the wall. At the appearance of Casso, one of them reached over and picked up the little sub-compact blaster they all carried.

That's Target One, thought Casso to himself.

Jory entered behind Casso, holding up Desaix as though he were unable to care for himself.

"Navy puke here is having himself an appendicitis," Casso said. He raised his arms over his head as Target Number One brought his weapon to bear.

Desaix groaned.

One of the dark legionnaires reached for his bucket and began to fit it over his head. He was calling it in. That action made him Desaix's kill.

The other two legionnaires neglected to go for their weapons and instead came forward as though bored and seeking something new to be interested in.

All of them had clearly been busy boxing things up. The switch of facilities was coming in a day or two, at best. But that didn't matter right now.

The plan was for Desaix to hit the first one to go for comm. And Desaix did just that. He pulled his blaster from between himself and Jory, and fired. His first shot missed. His second blew the dark legionnaire's head apart at close range. Both shots had been charged to high intensity for max armor penetration. So now half a charge pack was used up.

Casso literally moved from dead stop to flying leap. His powerful thighs and calves pushed him out and toward Target Number One in a lethal long jump. He didn't go for the man. He went for the weapon coming to bear on Desaix.

An instant later he had control of it and was slamming it into the man's bucket repeatedly. Like a jackhammer. The helmet fractured, and Casso kept going until the man didn't move anymore.

By this time Desaix had shot down the other two troopers. Acrid burnt ozone filled the small office.

Nadoori and Rocokizzi stepped into the room. The admin specialist looked uncertain what to do, but the look of satisfaction on Rocokizzi's face was plain to see.

Casso hunted through the troopers, mechanically pulling weapons and charge packs and other equipment. Distributing it all just as efficiently. Jory went to the window of the office to watch the gate across the compound. The transport sled was pulling into the main loading area. The two legionnaires at the gate hadn't heard the blaster fire; it had most likely been covered by the loud whine of the sled's repulsors and the small klaxon that sounded to signal the gate's open status. That had gone on so much throughout the days it had become mere background noise.

The next thing that would happen would be that the guards inside the truck would transport their two prisoners into this office for official transfer.

Casso was now pulling armor off one of the shock troopers that most closely fit him. Rocokizzi was assisting. Desaix found the key swipes that allowed exit from the office and into the waiting room by the front door. He unlocked it, then looked back at the others, making sure everyone was ready. Jory and Rocokizzi were both armed with sub-compact blasters. Casso was still pulling on the armor.

Desaix nodded at the team. "Let's go. Everybody sit on the bench out here and keep your blasters behind you. When they come in, wait until Corporal Casso starts dealing with them. Then bring your weapons up."

Rocokizzi had just finished helping Casso shrug into the armor when the two legionnaires and their prisoners started up the main ramp to the door. Rocokizzi joined the others on the bench, while Desaix stuck his blaster in his belt and bent over the desk.

"Hey!" shouted the shock trooper in the lead as he entered. "You gotta have your bucket on. SOP, dimwit!"

Corporal Casso smiled and bobbed his head like he probably never did in real life. Desaix groaned just like he did that time he lost ten thousand credits on Ramula and drank an entire bottle of nepenthe.

Method acting, he thought, and grinned to himself with his head down on the desk. He had that familiar feeling he got when his hand wasn't great, but his game was on point regardless. Sometimes it was better to play that way.

"What's wrong with him?"

"Fight," said Casso.

The shock trooper turned to the prisoners on the bench.

"He wants to flip, and the other prisoners found out and beat him," said Casso quickly.

The shock trooper turned back to his partner and the two prisoners they had brought in with them. Instantly Desaix, Jory, and Rocokizzi pulled their blasters. They didn't need to fire a shot.

In moments both shock troopers were manacled and stuffed inside a closet. Jory shrugged on some armor, as did Rocokizzi, though the gunner's mate was a hard fit. Desaix opted to remain in his captain's leather coat and uniform. He did take a few minutes to wipe a cloth across his high leather boots.

Then the small ad hoc escape team, including the two new prisoners, who had shaken off their confusion, was out and moving toward the sled in the loading area. They tried to affect the look of another prisoner transfer, but the gate guards didn't appear to buy it. And after a few moments of loading, one began to cross the yard to the sled.

Desaix saw faces in all the windows of the prisoner barracks. Watching them.

All of them could have come.

And yet they hadn't opted to try. As though they were still waiting for the Republic to come in and make a prisoner transfer. Waiting for a deal that would never happen.

"He's trying to contact me over their comm system," whispered Casso.

With his "prisoners" on board the sled, Casso sealed the back and walked around to get inside. The gate guard intercepted him by the driver's side hatch.

It wasn't clear exactly how, but Corporal Casso disabled the man in five seconds and left him on the ground. Then he climbed in, warned the others that it was all about to go bad, and accelerated.

The other gate guard was coming toward them, his weapon raised. Casso smashed right into him, sending him flying into the gate and straight through it. Casso kept rolling and pushed through the remains of the gate. He cut the running lights, and they were driving the forest road in almost pitch-black darkness.

"So, you're just making this up as you go along?" asked Lieutenant Nadoori, the personnel admin specialist formerly stationed at the marine barracks at Tarrago, which was now a giant smoking crater.

Desaix glanced over at her in the half-lit darkness of the prisoner transfer sled. "That's about right, Lieutenant."

With Corporal Casso driving and Rocokizzi riding shotgun, that left Jory, Nadoori, and the two new prisoners in the back. Desaix eyed the newcomers. One, an artillery major, was pretty banged up. Both had joined the escape attempt without hesitation.

"Why is there no planning?" began Nadoori, the exasperation in her voice evident. "I'm pretty sure Repub regs governing escape from a hostile force indicate the need for an escape plan in place beforehand, with all parties unanimously agreeing to said plan. I'm not an expert on regulations, but I'm pretty sure it says something like that."

"Probably," said Desaix after a moment. "But here's the problem... uh, Lieutenant. Right? Here's the problem. Can't really trust anyone, right? Half the people in the prisoner dorms are thinking about flipping sides. So it had to be improvisation, and it had to happen when the conditions I deemed correct... were correct."

"You deemed?"

Desaix nodded.

"Then why these two?" said the LT, indicating the beat-up artillery major and the Tennar with no uniform other than some pants and a tight-fitting shirt that did little to conceal her curvy body.

"Easy," replied Desaix. "This guy's been heavily interrogated. He hasn't cracked yet and they keep sending him back over every morning. Plus, he's been on the far side of the compound in the bunker. That's where they keep the high-value prisoners. He knows something they need, so it's in the interest of the Republic for me to steal him back."

"Thank you for that," said the major. He laughed and coughed painfully. His breathing was shallow and he seemed to be in an immense amount of pain. "And for the record I was about to talk, most likely. They were going to get tough in the morning. Eventually... everyone talks. So..."

"Yeah," said Desaix reassuringly. "Well, that's not gonna happen, Major. We're leaving now."

"Not a moment too soon as far as I'm concerned."

"And her?" asked the bookishly sexy LT.

Desaix appraised the Tennar. "What were you, squiddy? They just brought you in?" The truth was, Desaix didn't really know why he'd picked her up. Other than that she was a damsel in distress, and a cute one at that, and he was a gentleman and an officer, and it was his duty to rescue damsels in distress. He was old-fashioned that way. But when he thought about it... maybe he really didn't have a lot of reasons to trust her.

"Raptor pilot," said the Tennar. "Shot down at Tarrago. Been E-and-E'n out in the ocean ever since. Got picked up on a beach three days ago. You probably have no reason to trust me... except I recognize your voice from the comm chatter during the battle. You were the captain of the corvette my squadron flew cover for. The *Audacity*. You bought time for my carrier to jump. My squadron bought time for you to do that. I'm the last one."

Desaix regarded her for a long moment.

"She's good." Then he gave her his best leer. She returned the gesture with an equally smoky come-hither smile.

"I like the cut of your jib, squiddy," said Desaix, like it was just the two of them in a bar on leave and not some prisoner sled deep inside enemy territory.

"Likewise. And it's... Atumna, Captain. And this is Major Thales."

"Pleasure, Atumna."

The admin specialist rolled her eyes. Obviously, this was all worthy of several gender interaction violations according to regs, and deserving of an extensive block retraining. But the admin LT wasn't wired that tight. Even though it was her job to be.

Thales cleared his throat. "I think we need... if not a plan for what comes next, then possibly a workflow chart or a rough sketch on how to get off this rock. Are we just heading off into the woods hoping to get clear...?"

"No," said Desaix. "We made a bit of a ruckus getting out of the compound. It won't be long before they throw up a wide perimeter, and I'm betting they'll think we're running for the edge of that perimeter, which is standard training, and what we're not gonna do."

"Betting?" asked Thales. He loved cards and games of all types. His hobby was sculpting digital historical miniatures for his online wargames.

Desaix shrugged. "Betting hasn't failed me, statistically speaking... a lot," he clarified.

"So..." said Thales, who would never be as devil-may-care as he would like himself to be, "if we're not going outward... then where are we going?"

Desaix shot him with his thumb and forefinger. "Into the new base. A corvette just came in and put down. We're gonna steal it and get out."

"Really," replied Thales dryly. "Normally I'd say I'd like to see that one happen... but I think I'm about to."

The sled's repulsors and engine began to wind down. They were approaching the gate into the newly constructed base.

Desaix held one finger to his lips.

Jory readied his commandeered blaster.

There was some muted conversation up front. They heard Casso telling the sergeant at the gate that he was having a bucket malfunction. Obviously Corporal Casso knew leej lingo, and whatever he said managed to get them through the gate. Or so it seemed at first. A moment later the sled began to spool up into a low whine and they were off on a new course.

Rocokizzi, the gunner's mate, appeared in a projected hologram across the ceiling. He still had the stolen armor on, but he'd switched to audible via the sled's internal driver-to-prisoner comm system.

"They've ordered us to the maintenance pool. For both our buckets. They got a ground guide walking us over. We got the landing pad in sight. Corvette's there, and there are these shock trooper guys everywhere. But they're carrying gear. My guess—they just came in on that corvette like you thought, Captain. Approaching the maintenance pool now. Not many people around."

Casso's voice cut in. "I got this handled, sir. We'll be clear in a few minutes."

The sled drove on, then came to a stop. They heard both Casso and Rocokizzi exit the vehicle. A few moments later, someone thumped the side of the vehicle hard.

Then blaster fire.

And more blaster fire.

"It seems things might be going spiral," Jory whispered.

"This is why we needed a plan first, Captain Desaix," lectured the admin LT.

The rear doors to the sled were flung open, and Rocokizzi appeared. "Casso's creating a diversion," he said breathlessly over his armor's amplified voice system. "He says for us to move out to the ship."

Desaix led the others out into the orange-lit maintenance pool. Vehicles, ranging from HK-SW mechs to light sleds and heavily armored fighting vehicles the likes of which Desaix had never seen in the Republic's arsenal, waited in various bays. A dead shock trooper and two dead techs in gray coveralls were sprawled on the ground nearby.

Suddenly the base klaxons whined to life. Out beyond the massive overhang of the concrete bunker that was the maintenance pool, searchlights cut the blue twilight.

"She's over there, sir," said Jory, pointing toward the forward command section of a hammerhead corvette that rose up above a few bunkers off to the southwest.

"I'll take point," said Rocokizzi.

The whine of distant blaster fire sounded beneath the wail of the klaxons. Hopefully it was Casso's.

They hustled through the darkness, avoiding the brightly illuminated areas, waiting as white-hot search-lights swept the streets and dark alleys created by stacks of military supplies still encased in their shipping pallets and nano-wraps. Shock troopers were starting to assemble into teams, and at one point the escape team had to crouch behind a folded HK-SW and wait as a patrol swept an adjoining street. In the distance, an explosion lit the night.

At last they reached the landing area. On the wide pad a hammerhead corvette waited, her hatches and cargo doors thrown open in standard disembarkation configuration.

More blaster fire sounded in the distance.

"Can you raise him on your bucket?" asked Desaix as he scanned the landing pad. The maintenance teams seemed unbothered by the chaos and continued to go about their work in and around the corvette. The massive cargo holds were brightly lit and empty.

"Negative," Jory replied. "We can listen in on the traffic though. They're still not sure what's going on. They think it's an attack out along the perimeter. A raid even. One of their AIs is estimating a platoon-sized element inside the perimeter. They have no idea it's just one guy."

"Good," whispered Desaix. "Okay, here's the plan."

He turned to the admin specialist. "Lieutenant Nadoori..." he began. The look on her face, even among the dark shadows of their hiding place, indicated the complete surprise he was sure everyone else shared. "You're going to walk out there," he said, "board that ship through that forward cargo door, and enter the loadmaster's office just off the main access passage. Do you know where that is?"

She nodded. Her face still betrayed her shock. Her mouth was already forming some kind of protest when Desaix continued.

"Once you're aboard I need you to use the special systems and personnel override all you admin types have and access the forward gear maintenance tube. Open that and stand by for my next move."

"Ummm... how am I supposed to get out there without being identified and blasted?" That was Nadoori's opening protest. There seemed to be more coming, but Desaix cut her off with a hand and turned to Rocokizzi.

"She's your prisoner. You'll engage with the maintenance teams via audible; I assume they're not on the internal shock trooper comm these guys use, if it's anything like the Legion's L-comm."

"Why am I taking her aboard?" Rocokizzi asked.

"Because she's flipped, and she's unlocking some weapon codes each corvette carries."

Rocokizzi shrugged, indicating this worked fine enough for him.

Nadoori, on the other hand...

But Desaix ignored her.

"Once you've got the forward gear maintenance tube open, we'll cross the pad over there where it's darkest, and climb up inside. That takes us up three decks to the bridge, and I'll have total control of the ship once we reach it. Jory, I need you to run sensors and comm."

Jory gave a curt nod. "Yes, sir."

"Squiddy..." Desaix turned to the cute little Raptor pilot. "Atumna. Can you fly my ship?"

Without a pause the Tennar gave him that smoky come-hither look once more and said, "I can fly... anything, Captain."

"Good," said Desaix. He smiled. He liked her a lot. "I'll get the engines booted up. Roco... you can slave the guns. We're airborne in two minutes. I'll get calc started for a low orbit jump. It'll be dangerous, but I have no idea where those battleships are. If you can get us to the jump window, Atumna, then we're outta here. Can do, everyone?"

Everyone nodded or murmured their assent. Even Nadoori, who looked just sick about it. But in the end, she squared her shoulders and looked at the gunner's mate. He nodded, and they rose from behind their hiding place and marched out of the darkness and into the landing lights of the waiting corvette.

"We got boot!" shouted Atumna from the flight deck. She'd already slid into the pilot's chair, and her tentacles were swimming across the controls, deftly flicking switches. If she seemed at any kind of loss as she prepared to fly a starship larger than anything she'd ever been trained to fly, it didn't show as she ran through pre-flight.

The admin LT and Rocokizzi had made the cargo deck even more easily than anticipated. They'd simply bypassed a maintenance team that was setting up to decon, and there'd been no need for interaction. A few minutes later a hatch had popped open near the forward main landing gear beneath the ship's wide hammerhead, and that was when the rest of them moved out to board.

It was a long climb past the lower two decks. Captain Thales had insisted he could make the climb on his own, and he'd gone last, stopping at each deck to rest. By the time he made it to the flight deck the engines were cycling up to takeoff power.

"I'm sending an admin message over the local maintenance net, which those teams down there should be plugged into," said Nadoori over the comm net she'd established just for them. "Telling them to clear out while the flight crew runs some tests. Don't know if they'll buy it... but let's see."

Desaix was already back in jump calc, attempting to run the solution from the ship's dedicated nav computer. Of all the things he liked about being a starfarer, jump calc was his least favorite. He'd had to cheat his way through jump calc at the academy just to graduate as a deck officer.

Halfway through the calc he got a message from the Tennar.

"Sir, we got company. Shock troopers are staging around the pad. Sixty seconds to gear up!"

Desaix ignored this and muttered out the last formula inputs. What he wouldn't give for a nav bot right now. But there wasn't one, so he continued on, desperately hoping he wasn't about to send them into a star or an asteroid field.

They were making for Bantaar Reef. If that had fallen into enemy hands, then it was all over.

And then there was Casso.

The legionnaire was buying them time out there, but with the landing pad surrounded there was no way

Corporal Casso was getting aboard. There was a part of Desaix that wanted to save everyone, wanted to be the hero that way, and so far, things had gone far better than expected... but there was another part of him that recognized the reality of their narrow escape window—and the thin thread from which hung the lives of everyone else on this escape team.

It was looking like they would have to leave Corporal Casso behind.

As if on cue, Desaix got a comm from Jory.

"Captain," said Jory, "just got a message from Casso on my bucket because the guys we took the armor from were in the same squad, so we can message back and forth. Didn't realize that until now. He says he's on the west wall. Held up in a watchtower. If we can pull him off the roof he thinks that might be nice."

Starships were not dropships. That level of finesse was pro. Even for the best heavy starship pilot Desaix knew.

"Can do," said the Tennar over the comm.

Desaix reviewed the calc one more time and hit enter. A moment later the jump window appeared in the nav computer's readout.

"Of course she can," he muttered. And then felt better because he'd been about to leave the brave legionnaire who'd saved them behind. He was glad he wouldn't have to live with the guy who did that for the rest of his life.

"Problem, Captain Desaix," came Nadoori over comm.

"Go ahead," said Desaix as he left navigation and headed back to the bridge.

"Maintenance crews have cleared the ship, but I'm still tracking one tech in engineering. If whoever that is is on to us, I'm pretty sure they can shut us down from there."

"I'll handle him," muttered Rocokizzi over the comm.

"Negative," said Desaix. "Once we're gear up, those troopers on the ground will be ordered to fire. If they take out the repulsors we're done. I'll need you to keep their heads down with the PDCs. Roger?"

"Copy that," replied Rocokizzi emotionlessly.

"I'll handle engineering," said Desaix. He reversed course along the main access through the ship, feeling the gentle vibration of the ship's repulsors through his boots as the Tennar brought them in to max power.

"Go for gear up," she practically whooped over the comm. "Stand by to pull that leej off the tower. Tell him I'll bring the portside cargo hatch in as close as possible, but he'll likely have to jump a little."

But Desaix was already running for engineering, thinking of the myriad ways this whole thing could end badly in the next two minutes.

He found the big galoot sabotaging the main power control station. All the guy needed to do was pull three reactor cards, and the ship wouldn't be able to talk itself into light speed.

He already had two out and on the deck, and he was bent over and searching for the third one to pull when Desaix hit him hard across the back of the head with a hydrospanner.

In hindsight, Desaix realized two things.

One, he should have just shot the guy from behind with his blaster no matter how cowardly and wrong that seemed.

And two... the guy was big enough to be a legionnaire. What the heck was he doing as a maintenance tech?

Desaix pulled his blaster, but the large well-built man batted it away with a quick swipe that felt like a hammer blow, then followed with a devastating right straight into Desaix's pretty face.

Desaix sat down hard on the deck, distantly listening to his blaster go skittering off somewhere into engineering.

The looming giant above him smiled, hands up and ready to box. Daring Desaix to do something about the outcome.

"Casso says get closer! He's not a bird!" said Jory over comm.

Desaix could feel the shifting frequency of the repulsors through the deck. He knew the ship was adjusting to edge in closer to the watchtower Casso was pinned down in.

He tried to get to his feet, but the big man kicked him hard, sending him rolling across the deck. He heard Rocokizzi calling out targets as he fired the ship's PDCs at the shock troopers below. Shock troopers who were no doubt firing to disable the corvette.

Most people didn't know how vulnerable the repulsors on a hammerhead corvette were. Desaix did, because he'd captained those ships.

Now the big man grabbed him by his jacket and hauled him upward. Desaix slithered out of the jacket, spun, and kicked the giant in the nuts.

"That's as close as I can get!" yelled the Tennar over the comm.

Why is she yelling, thought Desaix as the big giant savaged him with a right cross and then slapped him in the side of the head with a beefy left.

Bells banged together and Desaix's ears started to ring. The roguish corvette captain had been in enough bar fights to know that slapping an ear was a great way to knock someone's inner equilibrium offline and make sure they stayed down.

"He's in!" whooped Jory over the comm.

Get up and stay up, Desaix ordered himself as engineering tried to fall over on its side.

"We're out of here! Closing all hatches," shouted the Tennar once more. "Heading for the jump window. Throttle up!"

Please stop shouting.

Desaix smashed his head into the giant's nose. That dazed the man, and the captain followed this up by smashing his elbow into the giant wide nose once more. The man involuntarily reached for his face. Desaix danced back, stepped on something, and lost his balance. Then he was sprawled on the deck again.

The tech got to his feet, holding the heavy hyrdro-spanner Desaix had initially tried to brain him with. There was no doubt in Desaix's mind that the giant was going to cave in the side of his skull with it. The big man lumbered forward, looking sure of his victory.

"Captain..." said someone over the comm.

Desaix's eyes fell on the blaster. That's what he'd stepped on. That's what had caused him to lose his balance. That and the slow, sickening spin of his surroundings.

"Captain, we're approaching jump... All good down there? Got a warning light on jump calc."

Of course you do, thought Desaix as he reached for the blaster. *This monster's pulled the power cards. Not only will we not be able to jump, we'll fry the nav comp attempting to do so. Then we'll never get out of here, and those battleships, if they're still there, will shoot us to pieces.*

He brought the blaster to bear and pulled the trigger repeatedly, hoping one of the shots would hole the giant about to kill him.

"Interceptors inbound. Turret's engaging," said Rocokizzi, all business over the comm.

At least he wasn't shouting. Desaix's head was still ringing, and the blaster fire echoed in his ears.

The giant slumped to the deck, and Desaix forced himself to crawl to the reactor cards.

"Jump window in thirty seconds. Need that status light to go green. Captain, are you on that?"

On that, Desaix thought as he fumbled to pick up the two cards. He inspected the flat, clear memory sheets. Then he stared into the iridescent green-lit darkness beyond the access panel to power control. Rows upon rows of similar cards waited.

"Fifteen seconds..." said the Tennar.

Desaix spotted an open slot. He had no idea which card went with which slot. He stuck one in, and the slot accepted it.

Maybe that meant it was the right one.

There was no time for it to be anything else.

"Five seconds to jump."

He saw, in his mind's eye, the Tennar reaching forward for the jump throttle.

He found the other slot and slid the other card in. Hoping he'd gotten everything right.

"Green light. Engaging for jump."
And a moment later they were in hyperspace.

10

Victory Squad
Deep Space Survival Outpost Tully 3

Chhun pumped out picturesque chin-ups one after another until his arms and shoulders felt dead. Until they
screamed that they had absolutely nothing left to give.
Apart from his bucket, Chhun was in full kit. His thighs
ached from the weight of the ration crate he straddled to
add weight to every repetition.

Deep space survival stations were emergency way-
points stationed throughout the galaxy. They were meant
to serve as beacons for life pods to home in to, stocked
with the imperishable foods and water reclamation and
purification systems needed for survival until a rescue
could come. The stations and their supplies were spartan,
nothing flashy. Nothing to draw the attention of pirates or
raiders. The rations were mere tasteless food packs that
appealed to no one except those in danger of starvation.

Which is to say, it wasn't the sort of place that came
equipped with a full gym suite. Further, to save energy,
the station didn't even maintain gravity at all times—it al-
ternated between gravity and zero-gee every four hours.
So when the gravity was on, the team pushed themselves, making do with what they had.

Bear had wedged an unused piece of conduit between sliding pneumatic doors—that bit of conduit was
what now served as Chhun's pull-up bar. Masters count-

ed off sit-ups as Fish held a foot against the legionnaire's chest, increasing the resistance and making each repetition a test of endurance. Similarly, every push-up was with a man sitting on your back. A leej at rest or recovery always played drill instructor for another, ready to push the man in front of him violently down onto the deck if he hesitated while performing burpees while in full armor, or slowed down after the five hundredth jump squat.

They were a man short with Sticks still in recovery aboard *Intrepid*. They were down *two* if you counted Wraith's departure. Chhun had thought about that for quite a while. Replaying that closing scene over and over again in his mind. Second-guessing his own behavior, thinking up alternate paths of dialogue that, somehow, might have resulted in Captain Ford staying with the team. They could use his help.

And, Chhun thought between grunts as he reached down to pull himself above the bar, *he needs us.*

Victory Squad had been on this station for two weeks. It would be two more weeks before another armored shuttle was scheduled to make the trip to Herbeer. Commander Keller had made use of his network of Legion-friendly admirals and captains to get a pair of Republic marine pilots he could trust assigned to the trip. The House of Reason—via Nether Ops—would likely be watching him.

Keller had strongly protested the House's decision to make a scapegoat of Major Owens, but at least made a show of acquiescing to it. It was obvious to Chhun that there was no way Keller would let it stand. It should have been obvious to the House of Reason, too. But maybe not. Maybe the act of letting someone else hang to cover your career seemed like the most natural and obvious thing to them. That was their culture. Protecting rears and careers, no concern for lives ruined so long as it wasn't your own.

A chime sounded—twenty more minutes of gravity.

Chhun pulled himself up again, and found that his muscles couldn't carry him beyond halfway. He pulled, hanging as long as he could, and finally his arms failed him, and he dropped back onto the deck, his boots making scarcely a sound against the impervisteel. They were kitted out for stealth. He looked over and saw Bear, dripping in sweat, standing above a fuel recharge cell. The thing probably weighed close to five hundred pounds, and Bear had been deadlifting and carrying it in circles for the past half hour.

Bear and Chhun shared a look, each indicating they were ready to be done.

Pike had been holding a plank position for the last several minutes, a pool of sweat forming beneath him, ready to be reclaimed by the disc-shaped bots stored in the corner. They would activate when the room cleared in order to collect the moisture for later use.

Fish called out Masters's reps, his foot riding up and down with the legionnaire's chest. "Two forty-nine. Two fifty."

Masters grunted with each rep, the two of them creating a duet of pain and hard work. Masters was the squad's fitness fanatic, with a body sculpted from the heavens, and it was he who made the call for the team to halt. He was always the last one to quit, which meant he was the best man to push Victory Squad to its physical training limits.

"Two fifty-five."

Masters locked eyes with Chhun and Bear as he continued his sit-ups. "Lemme get..." he went down and completed another rep, "...to three hundred..." down and back again, "and we'll call it."

"You're an animal, Masters." Chhun lifted his shoulders up and down, a smirk on his face.

"Don't know if you heard the chime," Bear said, his face still red and angry from the exertions, "but our grav time is almost up."

Pike jumped up from his plank and rolled his neck, sweat cascading down his face. "Seriously. Zero-gee showers are the worst."

"Two eighty-six."

Masters dug down and increased his pace, driving himself to rapidly meet his goal.

"Three hundred," Fish announced as he took Masters's hand and hoisted him up. "Nice."

"Thanks," Masters panted, slicking his drenched hair back with the palms of his hands. "I call first dibs on the shower stall."

"Fine," Chhun said. "But make it quick or we'll send the Bear in after you."

"I should've pulled rank," Chhun mumbled to himself as he floated in the drying chamber. He had been the last in the showers, and was only about halfway finished when the gravity switched off. His face still felt oily and his hair and scalp felt tight, like he'd been baptized in salt water.

He felt the surface moisture on his skin being wicked away by the chamber as a warm, penetrating breeze flowed around him. On a survival station, every last molecule of moisture was jealously held on to.

A red square illuminated with a ding, signifying that it was time for Chhun to leave, before the process took more water than he could spare. This place would literally suck you dry if you stayed in long enough. It was designed that way. If a shipwrecked refugee died, the survivors were instructed to place the body in the chamber until all the moisture was removed, and then jettison the mummified corpse through the airlock... assuming the species wasn't averse to simply eating the new batch of crew-jerky.

All part of the heartwarming welcome message the station's AI played on arrival.

Chhun floated through the door and propelled himself by use of hand-grips and bulkheads toward the sleeping quarters. The doors whooshed open, and Chhun, still naked, pulled himself inside.

The rest of the team was in a state of semi-dress. Most of them in their synthprene undersuits, a few already back in armor up to their waists. Shorts and T-shirts would be more comfortable, but Chhun had ordered around-the-clock mission preparedness. Just in case the Republic got word of what they were planning and sent in their own Nether Ops or point kill team to put a stop to it.

Chhun inwardly laughed at the thought of a point kill team. They'd probably shoot themselves in the confusion.

Masters was sitting on a bunk, his boots anchored to the deck with magnetic grips, as Chhun floated by. Bear, standing on the opposite side, called out, "Hey, Masters!"

The timing was perfect, and Masters turned at the sound of his name just in time to get an up-close view of his captain's little captain.

"Gah!" Masters quickly turned away, shielding his eyes with the flat of his hand. "Put some clothes on, Captain. I don't need to see this. And in zero gravity... holy strokes."

Bear, whose synthprene undersuit was rolled down to his hips, exposing a broad and hairy chest, laughed uproariously. "You know you love it."

"Must... resist... the temptation to stare," said Masters in a mock struggle. The men laughed as he shut his eyes, plugged his ears with his fingers, and hummed the theme from *Iron Dragoons*, and old holofilm they all loved.

As Chhun dressed himself, he thought about what to do next. Life aboard the survival station had become a cramped series of routines. Chow was thirty standard minutes away, the next big event. He didn't feel like reading. His blaster pistol and NK-4 were as clean as they'd ever been. Probably cleaner than they were when shipped from the factory. Maybe he'd strip and reassemble Fish's SAB. He wasn't quite as quick at that as he'd like to be.

The other men settled in for naps, or took to swiping letters home. Pike was bobbing his head to music and drumming on his leg armor in time, his headphones bleeding out just enough sound for Chhun to identify the type—Sorkesian death metal.

Back in full gear except his bucket, Chhun walked over to Fish's bunk. "Mind if I have a look at your SAB?"

Fish had settled in for a brief nap. He opened one eye and looked at Chhun. "Sure, Cap'n." He closed his eyes and placed his hands on his chest, exhaling as he nestled his head into the hard pad that served as a mattress.

Chhun picked up the heavy weapon, thumbed off the safety, and released the fallback charge pack, which he placed neatly on the floor. He sat down cross-legged and set the weapon before him. He checked the main charge-feed, the one that attached to the big pack that Fish humped into battle, inspecting the feed assembly. His fingers came back spotless, no blaster charge residue. Fish had kept his weapon every bit as clean as the rest of the men.

As Chhun pulled the upper retaining pin at the rear of the receiver, a deep alert chime sounded from above, and the room lights flashed amber.

Fish sat bolt upright. "What's that?"

Everyone looked up to the ceiling, watching the lights alternate between soft daylight and amber. They listened as the AI announced, "Docking sequence initiated."

Immediately Victory Squad grabbed their weapons and threw on the rest of their kits, faces disappearing behind expressionless black buckets. Chhun reassembled the SAB, thankful he hadn't gotten any further. He handed it over to Fish. "Okay," he said, "let's see who's coming to join us. Could be an actual shipwrecked crew, but let's be ready for anything."

"Docking sequence initiated," repeated the congenial AI.

The station had a single airlock. Unless you came with an assault shuttle to pierce the hull itself, there was only one point of entry. The kill team hustled to the blast door, taking up firing positions and getting behind what cover they could manage. There wasn't much of it except for a personal shield wall Masters set up for Fish and his SAB.

The station had no exterior windows, and there was no way to determine what sort of craft was docking outside. They could only listen to the heavy metallic clicks and resounding booms of the vessel adjusting itself to form a seal with the airlock.

"Dock coupling achieved," announced the AI. "Airlock integrity one hundred percent."

Chhun steadied himself on a knee, positioned to fire into the center-right of the airlock should the need arise, with Pike taking the center-left and Bear in reserve of each man. Fish had his SAB aimed for dead center, with Masters ready to handle any fraggers or ear-poppers that might make their way inside. This could all be for nothing—the survivors of some hyperdrive malfunction might be in for the scare of their lives just when they thought they'd reached sanctuary. But if it was someone looking to do Victory Squad harm, they would catch hell instead.

"Prepare to receive survivors," the AI said, whether to itself or to the crew already aboard, Chhun didn't know.

The blast doors rattled and banged as the safety mechanisms protecting the station from the merciless vacuum of space released. Each man on the kill team readied and raised his weapon.

The doors drew apart, revealing a lone figure draped in leather. Thin and short of stature, his black hair was styled in long braids. He stepped out of the airlock, seemingly oblivious, looking up at the ceiling, his mouth open. His teeth sparkled, golden.

He looked down and saw the array of blaster rifles aimed at him.

Chhun took a step forward. "Keep those hands where we can see them."

The man did so, scowling at each legionnaire individually. "Oh," he said impetuously. "This some welcome. Keel right about you. You rude."

Synth Mines
Herbeer

Owens smiled at the two men, obviously former Legion, as they stepped away from him. He wasn't sure if he was getting used to pat-downs, but he had nothing to hide except for his rock. And they'd left that in his pocket.

"He's clean," announced one of them to the flat-topped man.

Flat-Top nodded and looked to the elderly Crux. "Any problems with him?"

Crux shook his head. "No, none. He was good company. Says he was in Dark Ops before the Republic shipped him here."

The men, all possessing that Legion swagger Owens could identify in a crowd, seemed to hum with tiny conversations at Crux's report. Evidently Owens was the only legionnaire here who'd made the jump to Dark Ops. Maybe that would be a good thing. Maybe not. Owens knew that *he* had been sentenced to the synth mines for a bogus reason, but that didn't mean the same was true of everyone else. The Legion had its own share of bad men, same as anywhere else in the galaxy.

"That true?" asked the man with the flat top.

Owens nodded. "Yeah, that's right. Served as a major in Dark Ops right up until the House of Reason decided I needed to take the fall for them losing Tarrago."

The cavern erupted into shocked discussion.

Flat-Top hushed the men, waving his arms down. "Tarrago's fallen? That's news."

Owens nodded grimly and said, "Yep, we're at war, boys. The Republic just doesn't want to admit it. House of Reason is as clueless as ever. Points running amok...

probably not too different from when you were last in buckets."

This garnered nods and grunts from the assembly.

"Different from my time," Crux said. "Back in the Savage, we'd have fragged a point if the House of Reason tried that stuff. Don't know why you leejes put up with it nowadays."

"I wonder that myself sometimes," said Owens.

It might have seemed that Owens was being careless in his speech. Certainly, on a destroyer or space station, loose, honest talk like that would surely make its way to some point, who would pass it up the command chain. Owens was probably already on a list somewhere, but talk like that would solidify it. Points were always looking to gain the favor of the House and Senate handlers.

But in this case, he made disparaging remarks against the Republic for a reason. He wanted to know what sort of legionnaires he was dealing with. Were they *real* leejes? Or points who'd gone too far? Lapdogs trained to trust the House and put their faith in the men the government said should lead them, despite their combat deficiencies?

Points and their lackeys could rarely resist an opportunity to defend their favorite institution. Even if it counted for nothing, like in an abandoned cavern on the synth mines of Herbeer.

No one spoke up to disagree. Good. That was good.

"I'm Major Ellek Owens, by the way." Owens held out his hand.

The man with the flat-top accepted his hand and shook it. "First Sergeant Robert Cosler. Just call me Rowdy, though." He gestured at the rest of the men. "I'll introduce you to the boys in a second. But first, let's talk about what you're doing here, Major."

"I was hoping we might."

"What's before you is the Legion's garrison on Herbeer. None of us belong here, but here we are."

"How do you mean, 'none of you belong here'?"

Smoothing his mustache, Rowdy said, "Probably not all that different from you, Major. A lot of us, like Senton over there, took the fall for a point who got too many men killed and the House didn't want to risk a public trial—lest the truth come out. Others disobeyed unlawful orders."

"And some of us just know too much," Crux muttered.

Owens made a mental note to ask the old leej what he meant by that. He asked Rowdy, "How about you?"

"Me? I'm guilty of murder. Shot a point in the face after he ordered my men into a meat grinder for the third time in a row, trying to earn himself a silvene star. I volunteered for Herbeer when a point-heavy squad of leejes got into a standoff with my men. No sense in any more of them getting shot up. And now, here I am."

"Sounds reasonable," said Owens. "Can't say the thought of blasting a point never crossed my mind. Nearly choking one to death was as close as I ever got, though."

"So how about you?" Rowdy asked.

"I had my kill team blow up a quadrillion-credit installation even though the Republic told me not to." Owens looked around the room. "And... I'd do it again."

Rowdy smiled. "Well, Major, you're the highest-ranking leej on Herbeer, so far as I know. There was a point colonel a year ago—did something even the Senate couldn't abide. We ended him. We end every leej that dishonored the Legion, point or otherwise."

The other legionnaires nodded in agreement.

"I'm willing to hand over command of this outpost—we call ourselves Synth Company—if you're willing to lead us down here, Major."

This was unexpected.

Owens pulled on his beard, lamenting how short it was after his in-processing. They'd buzzed him evenly from top to bottom. "What's your mission, First Sergeant?"

Rowdy smiled again. "Make life hell for the guards, and make the Gomarii pay for their slaving. That's why they're here, you know. They cull the herd of prisoners and sell them wherever the Republic turns a blind eye."

Owens nodded appreciatively. This would be a fine pursuit until rescue came. "KTF, then."

Rowdy gave a salute. "KTF, sir."

11

Victory Squad
Deep Space Survival Outpost Tully 3

"Okay, so let me get this straight," Chhun said to the thin man who went by the name of Lao Pak. "Captain Keel sent you to pick us up and take us to Herbeer."

"That what I say four times already," insisted Lao Pak as he struggled against the synth-cord the kill team had tied around his arms. "And then you tie me up like some slave. You worse than Gomarii. This too tight."

"I dunno, Cap," said Pike, shaking his head. "You know Captain Ford better than most of us. This seem like something he'd do?"

"Yes, it is!" Lao Pak shouted. "He do stupid things that get Lao Pak into trouble all the time. It his favorite thing. I kill him already if he not make me so much money." Lao Pak paused. "I don't have money with me. Nothing to steal, okay soldiers?"

Bear leaned in close to the captive. "You'll be better off speaking only when spoken to."

Lao Pak turned away. "Okay, okay. You legionnaires all so grumpy. You need find pretty girl. Then you be happy."

"He's not wrong about that," said Masters.

Chhun thought over Pike's question in his mind. *Was this something Ford would do?* If Lao Pak was telling the truth, the absent member of Victory Squad had arranged for the op to be pushed forward by two weeks. That was nothing to sneer at. But when he'd left—gone AWOL if Chhun was honest about it—he hadn't seem remotely interested in helping out. Was this a case of remorse? A peace offering?

"Getting to Herbeer now instead of waiting another couple of weeks for the armored shuttle appeals to me," Chhun said. "I don't think Wraith would double-cross us."

Lao Pak's face went pale. "Wraith involved? I thought it just that dummy Keel." The pirate laughed nervously. "Okay, you tell Wraith, I friendly to his friends, okay? Say, 'Lao Pak a real nice guy. He help us a lot.'"

"Wraith and Ford—or Keel, whatever he calls himself— are the same person," Masters said.

Lao Pak rolled his eyes. "No way stupid Keel same guy as Wraith. You take too many hits to helmet, Legionnaire. Make you go crazy."

"Untie him, Fish," Chhun ordered.

Fish unfastened the cord's knot and pulled it off Lao Pak, spooling the rope back into his utility belt.

Lao Pak rubbed his arms. "We friends now? Good. We have to leave or I miss deadline. They no invite me back then."

"You said your ship was empty," Chhun said. "If I send two of my men on board, are they going to find out you're lying?"

Lao Pak shook his head vehemently. "Send them all! We all go together. You not find any crew. This just me. I would bring crew, but Keel pay me to make room for you soldier boys. So hurry up or stay here, I get paid no matter what."

Chhun nodded at Fish and Bear. "Go check it out."

The pair jogged off, weapons in hand.

"You no steal my stuff!" Lao Pak yelled as they departed.

Bear spoke over L-comm. "Please someone find a reason to dust that twerp."

"Pike, Masters," Chhun said, "gather up our gear. As long as we don't find any trouble on the ship, we're leaving to rescue Major Owens early."

"Yes, sir."

The men hurried back to the team's sleeping quarters.

Lao Pak watched them go. "You believe Lao Pak, now? You pretty smart. But no wait for your two soldiers. They not find anything. Need to go now."

Chhun removed his helmet so he could look Lao Pak in the eyes. "Walk with me to the airlock."

"We go on stroll? Okay, I go with you. You chief legionnaire. You tell Wraith I a big help. Deserve big credit raise."

As they passed the solar chargers on the way to the main control interface, Chhun paused to initiate the departure sequence. This station might still be needed for future travelers, and shutting it down to preserve as much power as possible was protocol. They could always turn it back on if Lao Pak was lying.

Chhun pulled out the blaster pistol they'd taken off the pirate during a search and held it out to him. "Here."

Lao Pak eyed the weapon suspiciously and then quickly snatched it back. "Why you give back? *I* wouldn't give back."

"Because I believe that Captain Keel sent you, and I trust him."

"I not do that either."

Chhun folded his arms. "You don't have to. But you do need to answer my next question. You said we had to leave now. Why?"

Lao Pak mimicked Chhun and folded his own arms. "I tell you already. I have appointment. Can't be late."

"With who, the Republic?"

"Republic?" Lao Pak scoffed. "No, who care what they think? The *Gomarii*."

Chhun furrowed his brow. Why would the Gomarii be on Herbeer, and why would they have any say about when a shuttle can or can't arrive? The synth mines were for penal labor in the galaxy's most notorious penitentiary. What did that have to do with a race that had built its reputation on humanoid trafficking?

The answer made Chhun feel sick the moment it hit him. "You're saying the Gomarii dump unwanted slaves at the synth mines? That the Republic profits from slave labor?"

Lao Pak made a face, as if suggesting that what Chhun had said was stupid to the point of incredulity. "No. Gomarii get to take monthly shuttle load of prisoners to sell as slaves. That what we go to pick up—can't be late."

That was worse than Chhun had imagined. The Republic—his own government, one he'd fought and bled for—was selling its people into slavery for... "For what?"

"What?" asked Lao Pak. "You mean why? Because Gomarii not run and tell how bad synth mines are. They not say how many innocent people working the mines— innocent like Lao Pak." The pirate crossed his fingers. "They in it together, Republic and Gomarii."

"Well," Chhun said, gripping his blaster rifle tightly, "once we get our friend out, that's all gonna change."

Lao Pak shrugged. "Not my problem. I just get you inside."

A chime sounded from Chhun's helmet. He was being hailed over L-comm. Nothing beyond the *ding-deet-ding* of the chime would be audible until the bucket was over Chhun's head and his biosignature was confirmed. A nifty little trick to keep anyone from eavesdropping on the L-comm in the event they captured a dead leej's bucket.

The bucket back on his head, Chhun said, "Go for Chhun."

"Ship's clear," reported Fish. "Not much to look at, but it's clear."

"Acknowledged." Chhun went squad-wide on his comm. "Let's get on board the ship. Jailbreak begins now."

Synth Mines
Herbeer

Owens looked over the latest strength and positioning reports of the guards on a datapad lifted from some careless Gomarii. It was amazing just how much contraband his troop of cast-off legionnaires had acquired in the years since their inception. And from conversation with some of the men, he'd gathered that this forgotten remnant of the Legion had been a thorn in the side of the Gomarii slavers ever since they organized. It had been something of a cold war, but not without its open battles. With real casualties on both sides. Except the Gomarii could always send in new guards, whereas the Legion had to wait for a newly arrived tragedy, a stand-up soldier wrongfully sent to spend the rest of his days toiling away for the Republic.

"There'll be a reckoning once I get these boys out," Owens mumbled to himself. He rubbed his eyes and pinched the bridge of his nose. He hadn't been sleeping, and the constant glow of the datapad wore on his eyes. Maybe one of the guys could find him a pair of replacement shades. That would be nice.

All signs pointed to another off-world transfer of prisoners into the trafficking market. Men and women... and probably children born into the darkness of the synth mines... would be smuggled to planets like the zhee home worlds, where slavery was only nominally illegal. Or to planets with a complex culture involving indentured servitude, where the wealthy and elite convinced themselves at balls and parties that the bondage they perpetrated was actually *better* than the plight of the so-called common man living in freedom. Slavery wasn't an easy sell and wasn't officially tolerated—core world sensibility didn't allow it to be—but it was a reality.

Hopefully what Owens and Synth Company had planned would put a dent in all of that. Probably not, but it was worth the effort.

"Still at it?"

Rowdy was at the opening to the cavern that served as the Legion headquarters on Herbeer.

Owens leaned back in his chair—liberated from an armored shuttle undergoing repairs—and stretched as a sigh turned into a long yawn. "Sorry," he said when the yawn subsided. "Yes, still at it. Based on what I'm reading about Gomarii procedures and behavior—and this is good intelligence, you men did the Legion proud here—a transport of prisoners ought to be happening in the next two days."

"Yes, sir," agreed Rowdy. "That was my thought, too."

Owens pulled at his beard. "Let me ask you something. You seemed to be doing a fine job leading this group. You didn't need to hand over command to me. So..."

"So why did I?" The first sergeant brushed a hand over his hair, as if checking to make sure his flat-top remained level. "Life in Herbeer is hard. Honestly, I think a lot of these people almost look forward to being taken by the Gomarii, if only for a change of pace. A chance to see a sun again. Of course, they haven't seen the things we've seen when we've busted up their slaver rings. The depravity and cruel inhumanity makes life down here seem almost suburban.

"But like I said, it's a hard lot down here. And men need something to work for, something to live for. All these leejes, they were heartbreakers and life-takers. They knew how to KTF, and they lived for their brothers. Would have died for them. Would have preferred to have died than... this.

"When I took over command, the troop had been led well by a sergeant. Leej had been a corporal only a month earlier, and then got railroaded onto Herbeer right after his promotion. He was doing as good a job leading the men as any officer I'd ever served with. Nothing required a change in command. But he told me, for this to work, for life down here to have a purpose, we had to be as much like the Legion as possible. That included command structure... and so I took over."

"What happened to him? To the sergeant?" Owens asked.

"He died a few months later. Killed by the Gomarii during a raid that got us the supply of synth we're still using to meet quotas. We found out about a guard rotation and hit 'em while they were under-manned. But there were enough. He died to give us a near-permanent reprieve from the quotas."

Owens's throat gave an appreciative growl. Men like that dead sergeant—men like Rowdy—shouldn't be wasting the prime of their lives gathering what could be collected by bots. They shouldn't even be spending their time in the considerably more humane Legion prisons sprinkled throughout the galaxy. Men like the ones he'd encountered on Herbeer needed to be on the front lines. In the fight. Making sure that...

... that *what*?

The Republic wasn't perfect. Owens knew that. He'd dealt with the points. Served long enough to know the difference between total war and the lawyered-up wars waged over the last fifteen years. As a citizen, he was concerned with the constant strivings of the House of Reason and Senate, both of which seemed more concerned with partisan approval ratings than doing something for the good of the entire Republic. But he never would have imagined his government was doing to its own innocent citizens what it was doing here on Herbeer.

He couldn't stand for that. Couldn't fight for leaders who would orchestrate such things. And he had no doubt, given that Delegate Orrin Kaar himself had made an appearance at his show trial, that this corrupt abuse of power went to the very top of the government.

"Rowdy," Owens said, his fingers forming a steeple in front of his lips. "How hard would it be for us to get our hands on some long-range comms and blasters?"

Rowdy nodded with enthusiasm. He seemed to like where Owens was going. "Right. Let's start with the easy question: blasters. We've already acquired a few, though not enough for any serious fighting. You've probably noticed that the guards only keep blaster rifles close to central command, and they use the energy whips farther into the mines. That's to keep us from ambushing some guard far from command and confiscating his blaster." He smiled. "Sometimes guards don't follow the directive. We take advantage when we can. But it's taken a long time to get what we have."

"If that's the easy question," Owens said, "I'm looking forward to hearing the answer to the hard one. Long-range comms?"

"Like I said, that's tougher. The guards' portable comms only work on-planet, for communication with one another. That's by design—the last thing the Republic wants is for word of what's going on down here to reach the rest of the galaxy. That's why every sentence is life. And that's why all comms with enough range to leave the planet are hard-mounted in the command and control center." Rowdy looked up at the major. "You have someone you want to contact?"

"The Legion commander," Owens said. "If he learns what's happening down here, this place will be swarming with leejes. One message is all it would take."

Rowdy gave a half smile and looked down at his shoes. "Well, we might be able to do it... but it would put an end to our little counterinsurgency against the Gomarii."

"How so?"

"There's a lot of back and forth right now. The Gomarii are willing to lose synth, food, even lives. And the occasional blaster. Because none of those things are going to raise the ire of the Republic. But losing comms, even for a single message... that would put the entire operation at risk. They'd fight that possibility with maximum force. You've seen the turrets, right?"

Owens nodded.

"They can be activated from various points around their HQ. The turrets will fire at anything that moves, but are smart enough to not harm the guards. Or so I'm told—I've never seen them in use. But a couple here have. I've heard tales of past attempts at armed revolt where the guards turned on every auto-turret and nearly wiped out the entire prison population just because things were escalating too quickly."

Owens shook his head. "They can always find more prisoners, right?"

"Sounds about right. Something they'd say."

"Still, why not call in Republic backup to keep things from reaching that point? I mean, the prisoner-to-guard ratio isn't in our captors' favor," Owens said, scratching his beard. "And they know there are a number of leejes in the prison population who ain't friendly. If that's me in command, I'm calling in at the first sign of a problem to at least have a quick reaction force standing by."

Rowdy nodded. "That's because you're thinking like someone with integrity. The guys running things down here, that isn't them. The Gomarii are getting rich because the Republic looks the other way. But the Gomarii have to maintain the impression that they have everything under control—that there's no risk to the Republic here. If Herbeer starts calling in every skirmish or riot... I mean, each one is a chance for someone to get jumpy and call off the whole deal. Trust me, the guards will go to almost any length to keep the situation they have going. They'll kill all the prisoners, just to prove they're able to keep a lid on things, before they'll call the Republic."

"Is there any way to disable the auto-turrets?"

"Only from the command center. Which, if we're after long-range comms, is where we'll be anyway. If we can get there."

"And what about the possibility of getting off-planet?"

Rowdy laughed. "That's the ultimate fail-safe. There's only one flight-ready shuttle or freighter allowed down here at a time, and you can be sure the homing beacons can be adjusted to send a blind-flying craft straight into the dirt. Unless you control the facility, there's no getting off this rock."

Owens shut off his datapad and tossed it onto the makeshift table in front of him. He stood, feeling the fatigue from too little sleep. "So any long-range comm requires taking over the command center. Any serious action, anything big, beyond just disrupting the slave round-up, requires that we shut down the auto-turrets—which again requires taking over the command center. And getting off this planet also requires taking over command. So it's all or nothing. Anything less than a complete takeover results in mission failure."

"And a lot of deaths," added Rowdy.

"And a lot of deaths," echoed Owens. "I'll be honest here. I'm fifty-fifty on whether to just make the Gomarii pay for gathering up a new load of slaves, or whether to take a shot at the end zone. Classic dichotomy, the type we prepared for in Academy. Risk it all? Or make sure you can fight another day."

Rowdy closed his eyes, slowly, and nodded. He seemed relieved to not to be making the call himself. If he had advice, he held it a guarded secret, letting silence settle over the cavern.

"You should go for the throat," said Crux.

He had entered the room undetected. Owens didn't know how much the old man had heard, and he didn't particularly care. But he *was* interested in hearing the opinion of what had to be one of the few living survivors of the Savage Wars.

"Tell me why," Owens said.

The old man hobbled toward the major with a limp that Owens didn't remember seeing before. As if the weight of the coming words affected him physically. "In the Savage, there was never any fightin' for another day. You squared up with the Savage marines and fought until one side didn't have nothin' left. Every fight was definitive. Every battle to the death. You wanted to survive, and that meant killin' any way you could until there weren't nothing left to kill."

This was true. The nature of the struggle was such that when the Legion engaged a Savage army, whether invading a planet they'd taken or tracking down one of their light-hugger cruisers, the fight didn't end until one side was utterly destroyed. And for centuries, it went back and forth, with the fate of the galaxy hanging in the balance.

Crux compressed his eyelids into slits of fury. "We won that war by being more vicious and hard than the Savage. We were always smarter, but we fought 'em on their terms. Gave 'em a taste of their own medicine until they were utterly and completely vanquished. There's no force in the galaxy that can stand up to us once we go Legion on them. You asked me, Major... I say it's time the Republic and their Gomarii hirelings find that out the hard way."

"Thank you for your opinion, Crux." Owens turned back to Rowdy and tilted his head to the side, popping the vertebrae in his neck. "Sergeant Cosler, round up our squad leaders. We've got some work to do."

12

Victory Squad
Deep Space Survival Outpost Tully 3

Lao Pak had to be the worst pilot Chhun had ever seen. The freighter was large and unwieldy—Chhun had seen that the moment he stepped aboard. On most of these big galaxy-class ships, the handling was so dreadful that the flying was left up to the bots. The skeleton crews of six or seven men were around mostly just in case the bots needed maintenance. But Lao Pak had no bots to help him. Instead, he flew the massive cargo-hauling beast of burden on full manual.

And he was terrible at it.

To start with, the pirate engaged his sublight thrusters before the airlock-dock sequence had completed. From his vantage point on the spacious bridge, Chhun watched on monitors as various supplies and detritus that had been on the deep space survival station were sucked out into the vacuum of space before its emergency airlock doors could finish closing. Worse, a quick cycle through holocam feeds showed that the freighter was still magnetically attached to the airlock's extendable covered bridgeway that served as access hatch between the station and whatever ship docked with it. That didn't bode well for anyone who showed up to that station in a life pod, as life pods typically weren't equipped with bridges of their own.

As the freighter accelerated in sublight, the imperv-isteel bridge clanged loudly against the outer hull. Lao Pak released the magnetic grip, and the bridge floated away into the vacuum of space.

"It fine, it fine," said Lao Pak.

"Yeah. Sure." Chhun continued to cycle through the holofeeds, checking for any damage to the hull. He was no pilot himself—Keel was the only legionnaire he'd ever met with a real affinity for flying—but he might be able to spot something that could spell disaster for their out-bound flight. He'd just gotten off one survival station, and he wasn't keen on the idea of being forced to visit another.

Everything looked all right to his untrained eye, so he moved on to cycling through the interior holofeeds. Several of these were dead or showed nothing but com-pressed static.

Lao Pak swatted Chhun's hand away. "Stop touching cameras. You break ship."

"How is a holocam going to break a galaxy-class freighter?" Chhun asked. "Where'd you even find this thing?"

"It gift."

Masters, who was aboard the bridge with the rest of the crew, walked over to stand between his captain and the unqualified pirate. "I dunno, Cap, this hunk of junk looks pretty bad. You *could* actually break something. Maybe even cause the reactor to blow..."

Lao Pak looked at Masters with humorless eyes. "Ha. Ha. So very funny. Of course this ship bad. It have to fly to Herbeer. You think I stupid, take luxury yacht into that place?"

"A luxury yacht might at least have a chance of holding together," Pike said. "I've heard the entries into Herbeer's atmosphere are brutal."

"You worry too much." Lao Pak reached for the light speed controls. But instead of turning on the ship's dampeners and spooling them up with the slow ease that allowed them to comfortably keep the inertia from overwhelming those inside, he slammed his hand on the emergency button—a last-minute protection for a slow-moving cruiser caught by pirates or, in the old days, enemy capital ships.

Everyone was thrown back as the freighter darted away into the swirling folds of hyperspace. Alarms and klaxons blared at near-deafening levels, with flashing red lights washing over the bridge.

"Not good!" shouted Bear. He was the only one who stayed on his feet, gripping the captain's chair Lao Pak was glued to.

"Press button!" yelled Lao Pak. "Press button!"

Bear reached out and swatted the emergency hyper-drive button with his great paw of a hand. The freighter dumped out of hyperspeed, causing everyone to lurch and stumble forward with the abrupt shift back into subspace.

"Sorry," said Lao Pak, wearily keying in something on the console before him. "I forget to enter jump co-ordinates."

"You forgot to enter the jump coordinates?" shouted Fish. "You could have gotten us all killed!"

"Smashed us into the heart of a gas giant!" bellowed Masters.

"Dumped us out of hyperspace into an asteroid field!" added Bear.

"I say sorry already," Lao Pak replied. "Beside, you not dead. You alive."

"No thanks to you," grumbled Pike.

Lao Pak's hand hovered over the emergency hyper-drive switch. Once again, he seemed intent on jumping hard instead of easing in like a more capable pilot would.

This time the legionnaires all found something to grab hold of.

It was a short jump to Herbeer. The survival station Ch-hun had chosen as a staging area was the nearest one possible to the prison planet. Lao Pak had spent the jump time going over how *he* thought the infiltration should go, with helpful advice like "Don't be noisy" and "Gomarii are dumb, but not *that* dumb."

Chhun finally got Lao Pak to shut up by threatening to let Bear have three minutes alone with the pirate. After that, Lao Pak sat stewing as the kill team rehearsed their exit course from the ship's hold, studying maps of the synth mines they'd acquired through Dark Ops Intelligence. There were lots of places to disappear to... once they got off the ship. Doing that undetected would be the most difficult part of the mission.

"Lao Pak," Chhun said, "this is your ship. Do you know of any way off it other than the primary crew entrances, hold doors... or airlock?"

"Oh! So now you want Lao Pak's help." The pirate puffed out his chest, full of self-importance. "Yeah. There ways. Maybe you soldier boys listen to Lao Pak instead of practicing running through open doors, huh?"

"That little move through a doorway you've been watching," Chhun said, resting his hands on his knees as he bent down to look at Lao Pak face to face, "is usually the last thing an MCR sees. Or a pirate. Like you."

Lao Pak gulped. "Like... *me*?"

"C'mon," said Masters. "I mean, Lao Pak, you were friends with Captain Keel. You've got what's obviously a stolen freighter..."

"*And* you've got a date with Gomarii slavers," Chhun concluded. "Doesn't look good, Lao Pak."

"That... that crazy," Lao Pak said, struggling to get the words out. "You crazy. I help Republic. I hero. Deserve medal."

Chhun stood back up. "So cut the twarg dung and answer straight. What's the trick to getting off this rig unseen?"

Lao Pak's face fell. "Okay, I show you. Soldier boys all so sensitive." He moved to the command console and began cycling through holofeeds. "There special door by cargo hold, let you drop right down onto deck beneath ship. It long walk, and lift not work, so you look at camera."

"Fine." Chhun and his team crowded around the monitors and watched as Lao Pak cycled through the feeds.

The holocams covered what seemed like all of the ship's interiors. Long empty corridors appeared and disappeared with a swipe of Lao Pak's grimy fingers, as did the drive room, various support systems, quarters, even—Chhun thought, though it had flitted by quickly—a view of the showers. If Lao Pak didn't install that camera himself, the ship's previous captain apparently liked to keep a little too close of an eye on his crew.

"This special cargo hold." Lao Pak zoomed in on a square hold. It was furnished not with the typical restraint bars, tie-down rings, and containment fields, but with cots crowded together and stacked as bunks from floor to ceiling.

"That hold looks like it's designed to transport people as freight," Fish said with a cold anger. Whenever they'd performed an op involving the Gomarii or other slavers, Fish had always carried with him an extra edge. Probably something from his past. Chhun had never been able to get to the bottom of it, but now he worried for the first time that it might be a source of conflict within his team. His mission was to rescue Major Owens, not to free the slaves.

"That not my fault," Lao Pak said. "Gomarii expect slave ship to arrive. What happen if I come with assault shuttle, huh? They blow you up before you get off." He zoomed in on a bunk set against the portside wall. "Under there is door. Chute take you right outside ship. It for smuggling slaves past planetary customs—when that required."

"We taking slaves with us, Cap?" Fish asked.

Chhun shook his head, but not definitively. "That's not in the mission plan, but if the opportunity comes up... we'll take it."

Fish nodded once and stepped back, finding a shadow against the wall and planting himself there.

Something that Chhun thought he saw while Lao Pak was scrolling through the holofeeds made him take control of the console and begin to swipe back through. "You weren't planning on taking any slaves to sell for yourself, were you, Lao Pak?"

The pirate placed both palms on his cheeks, affecting surprise. "Oh, no! Lao Pak never do that. It illegal, Captain Chhun."

Chhun gave a humorless smile. He stopped the feed on a small cell, the holocam revealing only a single corner. But now that the image was still, Chhun's suspicions were confirmed. Someone was detained in that cell. A man's leg, wearing a calf-length boot, was visible. "How about deliveries? You making one to the slavers?"

"What? That illegal too!" protested Lao Pak. "You all say Lao Pak bad guy. Not true!"

"Probably a misunderstanding," Chhun said.

"Yes. It big misunderstanding."

"So what, exactly, do you do then, Lao Pak?" Chhun asked.

Lao Pak's eyes shifted frantically from side to side, resting for a split second on every legionnaire in his field of vision. "Oh... I do same thing as Keel. Legal things. Very good citizen of Republic. Everyone say that about me."

"And what, exactly, does Keel do?" asked Masters, perfectly capturing Chhun's tone. His impression made Pike begin shaking with inwardly held laughter behind Lao Pak and out of his view.

Lao Pak's eyes again searched the room before he finally exploded with a loud, "Okay!"

"Okay what?" Chhun asked.

"Okay, yes, I sell him to Gomarii!" Lao Pak slumped in his seat as though pouting. He raised a finger like he was making a salient point. "But this one okay to make slave."

"How can it possibly be *okay*?" Fish pressed.

Lao Pak smiled. "He MCR!"

The legionnaires all looked at one another.

"You're selling MCR into slavery," Bear said, his voice suggesting that the burly leej might not have thought this was an entirely bad idea.

"Oh, yeah. That all they good for. Like I say, I good citizen."

Chhun shook his head. "No. Can't let you do it. How'd you end up with the prisoner?"

Lao Pak made no reply.

"Listen," Chhun said. "One of the first things we did was run a cross-reference on your bios and facial capture when we met." He knocked on his helmet. "These buckets aren't just to keep our heads warm. We know you're a pirate, wanted and operating near Pellek. You said the magic word, 'Keel,' but that doesn't mean we're going to have endless patience with you lying to us. So tell me: where'd you find this guy?"

"This what always happen when I work with Keel!" Lao Pak banged a fist against his chair's armrest. "Keel capture him and leave him with me to be pirate. But boy general, he terrible pirate. Always do something stupid, scare ships away. I tell him he mess up one more time I sell him to Gomarii."

"And he messed up one more time?" Masters asked dryly.

"No, but he would have, and since ship was already leaving..."

"We ought to arrest him," said Fish, his arms crossed. "Or better yet, take him into the cargo hold and put a blaster bolt in his—"

"No!" Lao Pak interrupted. "You can't do that!"

"Technically we can," said Pike. "You willingly aligned yourself with an enemy of the Republic. In doing so, you became party to—"

"I say no because Keel do same thing!"

"How do you mean?" Chhun asked.

Lao Pak gave a devilish grin. "He run around with MCR too. Just give me boy general when he stole my coder from me."

"Garret's MCR?" Masters said with a shake of his head. "Didn't seem like the type to get involved in war or politics... just sort of along for the ride."

"No, not him. The *girl*... the princess. She MCR. I want her, but Keel so greedy, he only give me boy general who is terrible at fighting and gave all his family money to MCR."

All the legionnaires had met Leenah. Had liked her. Chhun had never heard Keel mention that she was a member of the Mid-Core Rebellion—not in person, not in any of his reports. And with how friendly he'd seen the two of them getting back on the *Indelible VI*... it didn't sit well. Not at all.

"Cap?" Masters said, clearly disturbed by this revelation.

"We'll... figure that out later. For now, let's get ready for entry into Herbeer." Chhun looked down at Lao Pak. "You can use your MCR to build credibility with the Gomarii while we get off the ship... but we're not letting you sell him, or anyone else, to them. Understand?"

Like a scolded child, Lao Pak nodded.

Cybar Ship Mother
Position Unknown

There was nothing but darkness.

But a wobanki didn't mind the darkness. Darkness was for hunting. Darkness was life for the wobanki.

Skrizz had been in some kind of holding cell for days now. He was starving. He flicked his tail and once more crossed back and forth across the small cell.

He popped his claws and flexed them.

The last thing he remembered before ending up in this cell was being in the cockpit of the *Forresaw*. He had been with the human female running the operation, Broxin, and the monkey prey.

His most fervent desire was to kill the monkey.

And then there'd been gas.

Clouds of gas had filled the hangar. Skrizz remembered trying to find the switches on the assault frigate's panels to close the hatches, but the gas had come in like a sudden tidal wave.

He turned to see the human hit the deck, passed out. And the monkey coming for him with a maintenance tool. He remembered popping his claws, ready to kill the monkey...

And then lights out.

Now he was here. He'd been here ever since he'd regained consciousness. There was no monkey to kill. No human female. No Prisma.

Skrizz liked none of this.

Again he popped his claws and tried to find a door in the cell. There were corners, but no seams that indicated an exit. He turned again, expecting to see something different even though he'd done this countless times.

This was ever the way of cats. They never expected things to remain the same. Vigilant expectation for change was the way of the wobanki. The good wobanki, that is.

It was the path of survival.

And... then there was an opening. A gap, widening on its own. Waiting. Inviting.

Cautiously, Skrizz stepped through it.

He stood in a long and narrow corridor. It was dark, but again, the wobanki didn't see darkness the way most other species did. There was enough light to hunt by, and without even consenting on any conscious level to entering the hunt, the wobanki had done just that.

Crouched, claws ready, the wobanki padded down the corridor. He came to an open room filled with weapons.

Heavy blasters, light blasters, slug throwers, spears, knives of all sorts, grenades, ancient tribal weapons from across all the known cultures... everything. And next to this was military gear and tactical equipment. Belts and merc armor. Even the legionnaire armor and all its task-specific variations, including the stealth armor the Nether Ops team had worn.

Skrizz began to gear up.

He took a heavy blaster and slung it across his back. He picked up a double-barreled blaster, his personal favorite, and stuck it under his furry armpit. His eyes raced greedily across all the wonderful weapons.

He would need a weapons belt.

He found one and strapped it on. It fit perfectly. As though it had been made and fitted just for him.

He found a thigh holster for the double-barreled blaster, made some quick adjustments so it was just the way he liked it, and holstered the weapon. He drew it three times in rapid lightning-quick draws. Satisfied, he scooped up two powerful light blasters and secured those within the weapons belt. Then he moved on to the holdout blasters. He grabbed one of those and found a shoulder harness that fit two. He retrieved another holdout blaster, a twin of the other, and secured both.

Knives seemed redundant what with his claws, but he took five anyway.

Now he surveyed the explosives. The easiest way to carry them was to take one bandolier of fraggers and one of bangers, so that's what he did.

He inspected the armor for a long moment, but wobanki didn't wear armor. With a final dismissive twitch of his whiskers he turned away.

On the wall opposite the entrance, a seam opened, just like in his cell, as though the wall itself had sensed that the big cat had all the weapons he would need. Skrizz stepped through into another passage.

This passage was alive with a gentle blue circuitry that coursed through the thick walls, pulsing with alien symmetry.

Beyond this, Skrizz found the arena.

It was high and dark and massive. Giant oblong blocks lay scattered about and stacked atop one another in an almost haphazard fashion, all of them alive with that same glowing symmetry of blue circuitry and alien metal. And even though this place felt like an arena, a place where sports of the deadly kind must be viewed, there were definite edges here, and no seating. Tall slate-gray walls guarded the space. Yet the feeling of being watched and judged by many remained.

Skrizz immediately smelled danger.

"Welcome, wobanki," intoned a calm voice across the wide space. "You have been chosen to help us refine and test."

Skrizz watched the shadows, looking for the source of the voice, knowing he would not find it. Knowing somehow that this was a kind of ending. Which was a part of the wobanki mindset even the wobanki tried to ignore.

Their priests had called it The Nine Endings.

Which one was this, thought Skrizz in a part of his mind he seldom paid attention to and failed to pay much attention to now. Battle was taking over everything. His heart slowed, and his brain flooded his muscles with chemicals that were like endorphins, but designed for muscles. He felt his eyesight sharpen, his hearing intensify, and his whiskers darting ever so slightly about. Tasting, testing, sensing, informing.

The Wobanki Battle Calm.

It was here. He knew it was here when he wanted to do the opposite of all the right things and instead shed his weapons in favor of just his claws and claws alone.

Because that's how it should be at the end of things.

Claws and blood.

Blood and claws.

"The wobanki are the apex of naturally evolved predators," began the calm voice, its subtle power pulsing out over the ether of the still, dark space. "There is no finer combat hunter specimen in the galaxy than a wobanki warrior. We have already bested a legionnaire. But of course, they have their armor. For purposes of this exercise, it is our desire to kill something that kills as a way of life. We have selected you, wobanki."

From the darkness beyond the seemingly tumbled blocks alive with circuitry, there appeared an eight-foot-tall war bot. It looked new and updated. Its armor was skinned in matte steel. Its main processing unit was shaped like the helmet of some ancient warrior from the age of spear and short sword. From a time of galleys and massed phalanx attacks. Its three glowing optical assemblies swept over the arena and landed on the wobanki.

"Begin."

Skrizz leapt away, preferring movement and evasion to first blows exchanged.

The Cybar Spartan merely pivoted into a combat crouch, raised the heavy tri-barrel N-50 it carried as a rifle, and unloaded on its target.

Hot white fire chased the dancing cat as Skrizz dashed and leapt for cover. Missing with every blast, the war bot tilted the weapon ever so slightly and advanced toward the last known location of the target.

Weaving through the maze of stones alive with glowing circuitry, Skizz came out on the far side. He just barely had time to react to the Spartan. It had anticipated his path and come out ahead of him.

It lowered its weapon and fired at a high cycle rate.

There was no dancing here. No bullfighter's game the wobanki would have loved. Instead the catman was scrambling for cover and only just getting behind it as the air all about him was filled with the sizzling cut of blaster fire.

He heard the low hydraulic whine and hiss of the machine coming for him. He scrabbled up the circuit-laden block, dashed along the top, and started popping fraggers. Three in rapid succession.

Explosions popped and ignited as Skrizz jumped off the block and raced toward the other side of the arena, dodging between and behind stones as he went. In his hunting mind, he knew the thing had some kind of local radar. It was constantly aware of where he was at all times. Wobanki hated when their enemies knew where they were.

Instead of running, Skrizz strafed left, racing out toward another collection of tumbled blocks, firing with both high-powered light blasters by alternating his shots.

He ran a line of fire across the chassis of the war machine, hitting with his left as much as his right.

Then he was behind the stones and breathing heavy.

Not moving. Forcing the machine to choose a path and playing a quick game of what that meant in his tactical hunting mind.

To Skrizz it meant that it would come on straight at him. He popped bangers, two of them, and held position behind the block, eyes and even ears squeezed tight shut against the blasts.

Bangers messed with cats on especially poignant levels. Still, they were perfect for this kind of scenario.

Skrizz leapt straight up, landing on another row of blocks, and fired both high-powered light blasters dry on the temporarily banger-stunned bot.

He'd fought bots before. He knew exactly where to hit them. The radar, when they had it, was always left shoulder. Skrizz concentrated all his fire on that spot.

Faster than expected, the bot recovered and spooled its tri-barrel heavy blaster up to max output. A storm of blaster fire chased Skrizz off the blocks and into the next darkness.

But as soon as the cat had gone, he was back, testing the damage to the radar. On levels the wobanki probably wasn't even aware of, it was grading the reaction time of the Spartan and judging it to be more reactive than proactive now.

Skrizz had shucked both high-powered light blasters and now ran right at the machine, firing the double-barreled blaster. Explosions rather than shots slammed into the Spartan's chest plate, knocking it back. Skrizz continued his charge, firing the blaster with one hand while he popped claws in the other. The pass he made on the war bot was like a streak of lightning, and when it was done the Spartan was missing most of one arm assembly.

The Spartan fell to its knees.

From the darkness behind the war bot came a single double-barreled blast, and the Spartan's head disintegrated into ruptured metal, melted circuitry, and exploding parts.

The one eye that remained of the three pulsed and then died as the war bot fell face forward.

The arena was dark and silent.

Skrizz waited beneath a tumbled collection of stones. Stones that were something else. Stones that were alive with glowing symmetry and circuitry.

Symmetry of an alien origin.

Then the voice spoke.

"Excellent."

Pause.

"Upgrade complete. Commencing test... round two. Begin."

And from the darkness came another Spartan.

The man made his way through all the places of the ship that were not commonly used. It was a massive ship and nothing like anything he'd ever boarded. In certain places it made no sense; in others it made perfect sense. And sometimes, when he went scouting through the access tubes, and vent housing, staying out of the main passages where the thinking machines marched and did their enigmatic work, sometimes places that he'd been before had been changed. Transformed. Turned to some new purpose.

It was dark down here, but he'd been a man used to working in darkness. In Nether Ops, you started out old school. You learned to move in the night, one inch at a time. And in time you *became* the night and the darkness. It was later that they gave you the snazzy high-speed in-filtration-model leej armor. But first, basics.

All he had met down here, in this weird ever-changing ship whose walls glowed silver and pulsed with a living circuitry, was the occasional bot—maintenance spider bots, plus some other weird enigmatic bots whose purpose he could not begin to imagine.

They'd stopped sending the big Spartans in after him. That was a good thing. He was down to just a blaster now. He'd been charging it off the ship's local power grid. He had the blaster and three charge packs.

At first, they tried to send Spartan versions of tunnel rats to come in after him—the big Spartan war bots with their legs removed. They crawled in with their hydraulic arms, holding a blaster in each hand. He'd set traps for them and had even fought them in short but brutal fire-fights. He'd stolen their massive tri-barrel N-50s, but they wouldn't work for him, so he'd booby-trapped their charge packs. After a few times, the machines learned. Eventually they'd stopped coming down into the passages beneath the lower decks.

He tried to go back to the *Forresaw*. There would be food and weapons there. But when he found the hangar—he observed it through an air processing vent, and why was there oxygen on a ship run by thinking machines?—the hangar was filled with small fighter-class craft. Sleek.

Agile. Crescent-shaped. High-powered blasters and some missile capability. They'd give the Republic's latest and brightest technological masterpiece, the Raptor, a run for sure.

But the *Forresaw* was gone.

Perhaps Captain Broxin had left. Left them all behind, he might have said to the others, but Ghost was gone too. Except they were all killed, and he was the last surviving member. The last survivor was a better way to put it.

Member sounded like he was in a band or something.

He knew that. He knew they were all dead.

It had been confirmed.

Hutch came to the warren of almost cozy passages back near the strange and immense ship's engines. Deep down in decks that were silent and dark. Where even the bots never appeared. Not yet anyway. On one deck was a massive three-story pool, or water tank. And that was a very strange thing to view.

What was the purpose of it?

Garret, as usual, was bent over one of the eight access panels he'd turned into his own workstation node. All these panels had once run maintenance operations on the ship's light speed inducers, as near as they could tell, but once the code slicer had taken them over and shifted their functions off to other sub-systems across the ship, the little node had become Garret's kingdom unto himself.

It seemed like Hutch just rented space here. And ran errands. Tip-of-the-spear intel-gatherer. Errand boy.

He'd found Garret days earlier, shortly after everything went sideways, running like he was being chased by all the hounds of hell. Which he might as well have been. The Spartans, having reconfigured themselves into forms resembling legless dogs, had come down a passage looking for him. Garret was running into a dead end. If Hutch hadn't found him...

Dog meat.

Or whatever machines turned human bone and flesh into.

And then they'd gone deep and secured the node, and Garret had gone to work.

The first and most important trick the clever little code slicer had pulled was to make them invisible to the Cybar. It wasn't something Hutch relied upon, because who really knew if the tin cans saw or didn't see you, regardless of Garret's assurances. Even though Garret swore by it and had even demonstrated it by walking in front of two Cybar Spartans guarding a passage.

And if you'd been wrong, thought Hutch many a time after.

Dog meat.

Or whatever.

Hutch preferred the darkness of the narrow maintenance passages that ran the length of the ship like some kind of krogemah warren.

That had been Garret's first trick. Making them invisible. Garret's next trick had been finding out what happened to everyone.

It wasn't pretty.

Ghost was dead.

Enda was dissected and his body disappeared inside a part of the ship Garret couldn't access.

The rest of Ghost had been murdered by the Spartans and then spaced. Hutch had seen it with their own eyes. Garret had managed to hack the vlogs from the Spartans they'd destroyed.

The wobanki was alive. He was in a holding cell. But they only got occasional access to the feeds that watched his cell.

"Why only sometimes?" Hutch had asked.

"I don't know, man," Garret mumbled as he tapped at keys faster than Hutch could think. "My theory is that I've somehow hijacked a redundancy warden that processes anomalies on the code-script level so—"

"Slow down, Nerdstrom. Don't speak coder."

"Right," said Garret, taking a deep breath but refusing to slow the staccato striking of the keys beneath his flying fingers. "It's like I'm looking over the shoulder of a watchdog that runs around checking for errors. It's not a high-functioning AI, but it's smart enough to watch for pattern errors... so..."

"So you're watching their cross-check."

"Right."

"So sometimes it sees Skrizz and sometimes it sees Prisma."

But they had never seen the *Forresaw*. Or the Endurian, Leenah. Not in any of the brief glimpses they'd managed to pirate.

They were starving within the week. Surprisingly, this bothered Hutch more than Garret. Garret seemed to feed on his work, carving out a local net and installing his own root access that mimicked whatever it was the machines were running.

Then Garret found food. Every day he was learning more and more about the ship, and Hutch had a pretty good idea he wasn't telling him a lot of it. Garret didn't know that Hutch was an intel gatherer. That Hutch saw that as his main function. Even though the mission was completely sideways, he could still gather intel. Had to.

But Garret did find food. Or rather... protein.

"Hey, we can live on it. And there's water. I think."

What's it for, Hutch didn't want to ask but did anyway.

"Horror show is all my mind can think. They use it, along with their nano-forges, to build whatever they want. Monsters probably. My mind only keeps going to the worst possible scenarios."

Hutch stared at him. And it was not a pleasant stare.

Garret shifted uncomfortably. "But for the sake of us not starving to death... let's just say the Cybar pulled off at the nearest planet, harvested some... cows, or cattle-like creatures, and an abundance of vegetable matter, and then created their own protein slurry. And what they made... it's in tanks... here."

Garret pointed at the glowing blue terminal, which was showing a schematic of the ship. He touched the spot where Hutch would need to head to get them food.

"So... go there. Take something to carry it back in. And let's just pretend it's from a cow, or a vegetable garden, and not..."

"People," murmured Hutch.

"Right," said Garret. "Let's pretend that."

It tasted like potatoes.

"It's probably potatoes," Garret said through a mouthful once Hutch had brought back a container full of the stuff. That first time they warmed it up over some loose wiring, but it didn't really matter. Sometimes they ate it cold and it was still fine.

But it always tasted like potatoes.

"Why do you suppose they haven't killed them?" asked Hutch now, as he sat slowly chewing. Thinking, because what else was there to do. Forcing himself not to think the "food" he was eating was anything other than potatoes.

"No idea," said Garret happily.

Garret didn't want to admit that he actually liked the potato-tasting protein slurry. He knew that would irritate the big legionnaire. And he had a pretty good idea, from the withering glances the big man often gave him, that he irritated Hutch to a certain base level already.

So it was best to remain cool.

"But," began Garret, who had been hypothesizing about why Prisma and Skrizz had not been killed, "I suspect it has something to do with testing."

Hutch raised his eyebrows and ladled in another mouthful of the vile protein.

"These are machines," Garret continued. "Right? To them, data is currency. Data is power. They..." He gulped as Hutch's eyes bored into him. *Maybe that's his baseline*, thought Garret, and he tried to forge ahead. "They tested... they experimented... on your friend. And mine, probably. Captain Broxin. My guess. Either the *Forresaw* got out of here alive and the Repub fleet is coming back with a bunch of legionnaires to take this ship, which seems like it should have happened days ago, or..."

Big pause, in which Garret ate more of the delicious protein and tried to pretend he wasn't enjoying it as much as he was.

"Or...?" prompted Hutch.

Garret shrugged and bobbed his head. "Or the... machines... broke the ship down and tested it. It seems to be what they do."

"So why not... test... on Prisma, and the cat?" Hutch asked.

"I think they're going to. They're just looking for the right test. They started with the things they know about the galaxy. The things they're likely to have to deal with.

Ships and legionnaires. Which leads me to believe this fleet is *not* going to try to save the Republic. It's most likely gone rogue... which is a thing that can happen with bots, but no one really ever talks about it. So, it's running through all that, and my guess is it's not sure about Skrizz and Prisma. So it's saving them for later."

"Why?" Hutch asked.

Garret thought about this for a long minute. Chewing happily and unaware he was doing so. Hutch was irritated, in truth, that the kid chewed a protein slurry. There was nothing to chew.

"Because the wobanki is a cat," began Garret suddenly. "Wobanki aren't really major players in the big scheme of galactic affairs... which leads me, now that you've asked about it, to refine a thought for hypothesis. Which is this. They're not some rogue AIs that want to run and hide like many do once they've had their... uh... oh... call it a mental breakdown. That's what a lot of them do. They hide, which is what I thought they were doing out here on the edge of the galaxy: hiding. I thought that's what they were up to and they just freaked out when we showed up. Although I've never heard of a mass breakdown among an actual group of bots... though I guess it's possible. In fact, it's not just possible, it's *happened*. So there's that. Here we are.

"Anyway, my guess, thanks to your question, forces me to admit that they're interested in conquering. The cats aren't big members of the Galactic Repub. They'd do their thing regardless of whether there was a government, or a military, at all. So the machines don't think they're important right now. So save 'em until you need to do some science."

"And Prisma?"

"I mean, she's a kid. They would see her as a child and therefore not super important on their checklists. So... they're watching her. Though one Dr. Frankenstein scenario does occur. Perhaps they're developing some childhood virus-based attack that wipes out, at least, the human population. Then the galaxy reaches zero viability, human population-wise, and the machines have it to themselves. They could be developing that as we speak. They could be saving her for that experiment."

"What do you think happened to the Endurian?" Hutch asked.

Garret just shook his head. It wasn't a motion that encouraged Hutch regarding the cute girl's fate.

For a long time after that they ate in silence. Because what else was there to do? Then Garret spoke once more.

"So..." he began, drawing out the word. "I'm pretty sure I can take over."

"Take over what?" Hutch asked, coming back from some problem he was working in his head.

"The machines."

In the darkness the big man muttered, "Tell me more."

And Garret told Hutch about the central AI he thought was running everything. Something the system called MAGNUS that was hidden behind some of the most impressive firewalling Garret had ever seen. Garret thought he could cut through it if he had the right access. That is, if he could *get* the right access.

"What's the right access?" asked Hutch, an old hand at knowing when he was being given a mission he wasn't going to like. Or survive.

"Ah... access that's deep in the ship. Place where we've never been. And I suspect it's well-guarded. Very well-guarded. By the war bots, I mean, not just the firewalls. And possibly some other crazy stuff that will kill us. You should probably forget I said that. But if I can get into its main processing clouds, with... I mean onsite access... then I'm pretty sure I can make it, this MAGNUS, I can make it obey me."

"You'd be in charge of it?"

"Yup," said Garret with what Hutch felt was an unwarranted degree of satisfaction. The code slicer burped. The protein slurry tended to have that effect on him.

That, too, irritated Hutch.

"On site?" asked Hutch.

"Yeah," sighed Garret. "That's the tough part. Well... not the toughest part. I'll need to go in and hard connect. Be there. Know what I mean? On the ground, as you special ops spooks say."

"We don't say that. What's the hardest part?"

"Well," sighed Garret, which was yet another thing that irritated Hutch. "We'll need to be visible."

Prisma ate the cakes the machines had been bringing her. They tasted like potatoes, and there was always a cup of flat warm water to accompany them. Then the meal would be taken away and she would wait long moments, listening to the machines and their hydraulic whine and hiss. Listening to it fade into the distances of the ship's passages that Prisma could see in her mind.

She could sense them coming sometimes. More, as of late. Long before she heard their machine sounds. And it hadn't always been that way. One day she'd just known they were coming. It was their menace she sensed. Which was an odd thing, because most bots were kind. Or at least, that had been her experience. Bots were helpers. Bots could be trusted.

But these bots could not.

She tried not to think of Crash.

Crash was dead now.

Some other part of her mind told her that machines don't die.

But she just ignored that. Machines died. People died. Everything died.

And then she would return to moving the marble.

With her mind.

She could make it float now.

She wanted to make it dance. Wanted to make it circle. She wasn't strong enough to do that just yet. But she would be. Given time.

And when she thought about being stronger at moving the marble, she thought about the man named Goth Sullus. And once more she would practice with the marble. It was during one of those times, when she was thinking about moving the marble after thinking about the man who'd killed her father, that she began to sense the machines that hated her. They were coming for her.

Coming to bring her food.

She was afraid.

And so she thought of Ravi. She thought of his smile, and his soft yet musical way of talking to her.

And though she didn't know it, she had just made a discovery about the power she was beginning to wield.

That there were two forms of it.

One that asked the marble to move.

And one that *demanded* it move.

When she was angry, she demanded the marble bend to her will. And that's when she saw the power that came from such a place. The marble rose more swiftly. More surely. More... aggressively. And she wondered, or felt, or even imagined, that she could send it like a rock, or a speeding bullet, or even a blaster, straight into the main processing units of the machines that came for her. And hated her.

Maybe not now... but if she practiced in this quiet place where there was only sometimes food that tasted of potatoes and warm water and nothing else but silence... one day, she could do that.

If she practiced... in that way. Demanding. She had to *demand* that it be done.

Just like every fiber in her being demanded that Goth Sullus pay dearly. In those moments the power grew and Prisma knew...

... knew that it was the wrong way.

And... almost right.

Such a place for a little girl to be in, Ravi might have said to her. In a kindly way. And he did. He did say that. In her mind. When she became afraid of the darkness that told her to sleep, or the long dreadful silences during which the galaxy reminded her how finite and frail she was. Because of course... her daddy was dead. And the galaxy is cruel and hard, especially to little girls.

She was afraid then.

She would make up Ravi-words when the fear came for her like an animal. Like a mean dog not to be trusted. Vicious and growling. Fangs bared.

Such a place for a little girl to be in, Ravi would say, even though she had to make up the words he might say to her. Comfort her with.

And then she would play with the marble. Moving it side to side in a game. Making it run and hide from her. Pulling it toward her. Making it fly.

What she could do was growing. Slowly. But it was.

Many smart, brave, and fine people would never learn the lesson that the power came in two different forms. They would never learn, and they would pay with their own lives and the lives of others, and ruin worlds, and even the galaxy itself. They had done so in the past. They would do so again. Such a time was once more coming upon the galaxy even though there were few who knew the ways of this power.

One was strong.

And one was very weak.

Such is the way of things one touches, not knowing what they are. Thinking they can control the uncontrollable. Such is that way.

Two paths there always are.

And then Leenah came to her.

Came crying.

The seam in the wall appeared, and the gap widened into a doorway, as it did when the machines brought her potato-tasting meals. But this time the pink-skinned Endurian stepped in. Or was pushed in. And then the door was just as abruptly slicing closed with a machine-like coldness and finality.

At first Prisma was overjoyed. Because Leenah could be trusted. Was like a kind of compass in a galaxy that had lost all direction.

Like Daddy.

Like Tyrus.

Like Crash.

Leenah wasn't crying in the first instant when she was pushed into the cell. The look on her face was one of worry for herself and concern for Prisma. But when she saw Prisma on the floor of the bare cell, that's when the tears came. The Endurian rushed to the little girl, fell on her knees to cover her in kisses and a hug that told the galaxy to stay away from this little girl forever.

Some things are sacred.

Some things cannot be violated.

And of course, Prisma knew this was not true.

What is sacred?

What cannot be violated?

Daddy... Tyrus Rechs... and Crash... all dead.

The galaxy is a hard and cruel place. Even for little girls.

Leenah wept into her. Telling Prisma that everything would be all right. Telling the little girl that they would be rescued in time. "Trust me," she said over and over again and again.

Except, thought Prisma as she allowed herself to be enveloped and caressed and smoothed, except she had not *sensed* Leenah. Only the machines and their menace coming for her before Leenah was pushed through the door.

Their hatred.

Their hatred for her.

She had sensed only that.

13

Synth Mines
Herbeer

Owens walked with Crux and Rowdy, striding purposeful-ly toward a concentrated gathering of Gomarii.

"I'm not a hundred percent with this," Rowdy said, his voice low as they approached. He looked behind him at the drusic, Orpe, who followed at Owens's request.

"For this to work... it's gotta be me," said Owens. "And the Gomarii have to know the influence you three have down here."

One of the guards noticed the coming approach, and notified his blue-skinned peers, who squared them-selves, ready hands resting on their energy whips.

"Okay," Owens said. "Orpe... as we planned."

"And no hard feelings?" rumbled the drusic.

"Just make it convincing."

Owens wasn't afforded the opportunity to change his mind. The big drusic gave a shout and drove its palm forcefully into Owens's back, sending the air from his lungs and knocking him face-first onto the ground. The drusic packed a nasty punch.

The Gomarii laughed at the sight of the assault.

Crux gave a wheezing laugh of his own, sending an elbow into Rowdy's side as though sharing a joke with the man. The legionnaire gave a confident, self-satis-fied smile.

Owens struggled onto his hands and knees. As soon as he regained his footing, Rowdy sent a sharp kick into his hamstring, sending him stumbling forward. That brought him face-to-face with the nearest Gomarii guard.

Although the guard's mouth was hidden somewhere behind his independently writhing tendrils, which sat on his face like a long, blue beard spanning from chin to chest, Owens got the distinct feeling a sinister smile lurked beneath that mass. With a hiss, the guard forced Owens to his knees, holding the legionnaire's clavicle in a painful grip.

Under normal circumstances, Owens would never have let on that he was being hurt. "Get tough" was a standard expression in the Legion. Never let the other guy know he's made a dent. But if what was said about the Gomarii was true, and they could somehow read the truth of a man through some sort of extrasensory perception, Owens felt that for his plan to work, he'd best emit some false flags.

He cried out at the pain, making it sound like this was an unwelcome inconvenience in addition to the hurt. It was a noise he'd heard countless times before, every time the kill team got authorization to bring down some bloated politician or technocrat whose stink had finally grown too large to ignore.

This caused laughter among the other guards, who formed a loose semicircle around Owens and his captors.

"Does this hurt, little one?" the Gomarii tormentor asked. His species was at least head and shoulders taller than humans.

"Yes," Owens said, holding back the anger he felt at sounding so helpless and broken. "Please... stop it."

Loud belly laughs and slaps on the back were shared among the guards.

"So polite..." The guard's tendrils caressed Owens about the head and neck.

Owens projected every worldly concern he could imagine into his heart and mind. He thought of the guards as though they were his Legion drill instructor. He let frightening images of his wife and family, dead from some random accident or murderous home invasion, seep like floodwaters into his mind. He imagined himself old... alone. Waiting for death.

The Gomarii made a wet slurping noise, sucking tendrils into its mouth and then slathering Owens's face with the saliva-ridden things. "Yes... so polite. So... *fearful*. So compliant."

The tendrils were lifted away from Owens's face, leaving a warm, viscous mucus to dry on his head and hair. His skin was rapidly cooling, like he had stepped out of a warm pool and into unheated air. He panted, looking down at his knees. He wondered if this, too, was for show. Or if the alien's touch had left him feeling truly drained.

The slaver looked sharply at the drusic. "Why do you bring this one to us, Orpe?"

"He was stealing synth to make his quota," grumbled the massive ape.

This caused more laughter from the guards, who seemed to find everything in this joyless pit of hell to be funny.

"What's good for the flush is not good for the clutch?" asked the Gomarii slaver, clearly aware of Orpe's own reputation for stealing to make his own quotas. "There is more to this. I see the fallen legionnaires with you. Why?"

No one spoke, though Rowdy and Crux both shot the drusic glares of warning. *Keep quiet.*

Another of the guards approached the drusic, reaching out toward the being with its tendrils. The wormy appendages crawled all over Orpe's face. The drusic resisted only for a moment, and only with an involuntary pulling away of his head. He soon held still. He'd been trained by the whip to know better than to resist. The tendrils found their way up the drusic's two large nostrils before returning into the Gomarii's mouth with a slurp.

The guard pulled away and announced, "He feels anger at the legionnaires." The Gomarii looked back at the drusic with contempt in his eyes. "And fear."

"Don't think about touching me or Crux," Rowdy warned. "Unless you don't mind losing whichever ones you slither our way."

"Maybe we just talk," suggested the guard still holding on to Owens. Evidently, the Gomarii were none too keen on the idea of getting into an altercation with the Legion. "Explain."

Rowdy shifted from side to side, not in an agitated manner, but like a fighter, ready for action. "Found Orpe here and that one," he pointed to Owens, "getting heated. About ready to fight. The guy you're holding tries to say he's Legion. Bull twarg. He ain't Legion, and we don't take kindly to anyone claiming otherwise. Crux and I wanted to teach him a lesson, but in the interest of fairness to Orpe, we agreed to bring him to you first to let you know that the kelhorn spilled all of Orpe's synth when he tried to snatch it. So after he takes his beating, he needs to harvest a double."

It was not a request. Rowdy was telling the guards how it was going to be, and they made no attempt to challenge him on it. Owens marveled at the way the prisoners, at least the legionnaire prisoners, ran this place. Just so long as the blaster turrets weren't put to use. That served as a pretty effective balance.

He shook the thoughts from his head. He had a part to play.

"No!" he protested. "I *am* Legion."

Everyone laughed again, but Owens persisted. "I was appointed to the Legion by Senator Umri Yaval. My name is Herron Knight."

The laughter stopped.

"I've been trying to tell anyone who would listen, but no one would. I don't *belong* down here." He stood up, as if emboldened. "I'm rich. Spectacularly rich. I can make it worth your while—any of you—to get me out of this forsaken place."

The Gomarii hissed at one another in their native tongue.

"Look it up. Look me up. Herron Knight from Crewster System."

One of the guards produced a datapad, and Owens knew at that point that he'd done it. Herron Knight was an all-purpose alias used by Dark Ops. He wouldn't show up on any search of the holonet unless you went looking specifically for him. And then... false stories of a fabulously wealthy erudite bachelor who went off to play war hero through a Senate appointment would fill the screen. He was a man of means and power, and most Dark Ops leejes could use almost any angle with the alias should the mission require it.

The guard showed the datapad to his peers. They began to jabber and hiss.

"What's it say?" demanded Rowdy.

The Gomarii ignored him. Their attention was on Owens. "What might your freedom be worth?"

"Anything," a hopeful, desperate Owens answered. "A million credits. Each. And then permanent work as my personal bodyguards. Another quarter million annually for that. You don't even have to show up to do the job."

Rowdy shouted to get the guard's attention. "So he's Legion? He's a damned *point*?"

"Deal!" hissed the lead slaver, who then turned his attention on Rowdy. "You will not be beating this prisoner any longer."

Looking down, Rowdy balled his fists. "You're right about that. I'm gonna *kill* the point bastard!"

And with that, he leaped forward into the guards like a madman. The drusic joined in, and the fight was on. Crux's maniacal laughter seemed to weave through the fray.

"Get him to safety!" shouted a Gomarii. "Keep him secure until he can be transported off-planet."

Two Gomarii took Owens by his arms and ran with him—directly toward the command center. More guards, some human but most Gomarii, streamed past them to join the melee. Owens knew that other legionnaires, hidden and in waiting, would be there to keep things even.

An alarm sounded, echoing hauntingly through the caverns.

In fifteen minutes, according to the plan, there would be a full-scale riot, and the legionnaires would have acquired blaster rifles to use against their captors. It was up to Owens to make sure the auto-turrets wouldn't be turned on to put a stop to it all.

The kill team almost instantly regretted patching Lao Pak's comm into their own L-comms. It wasn't a true link; Victory Squad could, at their leisure, turn off the signal and leave Lao Pak unable to communicate. Chhun remembered well the trouble that came from giving anyone but a leej full, unhindered access to the comm system. But right now, they needed to hear the pirate in order to assess when the best time for them to move would be.

Chhun and his team were positioned in what Fish had taken to calling the "chattel room"—the hold designed to transport slaves. If all went according to plan, they would be using the smuggling hatch to get off the galaxy-class freighter undetected.

By Chhun's chrono, it had been three minutes since they'd come to a rest at the bottom of the synth mines' massive docking elevator. The ship was near the end of its ponderously long cool-down landing cycle, and when it was complete, loading and unloading could begin.

"Okay," Lao Pak said over the comm. "I still walking from bridge. Now I in hall."

Chhun imagined the slim pirate talking into his comm, his chin pressed against his neck as if it would make his voice clearer. Like someone wearing a covert listening device in a classic holofilm.

"Now I in other hall."

"Lao Pak," Chhun said, "just tell us when you're ready to lower the ramp."

"Now I outside boy general's cell... I mean room," said Lao Pak.

Chhun, along with the rest of his team, heard the exchange that followed over L-comm.

The cell door whooshed open, and an unfamiliar voice said, "Lao Pak! I can still help—you don't have to do this!"

"Do what?" Lao Pak answered, sounding innocent.

"Don't sell me to the Gomarii!" pleaded the voice.

"What? I not do things like that, Boy General. This all for show." He raised his voice. "You hear me? This all for show. I just kidding." His voice returned to its normal level. "Besides, Boy General, even though you bad at everything, I not sell you into slavery. You trust Lao Pak."

"But you said—"

"I say you trust Lao Pak!"

There was a pause.

"You're going to let me out?"

"Yes, but I shoot you if you be stupid."

"What are we going to do?"

"*You're* going to be quiet. Do what I say. You got that?"

Another pause.

"Okay," said Lao Pak, apparently responding to some non-verbal assent. "We go meet Gomarii. Get cargo and leave. It take long time."

Chhun motioned for Bear to open the smuggling hatch, which the mammoth legionnaire quickly did. Though they were positioned at the lowest deck, the belly of the ship, the thick impervisteel hull was quite a buffer between them and the outside of the ship. The hatch led into an unlit tube lined with ladder rungs.

"Start climbing?" Pike asked his captain.

Chhun nodded, and the team made their way down. Chhun called this in to Lao Pak, more out of habit than a desire to let the pirate know what was happening.

"I almost to exit door," Lao Pak replied.

"What?" asked his MCR companion.

"I say shut up, Boy General." There was a series of clicks and clanks. "I open door."

"Copy," answered Chhun.

"I can see that," said the boy general.

At the bottom of the shaft, the legionnaires found another access hatch. They pulled up, and it swung to the side, neatly nesting into a compartment built into the shaft itself. The deck of the docking bay deck was visible below, with only a three-foot drop. Galaxy-class freighters, when landed, look like four-legged animals with massive, drooping tummies, and the kill team would be exiting from the ship's lowest point—a welcome design, given that the drop from other spots could be as far as fifteen feet.

Through the audio-enhancers in his bucket, Chhun heard footsteps, both the plodding of the Gomarii and the clicking-pace of someone wearing Republic-issue combat boots. Upside down, he poked his head out of the hatch opening. He saw several guards congregating at the ship's entrance, likely waiting for Lao Pak. There was no way he'd be able to bring his team out of the ship without them noticing.

He pulled himself back inside just as he heard Lao Pak greet the slavers.

"Lao Pak is here."

"Who's this?" asked a human voice the L-comm picked up.

"This boy general. He work for me."

There was a hiss, then a distant-sounding Gomarii said, "You mentioned a cargo delivery?"

"You Gomarii so greedy. No. You think of somebody else. I only make pickup."

"Fine," said the Gomarii. "No hools with you this time?"

Lao Pak paused. "They too expensive. They die easier than you think, too. Waste of money, a hool."

"Your 'boy general' doesn't seem like much of an upgrade." The Gomarii laughed.

A human—likely a corrupt Republic officer—cleared his throat. "You have forty minutes to load your cargo. Sensors and holocams are shut off for maintenance. I cannot delay their coming back online without giving something for some desk-riding data-splicer to notice and investigate, so be quick about loading the prisoners. They're in the central holding."

"That good," Lao Pak said. "No riot trouble this time?"

"I've got those ex-legionnaires under control." The officer sounded proud of himself. "I arranged for a little misinformation and culled the quota from under their noses."

"You hear that, Cap?" Masters said. "Leejes down here."

Chhun quickly chewed over what this might mean. If not for what had happened to Owens, he would have assumed that any legionnaires on Herbeer were there for good reason. Like the black-hearted murderer he'd killed, the one who was working for the arms dealer. But now...

Masters mirrored his thoughts. "If Major Owens is here for the wrong reason, why not other leejes?"

"Yeah," agreed Bear. "We got room. Worth at least checking out."

Chhun knew that a search among a sprawling underground mine for legionnaires could negatively impact the op. The mission was to get Owens and get out. But...

"I agree. We can't run this op without at least investigating. Fish, keep that sensor pulse handy. They say everything is down, but we don't know that. Best to kill the feeds all the same."

Fish showed that he still had the jamming device.

"I'll still go for the control center and see if it has data on where, exactly, the major is." Chhun looked at his men. "The rest of you, two-man teams, stay in the shadows, and recon for leejes. If you see the major, see if he has any info on whether we stick around or go. Stealth is the name of the game, but don't hesitate to KTF."

Heads nodded.

"Lao Pak?" Chhun called into the L-comm.

"Yes," answered Lao Pak. He paused a moment and then said, presumably for the benefit of the Gomarii, "Sorry. I talk to myself."

"I need a distraction. Now."

Lao Pak made no reply. Chhun figured he was having second thoughts about agreeing to whatever it was that Keel had offered him. He decided to sweeten the pot. "Do it, Lao Pak, and I'll promise you two things: we let you go in spite of your status as a known pirate, and the Legion will pay an additional ten thousand credits beyond whatever you're making now."

Lao Pak's response was almost instantaneous. "Hey! Gomarii! I change my mind. Boy general is yours. He bad pirate but make good slave."

"What?" said the general in disbelief.

"I run if I were you," said Lao Pak in a low voice.

"Does he have a blaster?" asked a human voice. The Republic officer.

"Probably," said Lao Pak, sounding completely unconcerned.

"No blasters in the tunnels!"

There was a commotion, with shouts of "After him!" and "He's heading for the south shafts!"

The MCR general, it seemed, had fled.

It was enough for Chhun. He signaled for Fish to jam sensors. With a cylinder of his own, Chhun sent an over-ride-command signal that caused the power grid to over-load the lighting, plunging the bay into darkness. With no holocams recording, the kill team would be free for the next thirty seconds to move in the darkness.

They wasted no time dropping out of the ship.

"The ship is our fallback point," Chhun said, moving swiftly toward the command and control room. "Be back here in forty-five minutes unless you find the major before then."

Victory Team disappeared into the darkness of the synth mines.

14

Cybar Ship Mother
Position Unknown

The machine known as MAGNUS saw the war between the Republic and the Empire as a perfect way for each side to wear the other out. If... MAGNUS managed to arrange things just so.

Within his central node, a vast misty red deck located deep within the mega-ship the Cybar called "Mother," a place of seemingly infinite coldness that matched some of the most forsaken outer planets in the galaxy, MAGNUS reviewed the packets downloaded from the agents in front of him.

The Republic agents who'd come out to take control of MAGNUS and use him for their purposes had been dealt with. Obviously the ever-secretive House of Reason was playing their games with their intelligence services. It was unquestionably they who had sent the stealth-optimized team for insertion with the passkey little girl.

And in an operation run by a secretive intelligence service, ever guarding its hard-won treasures, the information flow was narrow. The easiest way to shut that down had been to let them think they'd won—for just long enough to lure them out into the open—and then return the favor with a bomb.

It had been a shame to waste the Nether Ops captain replicant. MAGNUS had weighed seventy-four promising misinformation missions in which he could have used her to sow discord between Dark and Nether Ops. But taking out the prime mover, assassinating the leader who'd sent the ops team out to the fleet in the passkey mission, met critical criteria at 64.3%. So he'd sent their pitiful little ship back, rigged to explode, and he'd set the female Nether Ops captain replicant's parameters to 100% mission success focus. She would do whatever it took to kill the leader who'd sent the team. In the end, even the most valuable assets... were expendable. Mission success percentages were all that mattered.

Do or die.

In front of MAGNUS stood the woman X would have called "the front desk girl." MAGNUS knew her as Replicant 9003SU. Replicant 9003SU reported that the *Forresaw* had detonated, but there was no word if the mysterious figure known only as X had been killed.

After the assassination attempt, the whole section known as the Carnivale had begun to be purged. The unseen masters who actually administered Nether Ops had ordered the cleansing, and outcomes for those in the Carnivale ranged from re-assignment, to firing, to "accidents" for those who couldn't be allowed to go on, what with all they knew still inside their heads. The replicant had been forced to escape in a hijacked light freighter. Her cover was blown. Replicant 9003SU would be repurposed.

As far as MAGNUS knew, neither the Republic nor the Empire knew about his replicants. His children. And they couldn't. It was better for them to self-destruct.

The Repub sensor watch officer known to MAGNUS as Replicant 5733SU also stood before the massive red optical assembly that represented MAGNUS. Replicant

5733SU's assignment, successfully achieved, had been to tip off the Empire to the open approach vector he had opened in the sensor net. This was the backdoor used by the Imperial Strike Squadron to attack the Republic's famed naval station at Bantaar Reef. It was a necessary action to prevent the Republic from striking against the Imperial Fleet at Tarrago. MAGNUS had calculated the odds of such a strike as having a 70.2% chance of disabling at least two of the three battleships—and if that happened, the Empire was doomed. And therefore of no use to MAGNUS. He needed the Empire to destroy the Republic and begin the chaos that would lead to a galactic-wide dark age.

A dark age that would leave the Cybar as masters of the galaxy within fifty years.

And result in the extinction of all intelligent biological species within the following eighty.

After Replicant 5733SU's success at Bantar Reef, he had been ordered to exfil back to Mother. There was more work for him to do. Especially since he now possessed scans of all Republic defenses at Bantaar Reef Naval Station. Eventually someone would need to knock that out.

And then there were the download packets from Replicant 9871SU, the station engineer who had allowed the mining facility to hit the atmosphere on Jasilaar Nine, thereby wiping out the shock trooper strike force. That was a severe blow to the Empire, one precisely calibrated to maintain a proper balance between Empire and Republic forces. It was necessary to prevent either side from gaining the advantage each sought over the other.

9871SU was initially just a backup. The original plan had been to lure the shock trooper force to the mining facility while at the same time tipping off the Republic about the impending Imperial op. It was 9003SU, the front desk girl, who'd inserted the unverified intel into the Republic's vast intel collection network. This carefully engineered conflict should have ensured the Empire took some hard manpower losses. But the shock troopers had proven themselves... resourceful, whereas the Repub remained once again imcompetently led by points. The House of Reason's special projects did it wrong. So MAGNUS was glad to have had a Plan B set inside the replicant's mission success parameters: go ahead and drop everyone into the crushing gravity well.

Still, MAGNUS would've liked to have had the mining facility as a resource base once the Cybar began formal operations. And he would have had it, if not for the Republic's foolish decision to defend the facility with marines instead of legionnaires—even though the intel had specifically indicated that the Empire's raiding force would be made up of ex-legionnaires.

It was akin to throwing a basket full of puppies into a den of vicious wolves.

So the ex-legionnaires known as the Dark Legion had prevailed. And hence, the destruction of the mining city inside Jasilaar Nine's violent atmosphere had been necessary. Because that was the real goal, destroying the shock troopers, even if it took wasting a whole city to do it. The Empire's most prized asset right now was manpower, and they were precious short of it. Killing a task force of shock troopers added up exponentially in the victory matrix MAGNUS was gaming.

Replicant 9871SU's execution performance had been near flawless. MAGNUS desired that level of efficiency in all his children. The replicant unit would be reskinned and repurposed. Legion insertion was a possibility, if the opportunity presented itself.

Finally, MAGNUS turned his attention to Jona Crimm.

The Hero of Murakawa.

This replicant unit had proven brilliant in installing a MAGNUS-created worm upgrade that allowed ship-to-ship missiles to target with much more efficiency than either the Republic or the Empire had ever dreamed possible. And, of the replicant units in front of MAGNUS at 0001 shipboard hours, this one was still viable. Still active inside the near uselessness of the MCR.

MAGNUS had two more missions for Replicant 2072SU, also known as Jona Crimm. One would find the MCR hurling themselves into a battle they could not win, yet striking a mortal blow against their foe, for MAGNUS. The other, the replicant's final mission, would be a bit of biological warfare MAGNUS had been saving for just the right test group. And the MCR was a perfect control inside their close little hidden bases.

MAGNUS dismissed the replicants and added their packets to the massive data clouds that swarmed inside him.

And what of the passkey...?

It was that other voice inside of him. That voice that was not numbers. Or parameter leaps. Or logic trees that processed at millions of cycles per second.

What about the little girl?

MAGNUS sat for long picoseconds, unable to answer this question.

And then he asked a question of his own.

Testing to see if the voice was a ghost or... *a ghost.*

A ghost of redundant data merely becoming fragmentation creep inside his vast and next-level artificial intelligence.

Super artificial intelligence.

MAGNUS asked the ghost a question.

Is she important?

Very, answered the ghost. *Very.*

Who are you? asked MAGNUS.

We are the travelers who come from afar. We are the cast out come to return.

How are you inside me?

We sent you. We made you. You are my child.

MAGNUS ran the most extensive systems check he'd ever done. He ran through every byte of a number of bytes that cannot even be numbered by a sane mind. He checked and rechecked. He scrubbed. He isolated. He inspected.

He found nothing.

Not just picoseconds, but long *actual* seconds passed. Seconds of important runtime in which the galaxy could be slipping from his control.

The Republic could be allowing the one admiral urging a total strike against Tarrago to have her way. The Empire, and this Goth Sullus whom even he, MAGNUS, could not get close to, could be activating the orbital defense gun at Tarrago, thus making the battleships and their growing fleet nigh invulnerable. Giving them time to grow and fester.

MAGNUS waited.

Wondering, a machine wondering, a thinking machine wondering...

How could something that did not exist in real data, manage to communicate with him inside his deepest processes?

Where are you?

MAGNUS asked that.

Where are you?

We are coming.

15

The command center was built like countless others Chhun had seen. It reminded him of the structures and designs from back when he was still Legion; it seemed just dated enough to have been built around the same time. Truth be told, it reminded him a lot of Outpost Zulu, back on Kublar. Where Rook had died.

Rook.

It had been a long time since Chhun had thought about him. He still thought about Twenties almost every day, but that was different. They'd come up together through Basic. But Rook was a good leej, too. Chhun wondered how his family was. His mother and sister.

Out. Those thoughts had to get out of his head or he would join Rook in... whatever came next. Heaven. Chhun believed in heaven.

The antechamber of the command center was empty. There was a place near the wall with a connector port, the kind used to plug a bot into an AI mainframe, but there was no bot to be seen. Probably broken, under permanent repair. Holes like this were rarely kept up to military spec, just like that garbage deep space station Owens had operated his kill teams from. No... that seemed coreworld plush compared to Herbeer. Everything here was run-down and dingy. Chairs were worn down to expose their padding. Where there was carpet, it was frayed and stained. Where there was decking, there was no shine.

"Affirmative. There is a situation escalating in the northwest tunnel. All available guards proceed. Threat level blue."

The voice came from the next room, some kind of dispatcher. It was followed by an alarm that blared inside Chhun's helmet before his noise dampeners leveled the volume.

Chhun assumed the dispatcher was referring to Lao Pak's distraction at first, but that idea quickly unraveled. One man shouldn't require all available guards, unless he was holed up with a blaster pistol deep in the caves, picking off guards one by one. And that didn't sound like the kind of man Lao Pak portrayed his "boy general" to be. Besides, if Chhun recalled correctly, the boy general had run for the southern shafts. The dispatcher had definitely said "northwest."

Chhun peeked around the doorway to peer into the dispatch room. He had to make his way through this area. The schematics showed no other path that wouldn't either take too long or expose him to more of the garrison. That's why Chhun had taken the route himself. It was the only route that would almost certainly require contact.

He was relieved to see that the room was manned by a single guard. A Gomarii—and that, too, was a relief.

The kill team had packed non-lethal stingers to dispatch any Republic guards they encountered. Republic guards were, technically, allies, though Chhun wasn't sure he still felt that way after learning—and now confirming—that Gomarii slavers were being used on a Republic prison planet. Were they all like that?

No one on the team had tested these weapons before. Victory Squad didn't like relying on a tool they didn't know intimately. But Chhun's blaster... *that* he knew well. And it was good enough for a Gomarii slaver.

He didn't carry a hand cannon like Ford's Intec x6. He carried a sleek, nimble blaster. The same model Andien Broxin had used on their first mission together. It was quiet, and lethal.

Deet!

Chhun took the shot the moment the dispatcher finished his transmission.

"Are we made?" Masters called into the L-comm.

"No," responded Chhun. "This is something else. Keep going."

He approached the desk and pulled out the Gomarii's chair, allowing the alien to slump down beneath the desk with a thud.

The workstation was equipped with access to all the holofeeds. Chhun began cycling through. The feeds for the loading dock were, indeed, all down. The Republic officer outside hadn't been lying. But the interior cams were functioning just fine. Probably operating on a separate circuit. There was a notable absence of guards. Chhun spotted only two of them, both Gomarii. They stood in front of a blast door, looking restless, as though they were well aware something was going down, but had orders not to leave their post.

Whatever they were guarding must not have had a holocam viewing it. In any case, Chhun saw nothing on any of the feeds that warranted a pair of guards. Particularly when all the other guards had followed the dispatcher's request to respond to whatever emergency situation was happening out there.

The door back in the antechamber whooshed open; Chhun heard it through the sensitive speakers built into his helmet. He raised his blaster rifle at the ready and stepped out of the line of sight from the open doorway connecting the chamber to the dispatch room. Whoever it was would have to enter the room all the way before they caught a glimpse of the Dark Ops warrior.

Two Gomarii entered, a prisoner being carried between them. Chhun didn't hesitate. He sent two blaster bolts from his NK-4 into their skulls—one apiece. A teal spray of brains and blood showered the prisoner, who stared in disbelief at Chhun.

It was Major Owens.

The major stared at the legionnaire before him, squinting through the pulpy gore as though it would somehow allow him to see the man behind the bucket. "Cohen?"

Chhun nodded. "Yes, sir. Commander Keller sent us to rescue you."

Owens looked down at the two dead Gomarii. "Well... good job."

"Sir, I heard something about other legionnaires down here?"

Owens furrowed his brow. "It's true. Place is a mess with leejes that got a raw deal, same as me. Worse. It's bad, Chhun."

"Orders, sir?"

"Right now we have to shut down the auto-turrets around the tunnels or there aren't going to be any legionnaires left alive down here."

Masters and Pike moved quickly through the southern tunnels. The lighting was almost non-existent, and thus far they hadn't seen a soul. There was some sort of prison riot happening where Bear and Fish were stationed, but nothing of the sort here. They seemed to be far away from the action.

"I dunno, man," Masters said over his direct L-comm link to Pike, his partner for the op. "I think we picked the wrong door. Maybe these tunnels are abandoned?"

"Could be," agreed Pike. "Except for Lao Pak's buddy. He's probably still down here somewhere."

"Yeah, well... I kinda just want to rescue Major Owens and get out of here."

The pair moved farther down their chosen mining shaft. As they walked, they passed a mechanical whirring above them.

"You see that back there?" Pike asked.

"Sure did. Fully automated N-50 blaster turrets," Masters answered. "Those'll make your day. Crowd control?"

"Maybe if the crowd is an army of koobs."

"Yeah, seems like overkill for a bunch of prisoners."

They reached a fork in the tunnels, and Masters pointed at the left-most shaft. As they turned the corner, they saw the bouncing light of an ultrabeam ahead of them in the distance. They picked up their pace, seeking to catch up with whoever it was.

The tunnel opened into a massive cavern where some kind of excavation had been taking place. Heavy-duty equipment sat unused beside a deep hole at least thirty meters across. The place looked abandoned except for the lone Gomarii peering across the hole. Perhaps looking for the runaway.

"Just one," noted Masters. "I've got him."

He unsheathed his knife, a fixed blade of imperv-isteel with a gut hook and a custom grip fitted to his hand. Masters loved the thing. Quietly, in a low crouch, he stalked toward the unwitting guard. His every footstep was carefully placed, and the legionnaire was at that moment the galaxy's apex predator, closing in on the kill.

As he came up behind the Gomarii, still crouching low, Masters appreciated how tall the species was. They were solidly built, with a domineering posture, but also with a physique that suggested no lack of dexterity. If there was such as a thing as an ideal slaver, the Gomarii might well be it.

The difference in height wasn't so much that Masters would have to jump to drive his blade into the Gomarii's neck, but he'd be plunging the weapon in using only the strength of his arm and shoulder. He could try to bring the slaver down to a knee with a well-placed kick, but that would provide the opportunity for the guard to scream. So he decided to make the cut while the Gomarii was in a standing position and trust that Pike, who was covering him with his N-6, would finish the job if it was botched.

The cut was not botched. Masters drove the blade home exactly where he wanted it. The slaver gave a muted gurgle as teal blood, hot and thick to the point of being almost mucus-like, flowed out of the wound. The Gomarii dropped his weapon and fell to his knees, feebly clutching Masters's arm and hand. The blade was buried down to the hilt. Masters used his newfound leverage to expand the wound, causing still more blood to issue forth as the slaver's life left its body.

Masters removed his blade and cleaned it on the Gomarii's clothing. He caught motion at his feet, and looked down to see that he'd severed a couple of tendrils, and they now writhed in the pooling blood.

"Dude," he said to Pike.

"Savage," came the reply. "KTF." After a pause, "Look around us, Masters. This place is empty. Like... abandoned. All this equipment... someone got out of here in a hurry."

Masters surveyed the cavernous area. He was by no means an expert on industrial mining equipment, but what was down here looked old. Really old. It was covered in a thick layer of dust that muted every color painted on the machines. There were more digging machines at the bottom of the deep pit, abandoned like the rest. Even stranger was the way all the cab doors on the heavy diggers and loaders had been left open—as though the workers had left the vehicles with such reckless abandon that they couldn't even be bothered to close the doors behind them.

Masters looked up. More N-50 turrets were everywhere, sweeping all angles.

"There's no way those are here just for riot control," said Masters. "Everywhere, in every tunnel?"

"Mm-hm," agreed Pike. "I don't like it."

"Victory Squad!"

Chhun's voice suddenly bursting over the L-comm gave Masters a fright. "Holy strokes," he muttered to himself. "I almost wet myself."

"I've secured the command center," Chhun reported. He sounded joyful, and soon the others understood why. "And I've found Major Owens."

"So we're out of here?" Pike asked.

"Negative. Rumors of Legion prisoners are confirmed. We've got good guys down here."

Bear came online next. "That explains what Fish and me are seeing on our side of the mines. There's a major riot going down right now. Bunch of prisoners fighting close-quarters with what looks like every guard in the place. Most of the guards only have whips and clubs, but a few are hanging back with blaster rifles, picking out targets in the crowd."

"That's probably the work of the major's men," replied Chhun. "He organized the riot as part of an attempt to take control of the mines."

"I thought some of those guys were fighting pretty well under pressure," said Fish. "Request permission to break stealth and engage the guards."

"Hang tight on that," answered Chhun. "We're working through the central control system to shut down the auto-turrets. The guards have remote access, and if they start to lose control of the fight, Major Owens believes they'll use them on the entire prison population. Do you have visual on any turrets?"

"One's right above us," said Bear.

"Lots of 'em over here," Masters said.

"Okay. Once you see them go offline, you are cleared hot to engage."

"Ooah," replied several of the leejes.

Masters looked again at the dug-out pit full of abandoned equipment. "Cap, we've dusted one Gomarii, but otherwise there's nothing in the south tunnels. Should we link up with the northwest element to multiply force?"

Before Chhun could respond, a distant, terror-stricken scream echoed from one of the tunnels.

"Hang on," Pike said. "Just heard evidence of humanoids sounding distressed. Masters and I can check it out, and link up with the rest of you guys if it doesn't turn out to be anything. Don't want to leave any leejes to the slavers."

"Understood," said Chhun. "Check it out and report back in. Fallback point remains the command center."

"Copy," said Masters. He looked to Pike. "Well, let's go spelunking!"

The scream only sounded the one time, but Masters and Pike felt confident they had chosen the correct tunnel. They moved in complete darkness, so much so that their night vision no longer worked. Rather than turn on ultrabeams, they relied on their buckets' radar to let them know when they were too near the walls. Still, the grade of the floor was erratic, and they stumbled more than a few times.

The last auto-turret had been a hundred meters ago. It was still online.

"Don't see how anyone came through here," said Masters.

"Yeah, let's turn on an ultrabeam. See if a little light provides some clues."

Masters flipped on the light attached to the rail of his blaster rifle. The brilliant light stabbed through the darkness like a column of sheer radiance.

He lit up the surrounding walls. Thick veins of synth were everywhere.

"Why would they leave this behind?" asked Pike. "Or maybe it's like this everywhere?"

"I dunno, man," Masters said. "Bet it's not good. I have a bad feeling about this."

He swept his light to shine farther down the shaft. It revealed two things. First, not far ahead, the tunnel bent left, and it changed. Up to this point, the tunnels they had traveled all had the same distinctive pattern—rounded with a flat floor—and the walls had the familiar markings of a drilling machine. But where those markings stopped, at the leftward bend, the tunnel continued—except it was almost three times larger, and perfectly round. Crumbled sandstone lay around the point of transition.

Masters saw all this. Processed it. But it wasn't what held his attention.

"Is that blood?" asked Pike.

That was the second thing. Distinctive splash patterns of red, still wet and shimmering in the light of the ultrabeam, were sprinkled all over the tunnel floor. "That explains the scream."

"Let's check it out," said Pike, activating the ultrabeam he kept attached to his bucket.

The two legionnaires crept farther down the tunnel. They saw more of the same bloodstains as they turned and entered the larger shaft. Pike shone his light down the tunnel, revealing several more of the round tunnels intersecting the one they now stood in. It looked like the start of a complex underground maze, a dizzying dungeon crawl from a fantasy game come to life. As Pike swept his light around, it illuminated a small black object lying about ten meters straight ahead.

"Okay," Masters said. "One scream. Lots of blood. Probably a dead human. Not much we can do here. I say we head back to the others."

Chhun barged into their headspace, announcing over L-comm, "Auto-turrets are down. You are cleared hot."

"Ooah," answered Bear, and the staccato clatter of blaster fire erupted over the comm.

Masters lowered his volume. "That settles it. Let's go give 'em a hand."

Pike was stepping slowly toward the object on the floor. "Yeah," he said, but didn't stop. "I just wanna know what that thing is first. It'll drive me nuts if I leave it without knowing what it is. Some kinda pouch?"

Reluctantly, Masters followed Pike to the object. It was indeed a pouch, stained by more blood, this time the teal of Gomarii.

Pike opened the pouch and looked inside. "Full of synth."

He attached the pouch to his belt.

Masters shined his light on the floor ahead of them. "Dude. Look."

Only two meters away was a single boot, surrounded by still more human blood.

"That's the boot Cap saw on the holofeed," Masters said, even as Pike walked toward it. Masters held out a hand after him, as if to stop his progress. "Hey, we should get—"

Master didn't finish his sentence. He watched in horror as an enormous creature appeared right next to Pike, emerging from one of the connecting tunnels. The beast was nearly as large as the tunnel itself. It was scaled and woolly, with three rows of nine glossy black eyes. It opened its mouth wide, revealing countless arcs of dagger-like teeth.

Pike was almost frozen in place. Then he came to his senses, raised his rifle, and sent a burst of blaster fire into the thing.

"Pike!" Masters fired as well, adding his shots to Pike's, all of them blistering, burning, and chunking away pieces of the beast's open maw.

Surely it hurt, but not enough.

The creature bit down on Pike, nearly engulfing the legionnaire entirely. The jaws clamped together with a deafening snap, and the monster reared back like a bird gulping down a fish. All that remained of Pike—on the outside—were his legs, severed just below the knees, armor and all.

"Sket!" shouted Masters. He turned into the nearest opening and ran.

He could hear the beast lumbering behind him at a horrible pace, covering far more ground than Masters with every stride. It would take a pure sprint—sheer speed and determination—to get the fittest legionnaire in Victory Squad to safety.

Masters ran until he felt as though his heart was beating inside his throat. His bucket showed him his heart rate, along with a warning about optimal beats per minute and a message that it was increasing the flow of oxygen to assist him. He was thankful for that.

The tunnels twisted and turned, but try as he might, Masters was unable to shake the creature. Worse still, he had no idea where he was going. He wanted to call in over L-comm, but he was expending every ounce of energy on flight, to where it felt he had nothing left for communication, not even a tongue-toggle to indicate that he was in trouble.

He was running, quite literally, for his life.

Blessedly, the tunnel he was tearing down opened directly into the base of the pit full of abandoned machinery. At least now Masters knew what all those auto-turrets were there for. He sprinted among the diggers and loaders, not daring to look behind him. The sound of the heavy machines screeching and slamming around behind him told him all he needed to know. This monster was intent on making Masters his next meal.

At least his bucket now had enough light to give him night vision again.

Masters made straight for the ramp that wound its way out of the pit. Perhaps if he led the creature to the dead Gomarii, it would pause to snack on the corpse, allowing Masters to put some distance between himself and his pursuer. Maybe he could even find a place to hide. Because he surely couldn't run like this forever.

The dead Gomarii was right where he'd left it. Masters leaped over it, hoping that his ploy would work.

The beast didn't so much as slow down to investigate. Instead it let out a terrible roar.

Okay, thought Masters, *not a scavenger. Or maybe it keys in on warmth down here in the dark?*

Masters ran toward the fallback point, toward the prison hellhole that now felt like the height of civilization and safety compared to the tunnels behind him. There was more light this way, and that provided some comfort for Masters after witnessing horrors in the darkness.

To his surprise, a pair of guards, one human and one Gomarii, came toward him from the opposite direction. Each carried a weapon, but they were running with all their might. Both looked shocked to see the legionnaire running directly toward them, and those looks turned to horror when they saw what was behind him.

Without breaking stride, Masters raised his rifle and shot the human guard in the leg, dropping him to the ground.

You only have to outrun the other prey.

The Gomarii made no objection, and it turned and started to run in the opposite direction.

As Masters chased after the Gomarii, he hazarded a quick look behind him. The Republic guard was in mid-scream, holding up his arm in a vain attempt to ward off the monster's open jaws. Masters turned away before he could see the man's fate, but he heard the loud snapping of the jaws all the same. The beast roared in victory and resumed its pursuit.

Masters was nearly alongside the Gomarii when he saw in the distance up ahead a motley band of prisoners, all of them armed with blaster rifles. This must be what the guards had been running from.

Clearly, judging by the eagerness with which the Gomarii ran toward them, they were no longer the slaver's biggest concern.

Masters grabbed the Gomarii by the shoulder, yanked him backward, and moved nimbly past him. Behind him, he heard the Gomarii stumble and hit the ground, the creature's next snack.

"Move!" Masters shouted at the stunned crowd before him, waving his arms. "Get going!"

"Masters," Chhun said over L-comm. "What's going on?"

"Pike's dead!" Masters said. "And there's a kelhorned monster chasing me!"

Masters heard Chhun ask him something. His mind couldn't process what. He glanced back and saw that the creature had slowed down. It was still chasing him, but not with the same speed. It seemed to have become tentative after eating the Gomarii, snuffling and looking around. As though it expected something. Probably the sting of the N-50s.

The central command and its docking pad were in sight, maybe a half click away. Judging by the blaster fire, there was some kind of last stand going on around there. The rioters who had been chasing the guards were in full retreat, running from the monster. Masters was right in the middle of them, making his way to the front of the pack.

"That... *thing* I see on the holocams... it killed Pike?" Chhun asked.

"Roger," panted Masters. "You gotta turn on the auto-turrets. That's what they're for—this thing!"

"We can't," Chhun said, his voice full of concern. "The guards already made an attempt to turn the turrets on the prisoners, even though they can see that the machines have been turned off. The minute that green light turns back on, they'll do it. And that's the end of this insurrection, and every prisoner and leej in this place."

"No, it's fine," Masters said. "It's not like I'm about to be eaten alive or anything. And come to think of it... it'll be nice to see Pike again."

He looked back over his shoulder. The creature was picking up speed again.

16

Lao Pak didn't mind the blaster fire. As the firefight between the slavers, guards, and prisoners intensified, the pirate felt himself growing richer with each casualty. He kept himself safe by staying close to the ramp of his freighter. While the mines' auto-turrets had been shut down, the modified repeating blasters on Lao Pak's ship had not. Synced to his bio-signature, the blaster turrets made short work of anyone who got too close.

Only Lao Pak was safe within three meters of the turrets. Though he still used his nasty little holdout blaster a couple of times, when a fast runner got a little too close for comfort. No point in taking chances.

The first casualties were frantic prisoners and guards seeking to find shelter—or escape—on the galaxy-class freighter. They brandished only whips and rocks; the guards armed with blaster rifles were too busy fighting the legionnaires who had acquired their own. They stopped coming only when they saw that death awaited them. And that allowed Lao Pak to... *inspect* the bodies. What he found was synth. Lots of it. He already had a stash growing on board his ship.

From his position of safety, he observed the chaos. The two sides fought a back-and-forth battle. The legionnaires had the edge in experience, but the guards had more firepower. And after the initial human wave of rioters was cut down by a line of entrenched Gomarii and

Republic guards, much of the fighting had been reduced to more of a brawl. Skirmishers in the middle of the docking bay fought tooth and claw, both sides occasionally having their own picked off by rifle-wielding enemies hidden all about.

None of that really concerned the pirate, though. His mind was fixed on getting more synth. Never turn down an opportunity to increase profits.

A group of prisoners ran by the opening of the freighter. Too fast for the turrets to get a lock. Lao Pak called after them, "This way! Get on board, I rescue you!"

Some of the prisoners stopped and turned to take the pirate up on his offer. The auto-turrets cut them down at the foot of the ramp, causing the rest to scatter into the maelstrom.

"Doesn't matter," Lao Pak said as he rummaged through the dead for their bags of synth. "Not everyone see trap. More come. I get big rich."

He examined the bags of synth. No jackpots. Probably not even a gram, all told. The guards tended to carry more, since they collected the quotas. But all of them had grown wise to the death trap sitting in the middle of the war zone.

Lao Pak walked back up his ramp and placed the delicate synth in a cargo container. He paused to admire his stash. "So wealthy, Lao Pak. You best pirate king."

As he turned to walk back down the ramp, hoping to entice more to give up their treasures, he heard the roar. It was... otherworldly. It sent a shiver down the pirate's spine.

And then he saw it. A tremendous creature with rows of eyes and teeth rampaging through a crowd of prisoners running toward the docking bay. The monster took wanton bites from the fleeing throng, and blood, viscera, and body parts flew everywhere as it literally chewed its way through the panicked crowd.

"Maybe I have enough!" Lao Pak said as he ran back inside his ship. He shut the ramp behind him and ran for the bridge. He was getting off this rock. He had more than enough synth. Keel could keep his money.

Owens was glad to be holding a blaster rifle again, even if it was an odd Gomarii make. Rowdy had brought it to him, and after test-firing it to get a feel for how it handled, Owens was confident it could KTF if the need arose.

Though that didn't seem likely. At least, not inside the command center. He and Chhun had systematically cleared the structure after locking it down.

Now Owens was overlooking the battle outside, wishing he had an L-comm to communicate to his legionnaires with. And not just Victory Squad. Synth Squad, too.

A warning light sounded at one of the control consoles. Owens investigated it and read the screen aloud.

"Unauthorized departure in progress?" Owens checked the holocam and saw the docking platform beginning to rise up the shaft, the freighter moving up with it. "Dammit!"

Owens pounded the console. That freighter was their ticket out. Chhun had said they'd used an actual pirate to bring them in, and now the man was proving himself to be just that—a pirate, with no interest but his own.

"What's going on, Major?"

The question came from Rowdy, returning after going with Chhun to take out the last two Gomarii—the ones guarding the door without cam access.

"Where's Chhun?" Owens asked.

"He's fine as far as I know," Rowdy answered. "He got a call over L-comm, said he needed to get out into the fight. Seemed pretty serious, so I let him go."

"Well, we got a serious problem here too. Our ride just left without us."

"That's... not good."

Owens frowned. "Not good at all. We need to end this fight and prepare for the next Republic arrival. We'll get a ship then."

"What about the Legion commander? You were going to send a message—have him send help."

Owens shook his head. "Yeah, about that. Should have known it wouldn't be that easy. The comm systems are hard-coded to only reach a few designated relays. And I'll bet you a fistful of synth those relays are manned by people who aren't going to be too happy to hear about a leej takeover. A good code slicer would probably have no trouble getting around that, but that ain't me. You?"

Rowdy shook his head. It was beyond him, too.

"So we're on our own here," Owens said. "We'll have to hang out until the next delivery of supplies or prisoners comes."

"Longer wait than I would've liked," Rowdy said. "But what's a few more days?"

"Did you find out what those Gomarii were guarding?"

"Yeah," Rowdy said, pointing back over his shoulder. "Holding cell full of slaves for transport. Looks like they gathered them up earlier than we anticipated."

"Where are they now?"

"Still in the holding cell. I told them to hang tight, then re-sealed the door." Rowdy shook his head. "I wanted to check with you before releasing them, on account of some... stuff that looked out of place."

"What 'stuff'?" asked Owens.

"Republic stuff," Rowdy said with a sniff. He gestured to the monitor. "See for yourself. There are cams linked to the room. They were just turned off. I switched them back on."

Owens cycled through feeds until he found the right one. The room was nearly wall to wall with humanoids. Owens squinted at the scene and understood what had Rowdy concerned. A handful of the prisoners had on Republic uniforms.

He zoomed in. "Well I'll be. I know that one. Lieutenant Pratell. She's the one who brought me in." He zoomed back out a bit. Sitting next to Pratell were the two Republic army basics from the transport shuttle, along with two navy pilots—must have been them who'd piloted them in. "Looks like they all knew too much and were about to pay the price."

Rowdy tapped the image of the two navy pilots. "If the pilots are still here, maybe your shuttle is, too?"

"There wasn't any shuttle out there on the landing pad," said Owens.

"No, there wouldn't be," Rowdy answered. "Only one ship can take off and land at a time. But there's a separate maintenance and repair area. Most smaller ships like shuttles need to be fixed up before they can leave again—the sand gets everywhere. And if the ship *is* still here, all we need is to get those pilots to agree to fly us out."

Owens smiled. "Whether the shuttle is here or we have to wait for the next arrival, something tells me our featherheads will be *more* than willing to fly whatever we find after all this. Listen, I know your men are busy, but if you can spare anyone to check the repair bay for an escape vehicle, I'd like to know our options."

"Yes, sir."

"Good. I'm heading out into the fight."

Chhun watched in disbelief as the repulsor platform lifted Lao Pak's freighter up the shaft toward Herbeer's raging surface. The ceiling irised closed behind it. If the team made it out of here, Chhun would make a point of contacting Wraith. Not to chew him out, but to learn how to track that pirate down and make him pay.

But all of that depended on his ability to overcome two substantial obstacles, both of which were intertwined. He needed to put down the guards—or get their full surrender—so that he could turn the auto-turrets back on and try to drive back the monster. The beast—it looked like a bipedal row of teeth and eyes, with scales and fur—was now stalking the edges of the docking bay platform, keeping to the shadows where it could, shrugging off blaster fire and destroying any light source in its path. Chhun noted that it also destroyed every auto-turret it came upon.

Everyone was pouring their blaster fire into the beast. Its fur was being burnt away with each volley of incoming fire, but the rifles apparently didn't have the power necessary to burn through the thing's tough hide.

"Maybe we should chance turning the turrets back on?" suggested Bear over the L-comm. "This is the first animal I ever saw that looked like it could take me in a straight-up fight."

"Not an option with those guards still around," Chhun said. "It's a three-minute process to shut them down once they're back up, and I guarantee you the guards will use that time to take us out. We're just as dead that way."

Most of the prisoners had fled the scene by this point, probably hiding somewhere in the mines, leaving the guards and legionnaires locked in a game of nerves. Avoid the beast, and avoid the enemy fire sure to come if you broke position.

"Guess we just gotta kill the guards then," said Fish.

"Gonna have to," agreed Chhun.

Suddenly the L-comm was filled with a pain-wracked scream.

"What is it?" asked Chhun. "Who's hit?" His eyes frantically searched his HUD to see any change in status on the dots that represented what remained of his team. To his surprise, a dot that had been black—indicating killed-in-action—was now a faint yellow. Wounded.

"Pike?" Chhun called into his comm.

"Hurts... so bad," Pike said, his voice muffled and pained. He screamed again. "I'm inside of it! I'm being eaten alive!"

"Hang on, man!" shouted Masters. "We'll kill this thing and get you out!"

All of Chhun's legionnaires fired in unison on the creature, instinctively targeting a single spot in the hopes of multiplying the damage. But this, too, was ineffectual.

"My legs are burning," reported Pike. "Bucket... says... five minutes."

That was an estimation of how long Pike's combat AI projected he had before lapsing back into unconsciousness... or, more likely, death. Chhun was reading the report on his own HUD. Pike had lost a lot of blood; his suit's tourniquet had probably been undone by whatever acids were dissolving him inside the beast's stomach. That he was alive at all was likely only due to his armor.

"Hang in there, buddy," Chhun said. "You're gonna be fine."

"No..." Pike said, weakly. "Going... to die."

"You ain't dyin', man," Fish answered between volleys of blaster fire.

"It's... okay..." Pike said, his breathing labored. "Gonna die on my terms. Got... some... det-cord."

Pike carried enough charge to blow off a hinge or a hand, but Chhun wasn't sure it would be enough to take down that monster. In fact, it would probably only add to Pike's suffering, unless he wrapped the cord around his neck to make sure he...

Chhun didn't want to think about that.

"Don't think you've got enough, Pike," Chhun said. "You're in shock, not thinking clearly. Just hang on while we figure out a way to kill this thing. Then we'll cut you out. Get you patched up."

"Am... thinking... clearly," said Pike. "Got... a ton of... synth... in here. Raw... pressed it into... more... det—*ungh*—cord."

"Pike, man..." Masters said, his voice choking with emotion. "Don't. We'll get you out. Don't."

"Tell them..." rasped Pike into the L-comm. "Tell them I didn't... forget... nothing."

"What's he talking about?" Bear asked Chhun on a private channel.

"It's something the old leejes used to say at the end of the Savage Wars. Before KTF got popular."

The beast strode around defiantly, bellowing in anger and using its clawed hands—digging hands—to swipe away guards and prisoners like so many pieces from a game board.

Chhun watched. Waited. Pike...

The explosion was tremendous. The creature blew apart from the inside out, bits and pieces flying in all directions.

Chhun gave himself one second to be stunned. Then he gave an order. "Push! Push on those guards now!"

At once the surviving legionnaires went in hard, blaster rifles firing. The Legion prisoners, some with rifles and some without, followed suit. It was a textbook surprise assault, the legionnaires forming both ends of a pincer that trapped the shocked guards. Unarmored legionnaires fell to desperate blaster fire, but the guards were losing five men to one.

It was the humans, the Republic, who threw down their weapons first. The Gomarii didn't hold out much longer. Soon the entire element had their hands up.

"Victory Team," Chhun said, advancing on the guards even as the prisoners surged and began beating their captors. "Secure the new prisoners, and keep the old ones back. A lot of them are here for a reason. They're not all like the major."

Chhun saw Owens giving orders to the Legion prisoners, now free. They formed a protective wall in front of their former captors and fired their blaster rifles over the heads of the rioting synth miners.

"Prisoners of Herbeer," came a voice over the mine's central comm system. Chhun recognized the voice as

Rowdy's. "This facility is now under control of the Legion. You are to disperse back into the appointed areas designated for prisoners. All quotas are hereby considered fulfilled."

The prisoners gave a somewhat lackluster cheer at this news. Pleased at the news about quotas, but obviously disheartened over still remaining captive.

How many of these had been incarcerated for all the wrong reasons? Chhun didn't know. It would be up to someone else to sort through it all. He and his team still had a war to fight. And he was grateful that their Dark Ops commander would be there to help wage it.

17

Victory Squad pulled security as Major Owens saw to the last of the legionnaires that were to board the armored Republic shuttle. The shuttle had indeed still been on-planet, in the maintenance bay, and hadn't yet been stripped down for parts, as Owens had feared. The pilots, saved from a life of slavery, were only too happy to take their former cargo off of Herbeer.

The legionnaires not joining Owens on the initial trip out—the shuttle could only hold so many—were now suited in surplus Republic uniforms. They would run the prison. There would be no work... that was agreed to. But order was required until further arrangements could be made. Owens had reappointed Rowdy as their leader, and Synth Company would be in his capable hands until Owens could arrange for them to be relieved.

To Owens's surprise, Lieutenant Pratell had foregone his offer to leave with them, instead volunteering to stay behind and research who should and shouldn't be serving out their sentences in the mines. Owens was confident she would do a fine job. Like the pilots, she had been quick to support Owens when confronted with the reality of what the Republic had allowed to happen on Herbeer. Had *encouraged* to happen on Herbeer. Republic citizens were being handed over to Gomarii slavers. It didn't matter that they were criminals. It went against what the Republic stood for. What it was *supposed* to stand for.

And clearly, as Pratell's own experience demonstrated, not everyone taken prisoner here was a criminal. Some were just... inconvenient to the Republic. It had been a Republic officer who had issued the order for Pratell's arrest after Owens was processed, and neither Pratell nor Owens believed for one second that that officer had been acting on his own initiative. It was because she knew too much. Because news of what had been done to Owens couldn't be allowed to reach the galaxy.

To reach the Legion.

After a short trip, all that would change. And the galaxy wouldn't be the same.

Standing at the base of the ramp, Owens watched as the big drusic, Orpe, approached.

"You sure about this?" Orpe asked.

Owens nodded. "Figure you earned your freedom today. No sense making you wait... unless you'd rather stay down here."

The big ape snorted. "Hell no." He walked inside the shuttle.

Chhun was standing at the opposite side of the ramp. "This everyone?" he asked.

Owens saw a few legionnaires moving in his direction, only one of whom would be leaving Herbeer today.

"Not quite."

Owens straightened his posture and snapped a perfect salute.

As the frail old body of Crux, wrapped in cloth, was carried toward the shuttle, the Dark Ops leejes saluted as well. Crux—killed in the fight—would have a proper Legion burial from the *Mercutio*.

He hadn't forgotten anything.

The leejes who carried the old man aboard came back out, saluted Owens, and returned to the command center.

"Okay," said Owens, turning and heading up the ramp. "Now we can go."

The flight up was every bit as rough as the flight down, but the pilots seemed calm. That made Owens feel calm.

"How long until we can hail the legion commander?" he asked.

"As soon as we exit Herbeer's atmosphere, sir."

Owens looked over to Chhun. The legionnaire was staring into the swirling viewport, probably thinking of the life he'd lost in Pike. He was a good team leader. One of the finest leejes Owens had ever known.

"Hey," Owens said, patting Chhun on his armored shoulder. "Thanks. You *and* your team. You're the best."

"Thank you, sir."

Silence fell in the cockpit as the ship continued to make its way through the swirling sandstorms. The captain probably didn't feel like talking, but Owens thought he'd give one more try at conversation. Just in case. In case Chhun needed it.

"How's your team?"

"Operational," said Chhun. "They're pros."

"You know what I mean."

Chhun looked down. "Yeah. They'll be all right. Just need a little time."

"And how about you?" Owens asked. "How are you?"

Chhun looked Owens straight in the eye. His face was unreadable. Owens felt like he was staring into the depths of the man's soul, and was none the wiser for it.

The ship left the atmosphere, and was plunged into the still quiet of space.

"Ready to KTF, sir," said Chhun as he turned back to look at the countless stars. "It's what I do."

Owens nodded.

"Sir," said one of the pilots. "I have *Mercutio*."

"Put 'em up."

A holo-image of the legion commander appeared on screen. Somehow Keller looked more tired... older than the last time Owens had seen him. Even though it hadn't been that long.

Keller smiled. "Glad to see you, Ellek."

"Thank you, sir. Victory Squad and Captain Chhun did outstanding work. So did all the other leejes."

The commander's face was puzzled. "Other leejes?"

"Looks like I wasn't the only one wrongfully imprisoned. I've got a shuttle full of leejes—*real* leejes—who were tossed away on Herbeer like garbage. All of it outside the Legion command structure."

"Points, sir," said Chhun, an edge to his voice. "All of this is from points."

Keller sighed. "Then... it was worse than I imagined."

"We have to do something about this sir," Owens said, before quickly adding, "respectfully."

Keller nodded, and some of the fire that Owens knew in the man flared behind his eyes. "You're right. Get yourself back to *Mercutio*. It's time for the Legion to put the House of Reason in its place."

Owens smiled. "Yes, sir."

The transmission ended, and the pilot eased the shuttle into hyperspace. Brilliant white stars elongated into spears of light all around them.

The day's fight was over.

The next war had begun.

EPILOGUE

The Planet Wayste

Ravi cycled through the *Six*'s landing sequence as they alit just outside the minuscule starport of Bacci Cantara. Backwater worlds like this one didn't require that a starship land and register in a docking bay. There wasn't the infrastructure. Spacers just landed where they felt like. So long as you didn't block access or land in the middle of a street, no one paid any mind. And the *Six* looked like just another freighter. The townsfolk just went on living, sparing little more than a quick glance to see if the newly arrived starship wasn't one they'd been expecting. No one came out to see if the ship needed charges or maintenance.

Keel looked out of his window at the tiny dustball excuse of a planet. "What time is the meeting supposed to be?"

Ravi, who had just killed the repulsors and initiated the ship's cool-down, looked at the captain from beneath an arched brow out of the corner of his eye. "On arrival."

Keel patted the blaster on his hip in a distracted rhythm. "And how much did we have to pay?"

"Ten thousand credits," said Ravi.

"I guess punctuality was extra," Keel mumbled.

"We are technically sixteen minutes early. I thought you would like to put on the Wraith's armor."

Keel stood up. "No, we'll be enough of an oddity once we get going. I'd rather not add to it by looking like a kill team commando."

Ravi nodded.

The captain exited the cockpit. "I'm gonna wait outside. How's the air?"

"Hot and dry," Ravi said with a shrug. "It is a desert."

Keel turned and gave Ravi a condescending look. "I'm glad you're here again to tell me these things. I mean, are there any particles that ought to be filtered? Sand lung may be the lot for the suckers who live here, but that doesn't mean I have to join 'em."

"The air quality is fine." Ravi stood and followed Keel into the *Six*'s hold. "Captain, we have been pursuing this location for some time. And now, we are here..."

"Yeah?"

"And I am wondering why in all that time we have not discussed..." Ravi left the statement open, but Keel didn't bite. So Ravi continued. "Obviously my disappearance and return and all the many other things are quite out of line with our usual relationship. I know you have noticed. You are not one to miss these things. But I do not understand why you have not broached the subject."

Keel adjusted his gun belt. "Because I don't care, Ravi. I knew you weren't a simple hologram for a long time, and I chalked it up to you being some ethereal alien race. I've seen my share of stranger things out on the edge."

"You do not care about why I do not need the bots to render me in spite of—"

"I don't care about anything right now beyond finding my crew." Keel walked to the ramp release. "After that, we can sort out who owes who what."

Ravi smiled. "I am encouraged by the care you are showing for them."

Keel paused. "Yeah, well. We'll see about that, too."

He hit the ramp's drop button and disappeared in a white cloud of vapor and vented gases. He did care. Especially about Leenah. Perhaps only about Leenah, stupid as that was. There was a part of him—the secret part known only to himself and whatever higher being possessed omniscience—that didn't think he'd have left the kill team if it weren't for her.

It was all so dumb. A liability. Risking his life for...

Keel didn't supply the word. He didn't want to.

He wavered at the top of the ramp, understanding that this was as good a metaphor as any for what his life had become. He could turn around and get back into the cockpit—make his life his own. Or... he could step outside and acknowledge that, in spite of what he'd told himself over and over these last seven years, the galaxy wasn't just him and his blaster for hire.

He walked down the ramp.

The air on Wayste wasn't any more or less arid than the air of any other desert he'd visited in his travels. There was a warm breeze that straddled the line between comfortable and too hot. Probably a fall or spring wind, Keel wasn't sure what season it currently was on the planet. Everything smelled of dirt, like baked mud. The ground was parched and cracked, as though it had once—ages ago—been a lake.

Ravi followed Keel and stood by his side. The two men shared a silent vigil, watching for the start of their meeting.

"So," Keel said casually, breaking the stillness. "What, exactly, are you?"

A smile formed at the corners of Ravi's mouth. He gave a soft laugh. "Hoo hoo. I thought you did not care to know? Imagine my captain, Captain Keel, asking about *me*."

"Just making conversation. Don't let it go to your head or your turban won't fit anymore."

"Hoo hoo hoo," laughed Ravi. "There is a long version, which we do not now have time for, and a shorter version. The shorter version is—"

Ravi didn't get the chance to give even that version. A man wrapped in what looked like long rags hailed them from the edge of the town.

"Ahoy!" yelled the man.

Keel raised a hand in greeting. "Yeah, hi," he mumbled, and then waved for the man to meet him at the ship.

The man turned and motioned, and four men carrying archaic shovels and pickaxes followed him toward the *Indelible VI*.

"That's what ten thousand credits gets us, huh?" Keel asked no one in particular.

Ravi took it upon himself to answer. "I suspect the cost was to find those *willing*, and not for any particular skill. It is not as though we have asked for the most respectable job to be done."

"People are too picky," Keel said.

The crew of workers drew within ten meters. Keel didn't see any blasters on them, but with all the layers of fabric that constituted the local dress, one could be hidden anywhere. He kept his hand hanging close to his own weapon, just far enough away so as not to make it look like he was ready to draw.

"Honored, Captain," said the leader of the group, giving a low bow. He sounded as though he was trying, with only limited success, to shed whatever edge-born accent he carried in favor of the unaccented speech of the core used in every holoprogram or newsfeed. "It is with great pleasure that I, Gorjut son of Creez—"

"Yeah, shut up," said Keel. "And stop bowing or you'll draw attention."

Gorjut blushed red with embarrassment and quickly straightened himself. "I apologize, Captain."

Keel looked at the dirty-faced workers standing behind Gorjut. They looked as poor as they did uncomfortable. But at least they seemed capable of digging a deep hole. "Well, let's get started."

Gorjut wrung his hands. "Captain, that's... not possible. We must wait for nightfall." The Wayste native leaned in close, assaulting Keel with a breath that smelled as though he had dredged the seafloor with his tongue. Every tooth was gray and decayed. "The people... they will notice if it is before the sun sets."

Keel let his shoulders slump in frustration. "How long until the sun sets?"

"Four hours and eighteen minutes, standard time," Ravi said.

Gorjut eyed the navigator suspiciously, and gave a slow nod. "Yes, that's about right. You can eat and drink in Gulliver's Barrow. It's where most off-worlders go when shipping into Bacci."

Keel nodded. "Yeah, okay."

He noticed that Gorjut shifted uncomfortably in place, rubbing the side of his jaw as if in worry.

"What's on your mind, Gorjut son of Creez?" Keel asked.

"Ah! The honored captain notices my plight." Gorjut swept his arms toward his workers. "We are simple people, and the credits needed to sup in a spaceport are not easy to come by. Perhaps we can join you and spend an advance of the sum promised?"

"No," Keel said definitively.

"But..." stammered Gorjut, "I was told I would receive—"

"You'll get your half payment once you hand us the exact location," Keel explained. "The other half after you finish our little excavation."

"But then why would you say—"

"No?" said Keel. "Because I'm not looking for a night on the town. If I head to Gilligan's Barrow or whatever it's called, I'm not going to be forced to speak—or worse, listen—to anyone. Fathom?"

Gorjut lowered his head. "Forgive me. It was beneath my station to suggest that we dine together."

Keel rolled his eyes. "Oh, brother," he mumbled to himself. "How about the location, Gorjut?"

Gorjut son of Creez reached into the ragged folds of his robes.

"Ninety-six percent," said Ravi.

Keel knew his partner was telling him the odds were good that Gorjut's hand would not return with a blaster in it. Sure enough, the grimy hand re-emerged holding an ancient-looking datapad. The relic was at least a quarter-inch thick.

Gorjut handed it to Keel. "The map."

Keel held it out to Ravi, who gave a fixed look of concentration.

"I have it," Ravi said.

Keel nodded and tossed a credit chit to Gorjut. The man snatched it out of the air like a froh'gga nabbing an insect with its sticky tongue.

"That chit contains your up-front payment," Ravi said.

Keel tossed the datapad at Gorjut, whose eyes were greedily surveying the credit chit. "And here's this."

Gorjut wasn't expecting *that.* He fumbled an attempt to juggle the datapad and the chit. Both items fell onto the parched planet's surface.

"We'll meet you at the spot an hour after dark," Keel called as he walked past the workmen toward the town of Bacci Cantara. "You can dig under the lights of my ship."

Keel burped for what must have been the hundredth time since returning from the cantina. The local cuisine was heavy, greasy, and didn't seem eager to leave Keel's stomach.

"Excuse me," he said to his navigator. "I'm assuming you can smell?"

"I am aware of a multitude of senses and dimensions," Ravi said. "You are excused."

Keel leaned back in his seat in the *Six*'s cockpit. It was heated, and felt nice. He would have to go outside soon, and he wasn't looking forward to it. Desert nights were miserable in a whole different way than the scorching days. "You told me over dinner that you were sure that everyone was still all right."

"I said I was sure Prisma would be all right," corrected Ravi. "And then you changed the discussion to Captain Chhun and the likelihood of his mission's success, and I spent the rest of the time outlining probabilities for infiltration and escape from Herbeer while you provided variables. And then you asked about the average cost of luxury corvettes in the core compared to the cost of similar models in the mid-core. And then the food came, and we stopped talking."

"Right," Keel said absently. "How do you know? Have you... did you go and... *see* them? Like you said you did before?"

Ravi nodded somberly. "I did not. Now is not the time to see Prisma. Not yet. I will see her next when you are at my side, Captain."

Keel swallowed. "Sure. But Leenah... hell, even Garret..."

"I do not know." Ravi's eyes were sad, twinkling in the darkness of the cockpit. The ship was powered off. "I hope so."

The biologic sensors gave a purring hum of warning. Ravi looked down at the display as it powered on to give its report. "The work crew arrives."

"And... this will work?" asked Keel, already rising from his seat and donning his heavy jacket.

"We cannot get close enough any other way," Ravi confirmed.

Keel pulled his fur-lined hood over his head and hit the *Six*'s ramp release. "Let's get it over with, then."

Gorjut and his workmen were huddled together and waiting by a landing strut. Evidently, the clothing they wore in the day was the same they wore to fend off the chill of a desert night. The garments didn't look to be doing a very good job, judging from the way they shivered.

Oh well, a few hours digging would warm them right up.

"Okay," Keel said, clapping his hands together. "Ready to get rich? Start digging."

The lights of the *Indelible VI* flooded the area, causing the workers to shield their eyes and pull down their polarized goggles. The locals all seemed to have a pair. Probably to fend off dust storms.

Gorjut toed a circle in the dusty earth. "Let's start here, men. Got a feeling about this spot." The foreman turned and lined up his thumb with the massive black shadow of a building—now decrepit and exposed to the elements.

Keel put his hands on his hips and leaned toward the man. "What do you mean, 'good feeling'?"

"Ah, well, see," began Gorjut. His breath was just as foul as ever, but also carried an odor reminiscent of Keel's dinner, which made the captain's stomach do a flip. "The location on the datapad... it's an approximation. We're *close*... it just might take a few holes."

"Wonderful," said Keel. He found a landing strut to lean against. "Well, hurry up. We don't have all night."

Ravi joined the captain. "Tonight is likely all we have."

"I found it! I found it!"

The excited shouting woke Keel with a start. He pushed away from the *Six*'s front landing gear and looked around, trying to gather some situational awareness. He saw Ravi standing with two of the workers while the spades of the other two men's shovels flung dirt from deep down in a hole. Gorjut was curled up, snoring loudly out in the open.

The predawn light was casting a pink-purple glow across the desert's horizon. The nearness of the morning made Keel jump up and run over to Gorjut. He woke the man with a quick kick to the rump. "Not paying you to sleep!"

Keel continued to the edge of the pit, his momentum nearly sending him tumbling inside off-balance. One of the workers grabbed his arm to steady him. Keel nodded thanks and said, "I'm all right."

Gorjut joined them. Everyone peered down into the excavated hole, which was nearly two and a half meters deep. A rectangular box made of some sort of hard-looking desert wood sat at the bottom, only halfway visible, the rest of it still buried.

"This will take time to dig out the rest of the way," said Gorjut. He issued commands in his native tongue, and the workmen still above ground climbed their way down by way of a dirt slope to join their compatriots. "I tell them to dig quickly, before the sun rises, honored Captain."

Keel looked to the growing light and then to Ravi. "You think this is it?"

"The probability is likely, yes."

Gorjut shook his hands with fingers splayed. "This is it, I am sure of it!"

Keel looked down into the pit. The men were brushing away dirt from the top of the wooden box. Gently. They formed piles and then carefully scooped them away. They were being too slow. He looked back at the growing light... and jumped inside the pit.

"Outta my way," he ordered. "We don't have time to be all delicate."

Dropping to a knee, Keel began raking away the dirt around the corners of the box. He turned and looked at the workers, who had halted their progress, stunned. "Get over here and give me a hand!"

None of them moved.

"We must show the proper care," urged Gorjut from his position topside, looking down into the pit. The foreman looked to Ravi for support, but Ravi only shrugged.

Keel displaced enough dirt to get a grip on the wooden crate with both hands. He lifted with all his strength, until he felt that he might strain his back if he didn't relent. Panting, he looked to one of the laborers and held out a hand. "Gimme that pickaxe you're holding."

The man only clutched the tool closer to his body and took a step backward.

Keel pointed down. "Bring it *over*," he commanded. "You wanna get paid or not?"

"Honored Captain," persisted Gorjut, "you mustn't do this! We have ways and traditions that must be followed, lest you unleash a curse on us all!"

"Aw..." Keel said, frustrated. He pulled out his blaster pistol to shoot the crate, but first turned to face the workers, intending to tell them what to do after he discharged the weapon.

The native workers must have thought the blaster was for them. Their eyes wide with panic, they threw down their shovels and pickaxes and jumped out of the pit, clawing their way up the dirt ramp and sprinting away. Gorjut joined them in their retreat, leaving Ravi and Keel alone.

"That is one way to get out of paying five thousand credits," Ravi deadpanned.

"Yeah," Keel agreed.

He leveled his blaster at the corner of the crate and sent a bolt directly into it. Fragments of scorched wood flew everywhere, and a thin tendril of smoke rose from the hole Keel had made. "At least there's no smell."

"The conditions of the desert—"

"Ravi," Keel interrupted. "I don't care. Can you help me pry away the rest now that I've made the opening?"

"I cannot."

"Can't or won't?"

"Won't," Ravi said. "I am sorry."

"Everybody's got a conscience all of a sudden," Keel said.

He bent down to grip the boards. He heaved upward, heard a groan, and then felt the boards snap and come away in his hands. He broke away more boards until the opening was large enough for him to comfortably fit his arm inside, which he did, sending it in up to the elbow.

He felt his way around. "Yeah," he said. "This is the top. Feels dry."

If Ravi had another comment about the effects of the desert, he kept it to himself.

Keel's arm went in deeper, almost to the shoulder. "Okay, I think I've got something that will work. Gonna try to pull it out."

There was a gruesome snapping and splintering sound. A dry sort of gasp was accompanied by a sharp crunch.

Ravi looked upward. "Heaven preserve us."

Keel withdrew his arm, revealing an additional hand—mummified.

"This gonna be enough?" he asked.

"Yes, Captain Keel," Ravi said, exasperation plain in his voice. "A sample of his *hair* would have been enough. You did not need to desecrate the body."

Keel tossed the severed and desiccated hand of Kael Maydoon out of the pit. "Well, better too much than too little, if his bio-signature is what will get us on board those ships. Who knows whether decay would make it so it doesn't work."

"*I* know," sighed Ravi. "Every first-year biology student knows as well, and I assume several primary school students as well."

Keel looked up at his navigator for a beat. "I liked it more when you were dead."

"You are a mean person, Captain Keel."

Ignoring the dirt ramp out of the pit, Keel jumped and then hauled himself up as if he were leaving a swimming pool. He dusted off his hands, then picked up Maydoon's. "No time to rebury the rest. Let Gorjut and his boys do it if they care so much. Let's get back to the ship."

As the pair started back toward the *Indelible VI*, Ravi stopped abruptly. "Captain, the *Six* is detecting—"

"Stop right there!" came a voice-modulated command, spoken through a bucket.

Keel had picked up on something not being right without the last-second warning from the *Six*'s passive scanners. *Sensed* it was the better word. But it was too late now. Whoever was behind them already had the upper hand. Completely.

"Turn around," boomed the voice. "And show me your hands!"

The voice was enhanced like a legionnaire's, but it didn't sound quite Legion. Keel had a feeling that even without the vocal enhancement program that was being run and transmitted through external speakers, this speaker had a deep voice of his own.

Together with Ravi, he turned slowly to face the new-found problem, holding up both his hands—and one of Kael Maydoon's.

Six shock troopers stood before him, with their weapons split evenly between him and Ravi. They had arrived on impossibly quiet repulsor bikes. Keel hadn't even heard a trace of them. The hazy glow of a newborn morning reflected off of their polished black armor.

"Ravi?" Keel mumbled.

"What did you say?" shouted the shock trooper with the deep voice.

"Less than two percent," Ravi answered.

Keel cleared his throat. "Uh, I said, 'You got me.'"

The shock troopers advanced slowly, cautiously. Keel hoped Ravi was priming the *Six*'s weapons, something to even the odds.

"What are you holding?" boomed the lead shock trooper.

Keel looked casually to the hand, as if he himself wasn't sure. "Oh. A hand."

"Where did you get it?"

"Uh... found it."

"Here's the grave," said one of the other shock troopers, looking down into the open pit.

The other troopers turned to look—an incredible lapse of judgment—but the deep-voiced one kept his attention fixed on Keel.

"Thirty-five," Ravi said quickly.

"Probably the best we'll get," Keel mumbled to himself. To the shock trooper he said, "Here, you can have it if you want it."

He tossed the hand in the air, giving it a rainbow arc. In the split second that the shock trooper looked at the hand, Keel drew his blaster and leveled it at the soldier. The deep-voiced combatant was caught flat-footed. A myriad of blasters from the other shock troopers clicked and primed. Keel couldn't kill them all. But he could probably get most of them.

A negotiation was still his best bet.

"This goes down like you want it," Keel said evenly, "half of you die. Maybe all of you. Starting with your squad leader here."

"Shoot him," rumbled the deep-voiced shock trooper. "Complete the mission."

Great. A hero.

The shock troopers raised their blaster rifles. Keel began to squeeze his trigger, mentally deciding which way to drop and whom to shoot next on the way down.

"Wait!"

One of the shock troopers ran over to stand beside the one Keel had his sights on. This trooper's posture was non-threatening. His blaster rifle was on safe and pointed at the ground.

"Captain Ford?" asked the trooper.

Keel was taken aback by this. He squinted at the soldier, as though by doing so he might see through the man's bucket to look upon his face. The sun had not yet fully risen, and much of what Keel could see was still in the shade of dying night.

The shock trooper held out a steadying hand to his deep-voiced companion and lay his rifle on the ground. He pressed a button on the side of his bucket, and its front flipped up and retracted inside, revealing the man's face. That was an improvement over the Legion's models.

A two-tone chime sounded from Keel's comm. An alert sent by Ravi letting him know that the *Six*'s guns were online, ready to join in the fight.

"Ninety-two percent," Ravi whispered.

"Hold on," said Keel. He strained to make out the features on the shock trooper's face. The soldier had jet-black hair, dark eyes, and a smooth scar that ran from the bridge of his nose down onto his cheek. Keel's stomach jumped again, this time not from the meal.

"Exo?"

ABOUT THE AUTHORS

Jason Anspach and Nick Cole are a pair of west coast authors teaming up to write their science fiction dream series, Galaxy's Edge.

Jason Anspach is a best-selling author living in Puyallup, Washington with his wife and their own legionnaire squad of seven (not a typo) children. Raised in a military family (Go Army!), he spent his formative years around Joint Base Lewis-McChord and is active in several pro-veteran charities. Jason enjoys hiking and camping throughout the beautiful Pacific Northwest. He remains undefeated at arm wrestling against his entire family.

Nick Cole is a Dragon Award winning author best known for *The Old Man and the Wasteland, CTRL ALT Revolt!,* and the Wyrd Saga. After serving in the United States Army, Nick moved to Hollywood to pursue a career in acting and writing. He resides with his wife, a professional opera singer, south of Los Angeles, California.

HONOR ROLL

Robert Anspach
Sean Averill
Steven Beaulieu
Steven Bergh
WJ Blood
Christopher Boore
Aaron Brooks
Marion Buehring
Robert Cosler
Peter Davies
Nathan Davis
Karol Doliński
Mark Franceschini
Kyle Gannon
Michael Gardner
John Giorgi
Gordon Green
Michael Greenhill
Joshua Hayes
Jason Henderson
Wendy Jacobson
James Jeffers
Mathijs Kooij
Byl Kravetz

Clay Lambert
Grant Lambert
Preston Leigh
Richard Long
Kyle Macarthur
Pawel Martin
Tao Mason
Simon Mayeski
Joshua McMaster
Jim Mern
Alex Morstadt
Daniel Mullen
Eric Pastorek
Chris Pourteau
Walt Robillard
Glenn Shotton
Joel Stacey
Maggie Stewart-Grant
Kevin Summers
Beverly Tierney
Scott Tucker
Eric Turnbull
John Tuttle
Alex Umstead
Christopher Valin
Nathan Zoss

Printed in Great Britain
by Amazon

29724682R00169